LF Today

a guide to success on 136 and 500kHz

Second edition

by
Mike Dennison, G3XDV
and
Jim Moritz, M0BMU

with additional material by Alan Melia, G3NYK

Radio Society of Great Britain

Published by the Radio Society of Great Britain, Cranborne Road, Potters Bar, Herts EN6 3JE.

First published 2007

ISBN 9781 9050 8636 8

Publisher's note

The opinions expressed in this book are those of the author and not necessarily those of the RSGB. While the information presented is believed to be correct, the author, publisher and their agents cannot accept responsibility for consequences arising from any inaccuracies or omissions.

Cover design: Dorotea Vizer, M3VZR
Typography and design: Emdee Publishing
Production: Mark Allgar, M1MPA

Printed in Great Britain by Latimer Trend, Plymouth

Contents

continued >>

Introduction

Amateur radio has always been about pushing back frontiers, whether the frontier is technological advance, or communicating with miniscule power levels or investigating frequencies that have never before been used for amateur transmissions. The relatively new low frequency amateur bands combine all three of these frontiers. Experimental radio of this kind can provide new research data whilst at the same time being a source of great satisfaction and pleasure for those participating in it.

LF Today aims to provide practical information and advice on tried and tested techniques for those starting out in low frequency amateur radio, and also to provide useful reference information specific to LF operation for amateurs who already have some experience of it, or those with a more technical background, who wish to develop the subject further. We have attempted to keep theory and maths to a minimum in the majority of the text, but have included useful formulas and explanations where these are of practical importance

This is the second edition of *LF Today*. Since the first edition was published, a great deal of experimental work has been done on the 136kHz band, including gaining a greater understanding of the sky-wave propagation mechanisms involved in both short-range and intercontinental communications. The many revisions and updates reflect this.

Another major change has been the issuing of several tens of Notices of Variation allowing special research work between 501 and 504kHz using an effective radiated power of just 100 milliwatts. Some of the work done so far has been incorporated into this book and, based on this, practical information on antennas, transmitters, receivers and propagation has been presented for those wishing to join in. Although '500kHz' is not technically LF (it is at the lower end of MF), many of the participants are those who have already operated on 136kHz and the now defunct 73kHz band, and most of the technology is similar.

We are indebted to all those who commented on the first edition, and all of the members of the rsgb_lf_group e-mail reflector whose combined wisdom and experience can be found in these pages. Thanks also go to those whose projects appear in this book. The chapter on propagation was once again contributed by Alan Melia, G3NYK, whose continuing work on the understanding of sky-wave propagation of small signals on low frequencies is unprecedented.

It remains only to wish you good luck with building, improving and operating your low frequency station. The authors have had several years of enjoyment doing just that, we hope you do, too.

Mike Dennison, G3XDV
Jim Moritz, M0BMU

1

Getting started

In this chapter:

- What can be achieved?
- Do I need a big garden?
- Simple antennas
- Receive antennas
- Using the shack receiver
- What you can hear
- Obtaining a 500kHz permit
- Join the club

THE 136kHz BAND became available to UK amateurs about ten years ago after a few years of experimentation on the unique, and now defunct, 73kHz band. The band extends from 135.7kHz to 137.8kHz, about the bandwidth of a single SSB station. In February 2007 the licensing authority, Ofcom, agreed to issue some amateurs with special research permits to operate very low power from 501kHz to 504kHz. This part of the spectrum was used for high-powered Morse code by ocean-going shipping for the best part of a hundred years, but by the start of the 21st century this activity had been rendered largely obsolete.

With worldwide contacts easily available on the HF amateur bands, some may wonder what is the attraction of operating in the kilohertz region where it takes an effort to produce a station capable of a range of a few hundred kilometres.

As any microwave enthusiast will tell you, it is this effort and the overcoming of obstacles that makes 'difficult' amateur radio so much fun, and ultimately so satisfying. It is no coincidence that many of the early LF experimenters were established microwavers. People frequently report their first low frequency contact as the most exciting experience in years of radio operating.

A word of warning, though. Despite the enthusiasm engendered by operation in this part of the spectrum, it is possible to get discouraged.

Demonstrating the joy of low frequencies at the RSGB HF convention are (front to back) G0MRF, G3GRO and G3NYK

A QRSS3 signal received in the UK from IK1ODO

As there are relatively few amateurs active, an efficient and versatile station is needed to stand a good chance of regular contacts. It is possible to achieve your first contact with a few watts of CW and a 'lash-up' antenna, but it is important to develop your station with more RF power, a more efficient antenna and additional modes.

Since it is easier to radiate an efficient signal at 500kHz then on 136kHz, many stations will try that frequency first. One aim of this book is to encourage newcomers to the low frequencies to go the whole distance and experience our lowest amateur band as well. The extra work involved will pay dividends, not only on 136kHz itself, but in developing techniques that will also improve your results on the easier band.

What can be achieved?

The typical range of a suburban station on 136kHz depends not only on the radiated power but also the type of transmission used. Conventional CW, typically at 12WPM, can provide contacts up to 1000km or so. Data transmissions using CW bandwidths may work over a similar range. Distances in the 1000+km range usually require 'QRSS' or specially developed data modes.

QRSS is extremely slow CW with dot lengths ranging from three seconds (QRSS3) to 120 seconds (QRSS120), generated and displayed by computer to provide a very low bandwidth and hence a much improved signal to noise ratio. Several UK stations have crossed the Atlantic on 136kHz using this technique.

It is difficult to assess potential ranges at 500kHz because of the very low power permitted - 100mW ERP at the time of writing - and the restriction of permits to UK stations only. However, ranges of several hundred kilometres have already been achieved and much longer distances are expected to be covered in due course, especially after dark.

As with any amateur radio, the actual contacts will depend on the amount of time and effort expended on chasing the DX, as well as transmitted power levels. At these frequencies, the amount of power radiated is greatly influenced by the antenna efficiency which is likely to be no more than a fraction of one per cent on the lower band and only a few percent on the higher.

On 136kHz, the UK licence limit is 1W ERP, but a large antenna and/or very high transmitter power is needed to achieve this. Most UK stations have an ERP of between 0.1 and 0.5 watts. At 500kHz, it is much easier to achieve the 100mW ERP so far permitted.

Proving that a large garden is not essential for LF, I5TGC has this ingenious roof-top installation

Do I need a big garden?

An efficient half-wave dipole for 136kHz will be over a kilometre long and hundreds of metres high. Even a quarter-wave ground plane will require a 500m tower and an earth system 1km in diameter. Needless to say, some compromises are needed to operate LF in a housing estate. Fortunately, it is possible to achieve usable efficiencies with 'domestic' antennas, especially on

500kHz, provided care is taken.

It is helpful to have enough real estate to accommodate, say, an 80m dipole some 10m high, but LF success has been achieved from very small gardens, and even the roof of an apartment block (see picture).

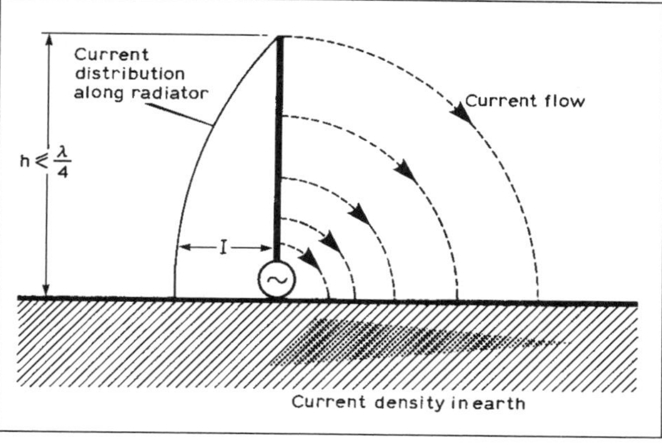

Fig 1.1: Current distribution of a short radiator over a plane earth

Several of the early experimenters on 500kHz have successfully used HF dipoles strapped as Marconi antennas and tuned against ground.

Simple antennas

Two basic types of antenna have been used for amateur LF transmitting: the loop and the Marconi. These will both be dealt with in detail later, but for the purposes of this chapter let's see how easy it is to erect a Marconi-style antenna.

Marconi discovered that a single vertical element would work as an antenna when a connection was made to ground to complete the circuit (**Fig 1.1**). He also found that by folding the top of the vertical parallel with the ground, the height - and hence the cost of the mast - could be reduced with very little reduction in efficiency. The resultant inverted-L and T antennas (**Fig 1.2**) are familiar to those who operate on the 160 and 80m amateur bands.

For our case, even an inverted-L is far too big. Fortunately, a Marconi antenna will work when its physical length is much less than a quarter wavelength, provided it is properly matched. Naturally, the efficiency is greatly reduced.

An established amateur radio station may well already have the basis of an LF Marconi antenna.

A dipole for 160, 80 or even 40m can be adapted by strapping the feeder and paying additional attention to insulation (see the antennas chapter). Even a G5RV could be used in this way. A tower or pole mounted HF or VHF antenna system might also be pressed into service.

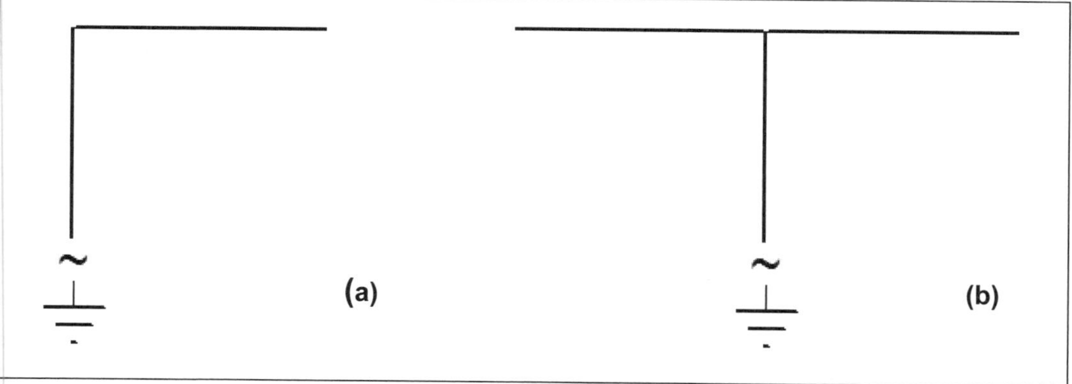

Fig 1.2: Reducing the height needed for a low frequency vertical. (a) An inverted-L and (b) a 'T'

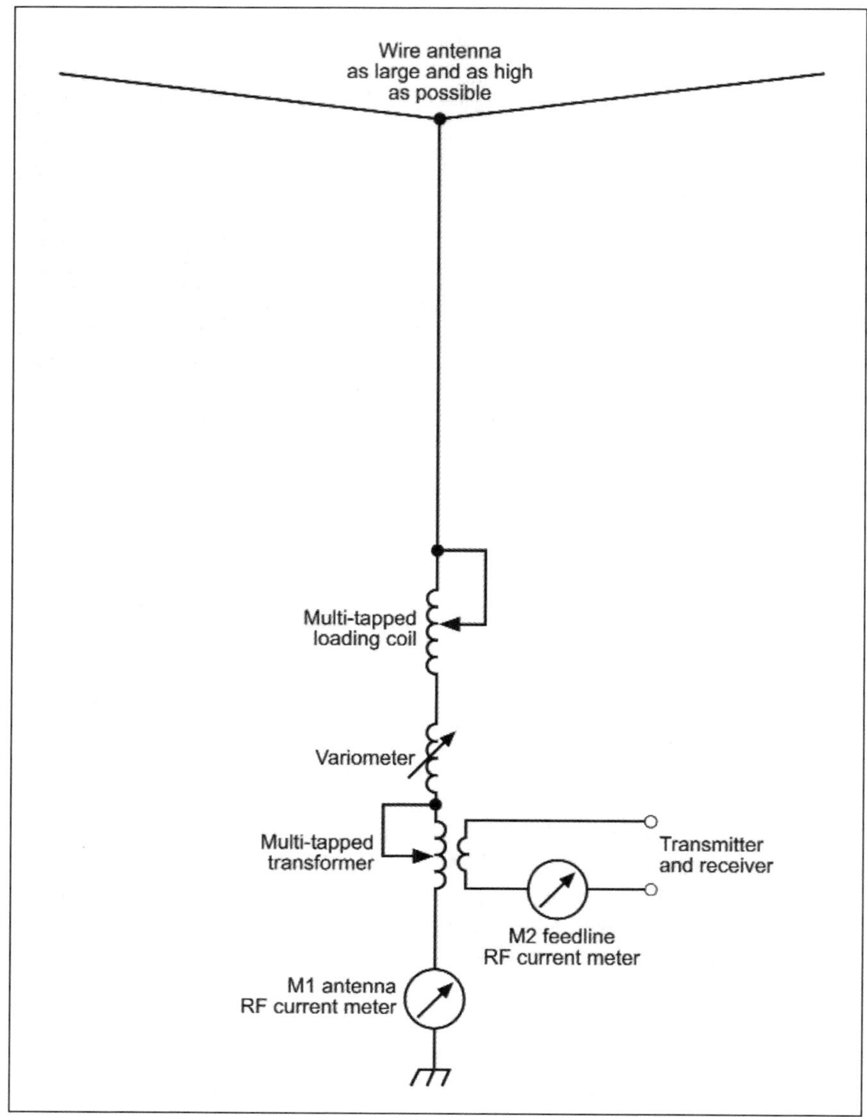

Fig 1.3: The typical arrangement of an LF antenna. The main element could be an existing dipole with the feeders connected together, or it could be purpose-designed

If started from scratch, an LF Marconi should be designed to have as long a vertical section as possible, and a top section giving as much capacitance to ground as possible without compromising on height (**Fig 1.3**). This need not be in the classic L or T shape. Anything that produces capacitance at a good height will work.

Since the resultant Marconi will be very short compared with the required electrical wavelength, the feedpoint will have considerable capacitive reactance. This must be compensated for (tuned out) by inserting an inductance - perhaps several millihenries - in series with the antenna lead.

A good ground connection is also required. For initial low power experiments, a single earth stake or a water pipe is a good starting point.

Although the theoretical feed resistance of a very short Marconi is a fraction of an ohm, this is greatly increased by the resistance of the coil together with earth and other losses. Your LF antenna may have a feed impedance much closer to 50 ohms than you would think.

Receive antennas

Even before considering transmitting, much can be learned by listening on the bands. Unfortunately, it is also a really good way of putting yourself off the low bands for life. This is because an unmatched wire plugged into a typical HF transceiver will often produce a lot of noise and no signals. No matter what antenna is used for your first excursion onto low frequencies, it is essential that it is resonated and (if it is a Marconi) tuned against ground.

A multi-turn receiving loop antenna for 136kHz, built by F6AGR

In the main, resonating involves winding a coil that can be adjusted from about one to three millihenries (perhaps 200 to 400uH for 500kHz). A proper earth is required - do not rely on the receiver being connected to earth through the power unit's mains plug.

An alternative, and often effective, receive antenna can be made by winding several turns of wire round a frame, parallel tuning this with a variable capacitor from an AM broadcast radio and coupling it to the receiver with a single turn loop. The antenna need not be placed high up, but must be mounted away from household wiring.

Using the shack receiver

Many modern HF transceivers tune down to around 100kHz, which theoretically makes them suitable for reception of 136kHz signals. However, the majority have greatly reduced performance at LF, often leading to early disappointment for the casual listener.

The recommended HF transceiver for 136kHz reception is the Kenwood TS-850 which performs very well and is available these days at a reasonable price second hand. Like many amateur band radios, however, it switches in an attenuator at 500kHz reducing its effectiveness for weak signal working. Conversely, the IC-706 has a better receiver at 500kHz than 136kHz.

The sensitivity of many radios can be greatly improved by using a pre-amplifier (see the receivers chapter), but this must incorporate tuned circuits to avoid amplifying huge non-amateur signals which will cause blocking effects.

Dedicated general coverage receivers, for example the AOR7030, are capable of good reception at both low frequency bands.

Suggestions for suitable radios, as well as pre-amplifier circuits, can be found in the receivers chapter.

If you have a TS-850, you are already well on the way to hearing amateurs on 136kHz, but it is less effective on 500khz

For QRSS reception, the receiver's oscillators must have minimal drift, especially if you intend to use the longer dot lengths.

Because the 136kHz band is so narrow, and to avoid interference from utility stations close to the band, it is highly desirable to fit a CW filter in the receiver's IF. This type of filter is suitable for all modes used on these frequencies. - there is no space for SSB transmissions.

What you can hear on 136kHz

Like many amateur bands, 136kHz is shared with utility stations and is also adjacent to them. **Fig 1.4** shows the European 136kHz environment.

It can be seen that DCF39, just above the band on 138.830kHz, is a potent signal which can be the source of receiver problems, but also makes a most useful beacon. This 50kW ERP transmission from Magdeburg, Germany, comprises a single carrier, interrupted every ten seconds or so by a data burst lasting about one second. Not only is this an excellent starting point for finding the band and testing receiver and antenna improvements, but it makes a good propagation indicator for stations outside Europe looking for DX signals.

A similar sounding signal, from Budapest, can be found on 135.43kHz; sidebands from its data bursts can spill into the lower part of the amateur band.

Within the band, around 135.8kHz, is SXV. Originating in Greece, SXV transmits teletype continuously. In the UK, it is audible during daylight hours

Fig 1.4: (left) The 136kHz amateur band as received in the UK, showing the close-in very strong utility stations, and (right) The relatively clear 500kHz allocation

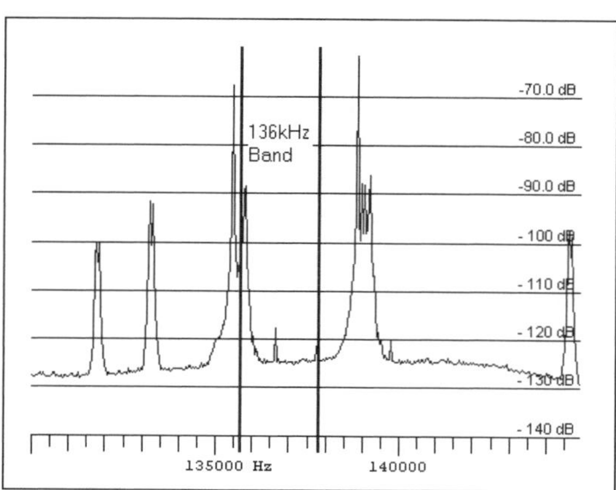

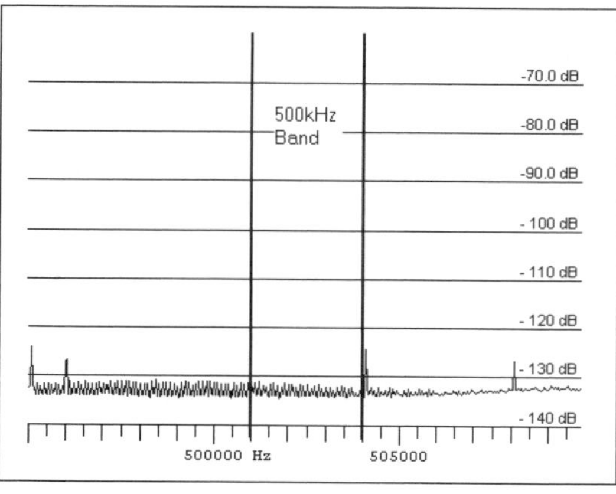

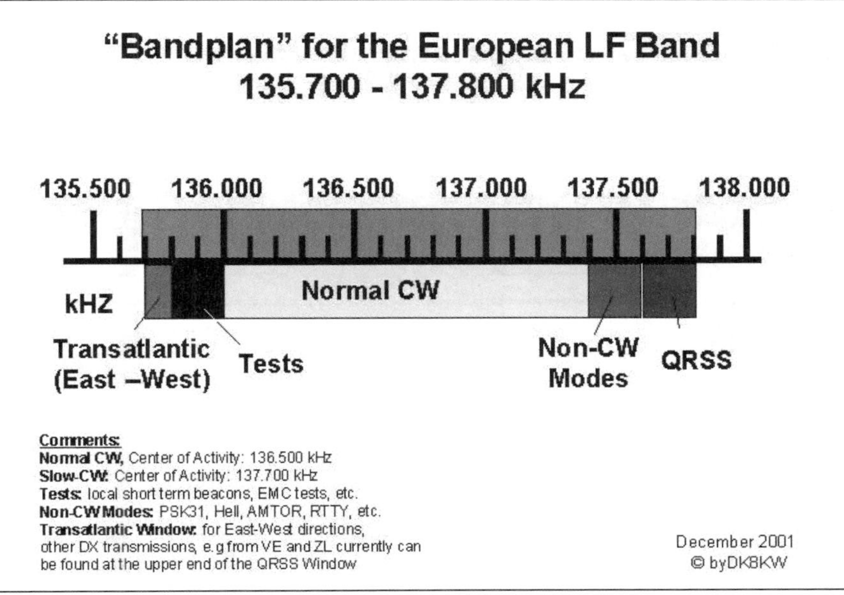

This early suggested bandplan for the 136kHz band has now been adopted informally by the IARU (see the operating chapter for the latest version). Note that the the East-West Transatlantic Window has now moved to around 136.3kHz

on a good receive set-up, but gets very strong at night when the signal is propagated by skywave.

Amateur CW signals can be heard in the middle of the band, from just above 136.0kHz to just above 137.0kHz. QRSS signals, which can be identified by ear as several seconds of carrier followed by several seconds of silence, are usually around 137.7kHz and occasionally close to 135.8kHz during inter-continental tests. Data such as PSK, and experimental transmissions. may be found between 137.4 and 137.6kHz [see operating chapter for the full Bandplan]. The best time to listen for amateur signals is at weekends.

With a good set-up, you should be able to hear CW signals from the UK and Western Europe and can read QRSS signals from as far as Eastern Europe and even America. More about DX-ing later.

What you can hear on 500kHz

Unlike 136kHz, there are no non-amateur stations inside the band and very few close by. The most obvious inband signal is the second harmonic of broadcast stations using 252kHz.

The closest out-of-band signals are aeronautical non-directional beacons (NDBs), most of which are below 434kHz, but these can provide some reassurance that your receive set-up is working in the absence of amateur transmissions. A comprehensive list of NDBs can be found at the Beaconworld web site [1].

Amateur stations are active mostly at weekends. Some transmit test beacons from time to time using CW or QRSS3, or both. Beacons and QRSS transmissions tend to be higher in the band, though at the time of writing there is no formal bandplan. Most two-way contacts are made using CW.

Currently, only UK amateurs can run conventional amateur radio stations on this band, but there are experimental German, Swedish, Czech and US beacon transmissions (usually QRSS3) between 505.0kHz and 505.2kHz. The Europeans have been successfully received in the UK.

Part of Ofcom's application form for operation on 500kHz

www.ofcom.org.uk OfW306

Application for an Amateur Radio Special Research Permit

This form should be used to apply for a Special Research Permit, which, if granted, will be issued as a Notice of Variation to an existing Full Amateur Radio Licence.

Applicant

Family name		Callsign	
Forenames		Date of first issue	

Obtaining a permit to transmit on 500kHz

Unlike the 136kHz band, which is included in the standard UK Amateur Radio Licence, transmitting on 500kHz is by special permission only. An application form for a Special Research Permit is available from Ofcom [2] or may be downloaded from Ofcom [3]. Advice on how to make the application can be found at the RSGB Spectrum Forum web site [3].

At the time of writing permits are being issued on a case by case basis to Amateur Radio Full licensees only. The original Ofcom announcement said:

> *"Due to the usage of the spectrum around 500kHz, applicants should pay special attention to demonstrating technical and operational competence in terms of transmitting within the frequency and Effective Radiated Power parameters agreed with Ofcom. Previous experience at 73kHz as well as 136kHz will be considered desirable in this respect to ensure adequate steps are taken to limit any potential interference."*

The initial permits were for a maximum of 100mW ERP from 501.0kHz to 504.0kHz using a variety of low bandwidth modes. They were for a maximum of 12 months commencing 1 March 2007. Any future amateur use of this part of the spectrum will undoubtedly depend on the results of this experiment.

Join the club

If this chapter has got you interested, the next step is to join the RSGB LF Group which is a type of e-mail forum known as a reflector. After signing up (free), you will receive in your e-mail inbox a copy of every e-mail sent to the reflector, and you will be able to post messages to the group. There is no junk mail, just news and comment, plus technical discussion and advice. This is where you can ask questions on LF matters, no matter how simple or complex, and you will get replies from experienced, knowledgeable and friendly people. To join, simply send an e-mail to: *majordomo@blacksheep.org* with no subject and only **subscribe rsgb_lf_group** in the body of the message. A welcome message will be sent back, and you should then receive several LF-related e-mails each day.

References

[1] *http://www.beaconworld.org.uk*

[2] Ofcom Licensing Centre, Amateur Radio, Riverside House, 2a Southwark Bridge Road, London SE1 9HA. Tel: 020 7981 3131.

[3] *http://www.ofcom.org.uk/radiocomms/ifi/licensing/classes/amateur/Notices/20070221*

[4] *http://www.rsgb-spectrumforum.org.uk/ofcom_501kHz_%20srp.htm*

2

Receivers

In this chapter:

- What is needed
- Suitable commercial receivers
- Improving your receiver
- Receive pre-amplifier
- Preselector, pre-amp and converter
- Software defined receivers
- 'SoftRock Lite' modifications
- Home made receivers

THE RECEIVE ENVIRONMENT at 136kHz is unique in that the amateur signals can be extremely weak, whilst very strong non-amateur transmissions are present on the antenna. This leads to the conflicting requirements of good sensitivity and resistance to blocking.

Amateur signal levels are also very low at 500kHz, but there are very few close-in commercial stations. This simplifies the design of an efficient receive set-up.

Frequency stability is an issue when receiving very slow QRSS, and a good noise blanker can help during the summer months when static dominates.

What is needed

Tuning the antenna to resonance is vital for transmitting but easy to overlook when just receiving. Amateur stations may be received at 500kHz on an untuned antenna, but better results will be obtained when the system is tuned to resonance. On 136kHz, however, tuning the antenna is essential to be able to receive any amateur stations. Some antenna tuning arrangements are shown in **Fig 2.1**.

It is also vital to site the antenna away from sources of local interference. This topic is discussed in detail in the operating chapter, but for the moment you need to be aware that local electrical noise and static crashes can be a major problem at LF.

A radio with poor sensitivity is capable of receiving non-amateur signals at LF, and this may lead the beginner to believe it is satisfactory. Unfortunately, amateur signals are several tens of decibels closer to the

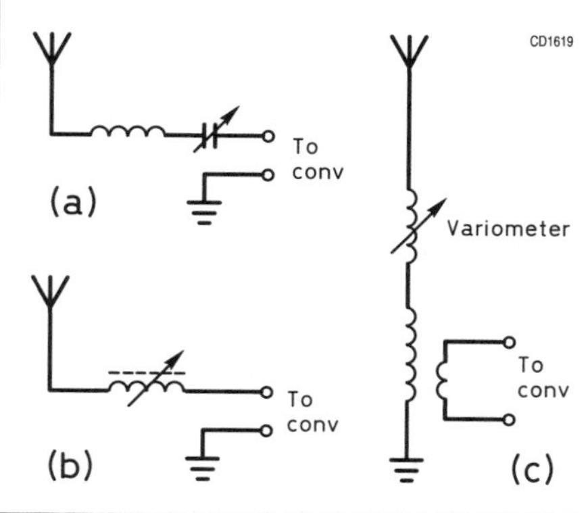

Fig 2.1: Methods of tuning an LF antenna. (a) and (b) are adequate for receiving, whilst (c) is typical of a transmitting installation. Note that an earth connection must be used with these arrangements

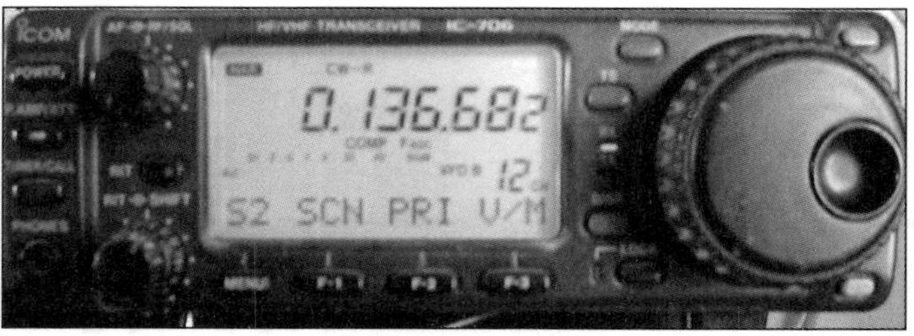

The IC-706 is stable and has frequency readout down to 1Hz. It is good for 500kHz but needs a pre-amplifier to be efficient on 136kHz

noise level. For instance, DCF39 on 138.830kHz should be well over S9 on your s-meter if amateurs are to be received satisfactorily. A good rule of thumb is to have a system capable of hearing a constant background crackle in the absence of signals (and thunder storms) - this is the so-called 'presence' that will be familiar to experienced HF operators.

Ideally, your receiver should be capable of sufficient sensitivity without modification (see below) but in many cases sensitivity can be improved by the addition of a *tuned or filtered* pre-amplifier.

Plainly, good dynamic range is important in a 136kHz receiver, as is proper gain distribution. An RF gain control and switchable AGC are both desirable. Requirements for 500kHz are less stringent.

Since all modes used at LF are narrowband, any receiver should have a narrow IF filter, or at least provision for fitting one. Again, the absence of close-in high-powered utility stations makes selectivity less of an issue at 500kHz.

For conventional CW or QRSS3 operation, all modern radios have adequate frequency stability. If your interests lie in digital modes or in working DX using extremely slow CW (eg QRSS30), a high level of stability is required.

Frequency readout is often confused with frequency stability, but a readout to 1Hz does not mean the radio will stay within 1Hz for long periods. Conversely, some radios will have excellent stability but have a readout in 10Hz steps. Again, this is of no consequence for CW operation, but for QRSS the ability to set the receiver accurately to 1Hz can be useful. Note, though, that provided the receiver is stable, it is possible to use software to improve on a poor frequency display - see the chapter on advanced techniques.

Lightning static is audible for most of the time at LF as there is usually a storm of some kind within 2000km or so. This dramatically increases in the summer months, leading some to abandon the low bands. A really good noise blanker can be an asset under these conditions, though few commercial radios have this.

Suitable commercial receivers

A few transceivers, and rather more receivers, have sufficient sensitivity on the low frequency bands. Some work better on 136kHz than on 500kHz where an attenuator may be fitted to reduce blocking on the Medium Wave broadcast band. More radios will perform better at the higher frequency. Many will work fine on both bands with the addition of a pre-amplifier (see later).

Top of most 136kHz, operators' shopping list is the Kenwood TS-850, but don't assume that all of the more recent Kenwood models are an improvement on this band. The '850 has excellent sensitivity and a clean DDS. A range of CW filters can be fitted both at 8MHz and at 455kHz, allowing very high skirt selectivity. It performs poorly at 500kHz because of its MW attenuator, but this can be removed [1] or the receiver set to 499.98kHz and the RIT used to tune a little higher (note that the RIT range can be increased to 2.54kHz by changing programmable function #17). The 10kHz IRT on the TS-930 can be used in a similar way and its transverter port makes it easy to get a fully-featured LF/MF

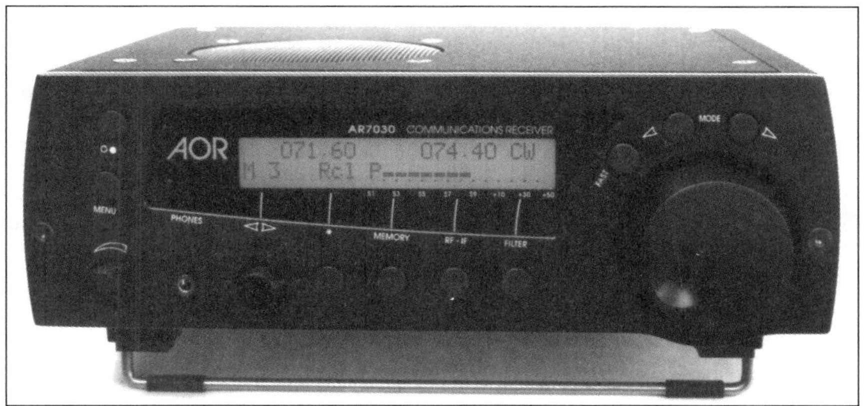

The AOR7030 is a receiver that performs very well at low frequencies

radio with an external transverter. The TS-440 is also very sensitive and, provided the internal 20dB attenuator is used, the intermodulation behaviour is very good. The noise blanker in the TS-870 is reported to be effective, and the receiver is ideal for use with large antennas, though LF sensitivity is not as good as the TS-850. The TS-140 is described as adequately sensitive for 136kHz.

The Icom IC-706 (Mk1 and Mk2) has excellent stability and the frequency can be set in 1Hz steps. However, it is insensitive at 136kHz and benefits greatly from an LF pre-amplifier. When used on 500kHz a low pass filter with a cut-off of 600kHz [2] keeps broadcast band signals out. The AGC cannot be switched out, but there is an RF gain control. A fixed audio level is available on a rear socket which is handy for connecting to a computer sound card for QRSS, etc. The noise blanker is totally ineffective at LF. Similar performance has been experienced with the IC-718 and the IC-756 PRO. The IC-751A has been used successfully on 136kHz after the addition of an AF filter, although the frequency stability has been reported as inadequate for QRSS. Other LF operators use the IC-761, IC-765 and IC-781, adding CW filters in both IFs.

From Yaesu, the FT-990 is very sensitive and has built-in DSP to supplement the very good optional CW filters; the AGC can be switched out. The FT-817 requires an external preamplifier for LF.

Dedicated receivers are more likely to perform well at low frequencies. The Yaesu FRG100 is reported to be sensitive and stable, and as good as the TS-850. Tuning well below the 136kHz band, the AOR7030 is useful for LF work with good sensitivity, 10Hz tuning steps and optional 300Hz or 500Hz IF filters. JRC's NRD-345 is sensitive and stable, and has several optional narrow filters; the NRD-525, 535 and 545 are described as very good and the NRD-91 tunes down to 10kHz. The Icom IC-R75 can be fitted with an oven controlled oscillator and is very sensitive; the AGC can be turned off. Lowe's HF-150 has good IMD performance, but no CW filter, RF gain or AGC off switch; the HF-225 has a 200Hz filter at AF. Other receivers that have been used at LF include the Ten Tec RX-320 (with AMRAD modification [3]), and the Cubic R3030 and R3090.

Receivers intended for commercial operation, are also likely to perform well, though some may have keyboard entry rather than a dial for tuning. Most have high stability oscillators tunable in 1Hz steps, have AGC that can be switched off and will have outstanding IMD and cross-modulation performance. The Racal 1792 also has IF passband tuning. Another useful receiver is the Harris

> Note: The advice on commercial receivers given in this chapter is based on user reports and is intended purely as guidance. Actual performance may vary from one equipment to another. Potential buyers are advised to make their own tests on the radio before parting with their money.

RF590 which has good sensitivity and an effective noise blanker. From Germany, the EKD300 is reportedly a good performer. The RA6790-GM tunes down to 500kHz, and is sensitive but is described as "a bit quirky" and "the membrane keys are a bit hard on the fingers."

Vintage receivers
Some 'boat anchor' radios tune to 500kHz and even as low as 136kHz. These do not have the 'brick-wall' selectivity required to avoid the very strong utility signals adjacent to the 136kHz band, but may well have adequate sensitivity for your first attempts at receiving on 500kHz.

Selective measuring sets
Used for making measurements on analogue telecommunications systems, selective measuring sets (SLMS, or sometimes TMS) can make good LF receivers. They almost all cover frequencies down to VLF and some include the HF spectrum, too.

The advantages of going for this type of receiver are: adequate sensitivity for amateur use, good dynamic range, a calibrated input attenuator, an output meter with a readout to 0.1dB, probably a very narrow IF filter (less than 100Hz), good stability, constant sensitivity over a wide range of frequencies and the possibility of a matching oscillator that can be locked to it. They are also ideal for making accurate field strength measurements (see the Measurements chapter).

On the debit side are: no AGC, sometimes no SSB or CW demodulator (this can often be overcome by connecting your station receiver to an IF output socket), often no intermediate-bandwidth filter (just speech bandwidth and sub-100Hz) and a greater size and weight than most amateur specification radios.

Since an SLMS can be picked up second hand (check eBay regularly) for £100 or less, it is often a good investment. Look for the East German MV61 or 62 'Pegelmesser', Siemens D2155, Wandel and Goltermann (W&G) SPM-3, SPM-12, SMP-30, SPM-60 or similar.

More on using these sets as LF receivers can be found at [4].

Improving your receiver

Many receivers will benefit from a preamplifier. However, do not under any circumstances use an untuned circuit. In addition to amateur signals, this will amplify non-amateur transmissions such as MSF on 60kHz, the BBC on 198kHz or medium wave broadcasters, which will lead to an increase in noise and intermodulation products. Too much gain should be avoided, so a gain control or switched attenuator before the amplifier would be useful.

To check the intermodulation performance of your 136kHz receive set-up, listen on 138.000kHz. If you can hear a rough-sounding signal pulsing on and off once every second you have a problem. This will be a mix between the BBC on 198kHz and the Rugby time signal on 60kHz. The fix is better gain distribution - probably less front-end gain - and better input filtering. Note that late at night it may be possible to hear noise modulated by broadcast signals close to the top or bottom of the 136kHz band. This is believed to be ionospheric mixing - the so-called 'Luxembourg effect' - and cannot be eliminated by improving your receiver.

It is possible to operate on LF using a receiver with an IF bandwidth suitable for SSB. However, this will cover the entire amateur band! Since all transmissions are narrowband any serious operator will invest in a CW filter, preferably the best available and if possible fitted to both IFs. Since there is very little Morse above 12WPM, an IF filter of 250Hz, or even narrower, can be fitted. An analogue or DSP audio frequency filter can be a helpful addition, but is not an adequate replacement for good IF filtering. PA0LQ's design for an active audio filter designed by can be found at [5].

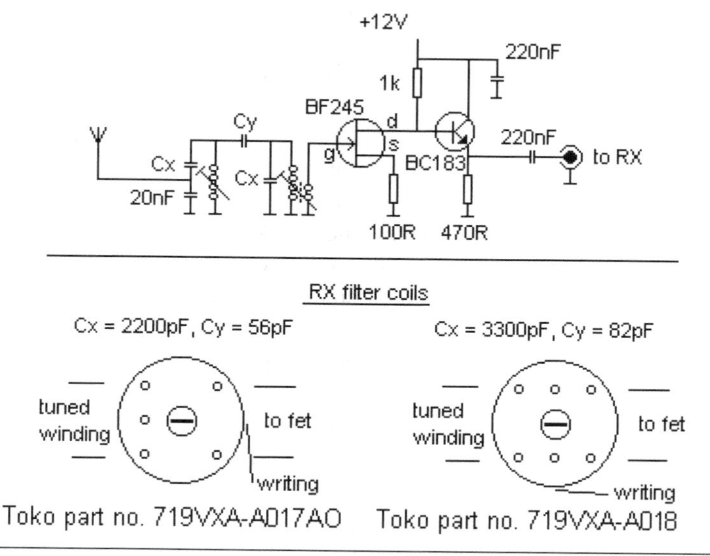

Fig 2.2: An LF pre-amplifier with 10dB gain and high selectivity. Two alternative Toko coils are shown. The amplifier was designed by G3YXM and is available ready built from G0MRF (see Appendix 2)

Turning down the RF gain control may well produce a better signal to noise ratio. In some cases, especially for QRSS operation, it may be useful to turn off the AGC - note that some transceivers do not allow this.

What if your trusty HF radio has all of the above features, but does not tune down to 136kHz, or performs badly at 500kHz? All is not lost, as a properly designed LF converter will extend the frequency range.

Receiver preamplifier

Most modern receivers covering the LF/MF range have a nominally 50-ohm input impedance that is not well matched to typical receiving antennas used in this frequency range. In amateur-type rigs, the general coverage receivers often have poor sensitivity in the LF/MF range, or coverage may not extend to lower frequencies at all. In most cases, adequate reception performance can be achieved using an existing receiver together with suitable preselectors, preamplifiers or converters. The requirements for these input circuits depend on the type of antenna to be used for reception, as well as the receiver capabilities.

A suitable tuned amplifier with moderate gain and a sharp band-pass response about 3kHz wide, is shown in **Fig 2.2**. More gain can be had by connecting the FET gate to the top of the second tuned-circuit, instead of the overwind. With this method, you could use any variable inductor with an inductance of around 680mH. Even if adequate sensitivity is available, most commercial receivers have a broadband front end so additional signal frequency tuned circuits, such as those shown in Fig 2.2 may help avoid blocking effects.

Preselector, preamplifier and converter

The circuit blocks described below have been in use at M0BMU for some time, and combined together in various configurations have proved to be a versatile interface between a wide range of receiving antennas and receivers to provide good receiving performance in the LF/MF range.

For many receivers of good to 'average' sensitivity at LF, the preselector will be sufficient by itself when used with reasonably large loop or wire antennas to bring the band noise above the receiver noise floor. At M0BMU, the preselector has been used like this with a Racal RA1792 receiver, and an Icom IC718 transceiver.

For receivers with very poor sensitivity, for example the Yaesu FT817 at 136kHz, adding the 20dB preamplifier after the preselector will give a sensitivity improvement, however the the combination of preselector-plus-converter gives better results, with the receiver used as a HF tunable IF. Small tuned loop antennas benefit from the 20dB preamplifier, used directly with a reasonably sensitive receiver, or to feed the converter. If additional gain and filtering is required, this can be achieved by connecting the preselector between the preamplifier output and the input of the converter or receiver.

Preselector for 136kHz and 500kHz

The basic preselector circuit is shown in **Fig 2.3**. It provides an antenna tuning and filtering function, along with considerable gain to drive a low-impedance receiver input. The tunable L-C input circuit has a narrow bandwidth of a few kilohertz, which substantially reduces the level of unwanted signals at the receiver input, particularly Medium Wave broadcast stations.

A compound FET/bipolar unity-gain buffer amplifier provides a low output impedance to drive the receiver, with a very high input impedance to minimise loading of the tuned input circuit. Although the follower has a gain around unity, the circuit has considerable overall voltage gain due to the impedance step-up of the input tuned circuit.

The input circuit can be adapted for use with wire antennas, or various types of loop antenna, as shown in **Fig 2.4**. For use with a wire antenna, a shunt capacitor is added to the input circuit (**Fig 2.4(a)**). The value of this capacitor controls the impedance transformation, and so acts as a sort of RF gain control - larger input capacitors result in lower signal level at the preselector output. This capacitor should be selected to provide the minimum gain that achieves adequate signal-to-noise ratio. For short wire antennas of 5 - 10m, a 1000pF capacitor is typically about right, whilst up to 10nF can be used with larger long wire antennas. A wire antenna may be connected to the preselector input through a coax feeder, in which case the capacitance of the coax cable makes up part or all of the input capacitor. This allows the antenna feed point and earth connection to be well away from the shack, which can help to reduce noise pick-up.

For use with untuned loop antennas (**Fig 2.4(b)**), the shunt input capacitor is omitted, and the loop connects directly to the input, effectively forming

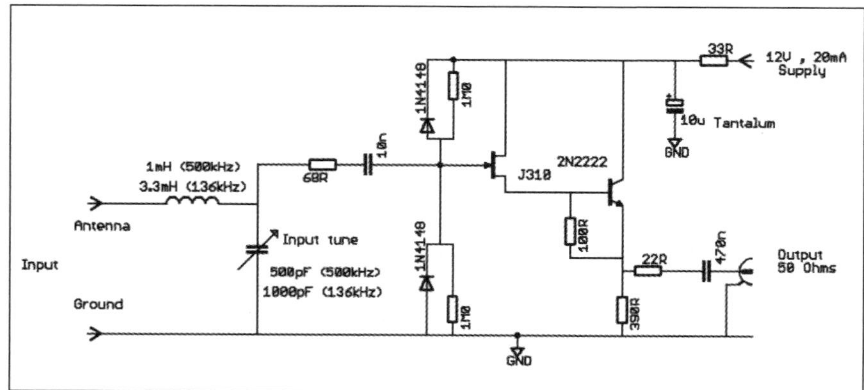

Fig 2.3: LF/MF Preselector - input connections for different antennas are shown in Fig 2.3

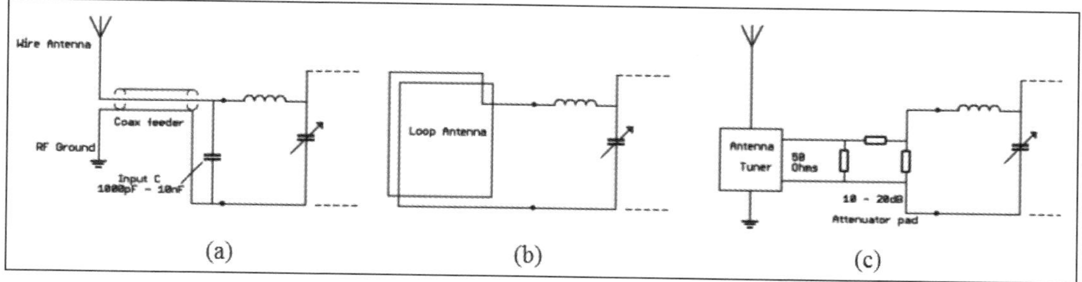

Fig 2.4: Using the preselector of Fig 1 with (a) wire antennas, (b) loop antenna, (c) operation with 50 antenna tuner

part of the tuning inductance. This arrangement gives quite a large voltage step-up, and the overall voltage gain can be 30dB or more, boosting the generally low output from the loop antenna. The antenna may be a large single turn of wire with an area of $10m^2$ or more, or a smaller, multi-turn loop.

A 1m x 1m, 10 turn square loop has been used satisfactorily with this circuit for 136kHz reception, with five turns used for 500kHz. Loop antennas may also be connected to the preselector input via a considerable length of coax, allowing convenient tuning from the operating position.

The preselector may also be used in conjunction with an existing transmitting-type antenna and tuner providing a 50 ohm match, in order to provide additional gain and filtering. In this case, the signal level at the antenna tuner output will probably be quite large, and an attenuator pad can be inserted between the antenna tuner and the preselector (**Fig 2.4(c)**) to reduce the signal level and also reduce tuning interaction between preselector and antenna tuner. The input as shown in Fig 2.3 can also be connected directly to a low impedance source, such as another preamplifier, or an active antenna. Used in this way, it functions as a tuned preamplifier with around 30dB gain.

The preselector circuit can be used over a wide range of frequencies by choosing appropriate values of input tuning inductor and capacitor. Values in Fig 2.3 are given for 136kHz and 500kHz, and a band-switched version of the input tuning circuit covering 10kHz to 600kHz in five overlapping bands is shown in **Fig 2.5**. The band switch selects a tuning inductance between 1mH and about 250mH, which is resonated by both gangs of a 500pF + 500pF tuning capacitor, except on the highest band, where only one gang is used.

The inductors used in the prototype were small radial-leaded filter chokes wound on a ferrite bobbin (eg Panasonic ELC series, Wurth Electronics WE-TI series, available from RS components [6]). The inductance values are not critical, and other types of inductor with a Q of 50 or more at the receive frequency should be satisfactory.

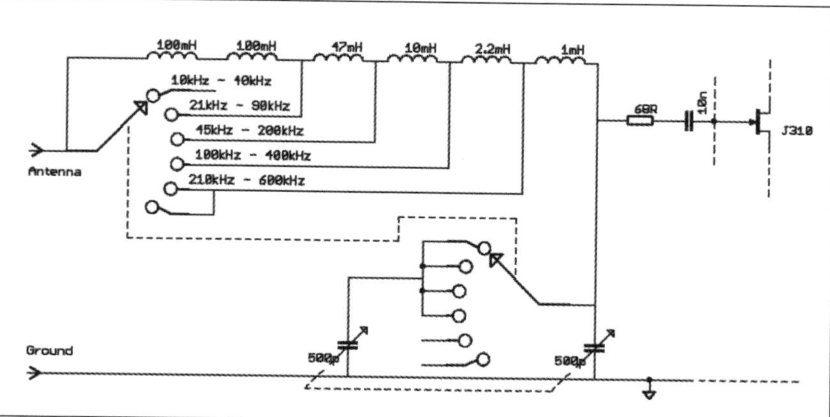

Fig 2.5 10kHz - 600kHz multi-band input circuit for preselector

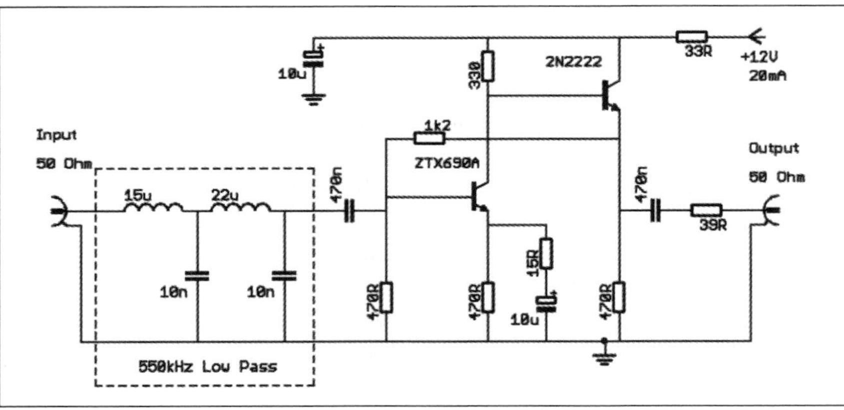

Fig 2.6: 20dB preamplifier

Pre-amplifier

For particularly insensitive receivers, more gain may be required than is provided by the preselector by itself. Also, small tuned-loop antennas have quite low signal output and require a low-noise preamp with 50-ohm input and output impedance to drive the receiver. The preamplifier circuit in **Fig 2.6** gives about 20dB of gain through the VLF, LF and MF ranges. The ZTX690A transistor gives a noise figure of about 3dB in the LF/MF range in this circuit; if low noise is not so important, other transistors such as the 2N2222 can be used with a few dB increase in noise figure. The preamp is shown with an optional low-pass input filter with cut-off frequency around 550kHz; this is advisable in order to reduce the level of broadcast signals reaching the receiver.

LF/MF to HF converter

Fig 2.7 shows the converter. It uses a 4MHz crystal oscillator and broadband diode mixer module to up-convert input signals from a few kilohertz up to the 550kHz cut-off frequency of the input low-pass filter, to an output range of 4.00MHz to 4.55MHz.

Fig 2.7: LF/MF - HF Converter

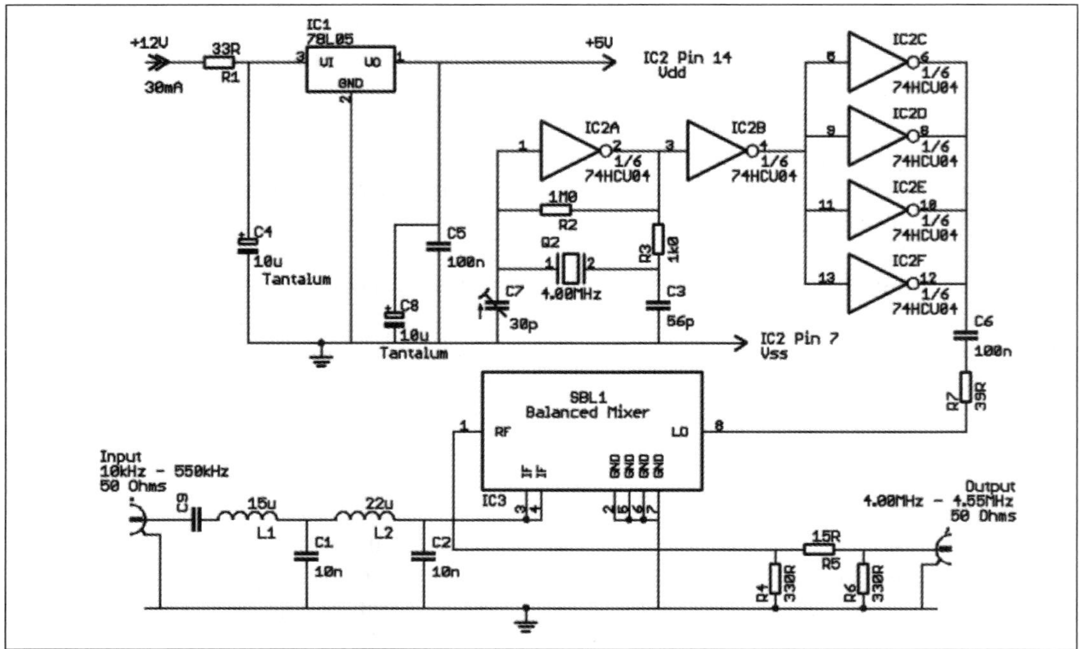

The LF/MF input signal is fed into the DC-coupled IF port of the SBL-1 mixer, and the HF output is taken from the RF port - this allows input frequencies below the 500kHz minimum of the RF port.

The crystal oscillator uses one gate of a 74HCU04 hex CMOS inverter IC, with the remaining five gates used as a buffer amplifier to drive the diode mixer. A wide range of other crystal frequencies could also be used to obtain different output frequency ranges if preferred; due to the broad-band nature of the mixer, no further modification is needed other than to change the crystal. An oscillator frequency below 2MHz makes the circuit more susceptible to IF breakthrough and image responses, while frequencies much over 10MHz will lead to reduced frequency stability, which may be a problem when narrow-band modes such as QRSS are being received.

The converter output has a simple -3dB attenuator pad to reduce the effect of output impedance variations on the mixer; the circuit therefore has an overall loss of about 10dB. No post-mixer amplifier stage is included, since most HF receivers include a low-noise preamplifier that can be switched in to perform this function. The crystal frequency can be adjusted by setting the HF receiver to exactly 4MHz (or other crystal frequency), and adjusting the trimmer capacitor so that the oscillator signal is exactly centred in the CW passband of the receiver. The received input frequency is then the value displayed by the receiver, minus the crystal frequency. This converter gives good performance from 550kHz down to very low frequencies, and for receivers with very poor sensitivity at LF or MF will often give better results than the addition of high-gain preamplifiers. It is also an effective way of extending the lower frequency capability of HF-only receivers.

Software Defined Radio Receivers

With the availability of low-cost personal computers with powerful digital signal processing capability, software-defined radio (SDR) has become practical for use by LF and MF amateurs during the last few years. Several suites of SDR software have been made available free of charge for amateur use [7, 8, 9]. These are generally used in conjunction with the PC sound card for analogue to digital conversion, and an external I/Q down-converter to convert the signal from radio frequency down to the audio range where it can be handled by the sound card (for a detailed tutorial on such techniques see [10]).

PC-based spectrogram software has been used for several years in conjunction with conventional receivers for the 'visual' LF operating modes such as QRSS; SDR is the natural extension of this trend. The narrow bandwidth of the 136kHz and 500kHz allocations are well suited to sound card based SDR receivers, since the whole band can easily be accommodated within the sound card input bandwidth, allowing all tuning and channel filtering functions to be performed in the digital domain, and a simple fixed-frequency crystal oscillator to be used for down-conversion. Modifications to the well-known 'SoftRock' SDR receiver kits to enable 136kHz and 500kHz reception are described below.

General coverage SDR receivers are also becoming commercially available to amateurs at reasonable prices. The WinRadio G313 is reported to perform well. The RFSpace Inc SDR-IQ receiver [11] has been used successfully by KL1X for LF and MF reception at a variety of exotic DX locations. I2PHD has a web

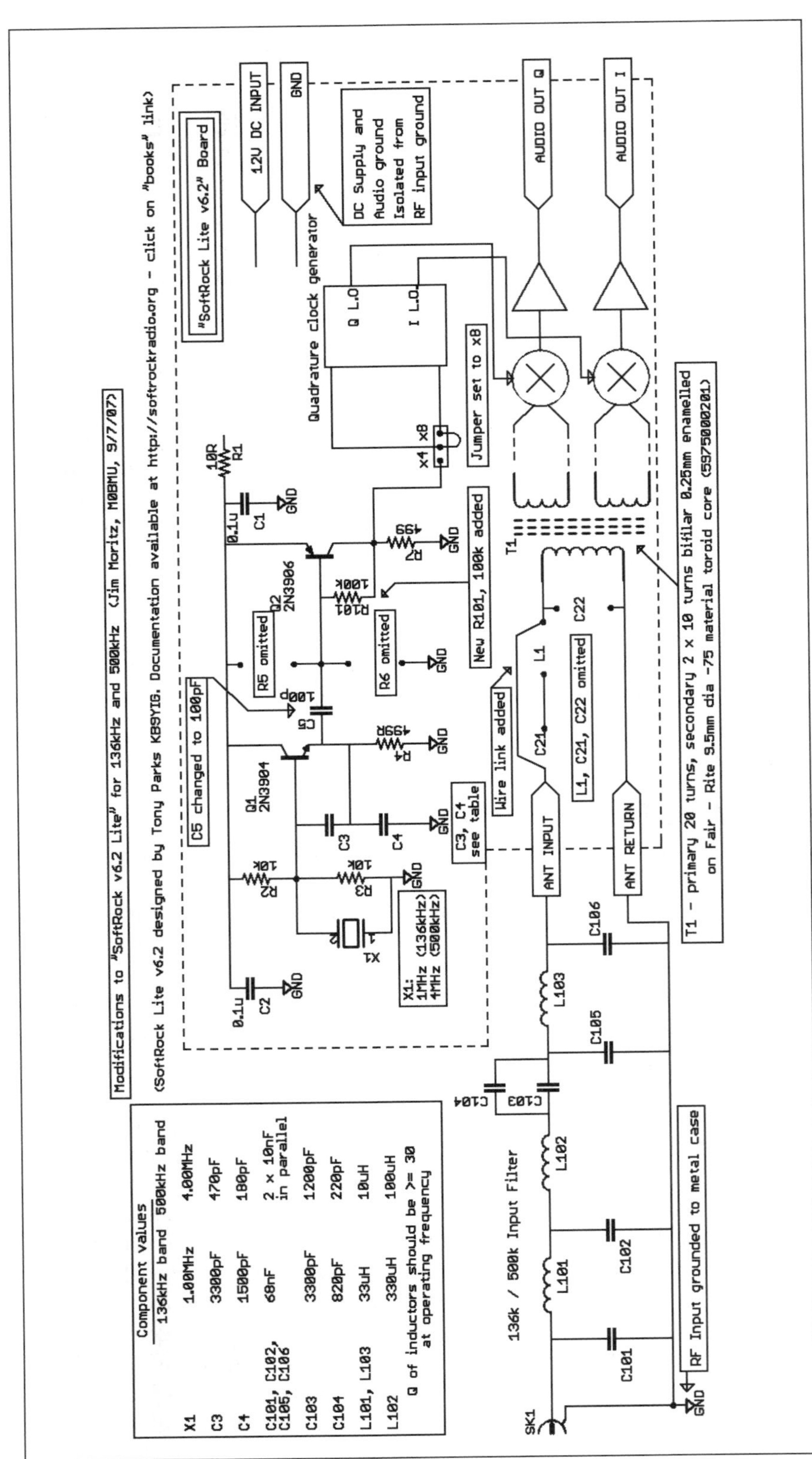

Fig 2.8: Modifications to SoftRock Lite v6.2 for 136kHz and 500kHz

page [12] showing his own experiences with this receiver. The SDR-IQ allows recording of up to 190kHz of the spectrum at one time.

'SoftRock Lite' modifications for 136kHz/500kHz

The SoftRock software-defined radio kits designed by Tony Parks, KB9YIG, have been popular as an entry-level SDR project for the HF bands (see [10] for much more about this receiver). The same concept, with suitable modifications, is well suited to the narrow 136kHz and 500kHz allocations.

The modifications described here were applied to the SoftRock Lite v6.2 kit, but other similar SDR boards could be modified in a similar way. **Fig 2.8** shows the modifications to the SoftRock circuit (complete documentation of the original circuit is supplied with the kits, and can also be downloaded from [13]). Two major changes are required for 136kHz or 500kHz; the local oscillator frequency is changed, and the input bandpass filter is re-designed.

For the 500kHz band, the crystal frequency is changed to 4.0MHz, and for 136kHz a 1MHz crystal is used. With the "x8" jumper on the PCB fitted, this gives local oscillator frequencies of 500kHz and 125kHz respectively, giving tuning ranges of 476 - 524kHz, and 101 - 149kHz with a 48kHz sample rate. The existing SoftRock oscillator/driver circuit just works at 4MHz, but not 1MHz. Fig 2.7 shows changes to the circuit to obtain better oscillator waveforms at the lower frequencies. 4MHz crystals are easily obtained; M0BMU had several 1MHz crystals in the junk box, but these are less readily available. An alternative would be to use a 1MHz DIL oscillator module, with its logic-level output connected directly to the divider flip-flop.

The original SoftRock input filter could be re-designed for the LF/MF bands, but the components required would be too big for the tiny PCB, and the rejection of LF and MF broadcast stations near harmonics of the local oscillator frequency would probably not be good enough. Instead, the original tuned input transformer T1 is replaced by a wideband ferrite-cored transformer, and off-board filters were designed with increased rejection at harmonic frequencies. As in the original SoftRock design, component values are fixed, and no adjustment is required. Values are shown for each band. For the 500kHz band, small axial-leaded inductors the size of half-watt resistors were used and were quite satisfactory. For the 136kHz band, this type of component has insufficient Q, leading to high insertion loss and a poorly-defined filter passband. Instead, slightly larger radial-leaded chokes wound on ferrite bobbins (eg Panasonic ELC series [6]) were used. Their Q of around 40 was adequate.

The tiny SoftRock version 6.2 receiver

Both 136kHz and 500kHz versions have been used, mainly with I2PHD's Winrad software [9] and DL4YHF's Spectrum Lab software [8], both with excellent results. If the connections to the PC sound card input are made according to the details on the SoftRock kit schematic, the 'reverse I and Q channels' option should be selected to give correct sideband selection. The phase and amplitude balance between I and Q channels should be adjusted to obtain maximum rejection at the 'image' frequency of the centre of the amateur band (about 497.5kHz for the 501-503kHz band, 113.2kHz for 136kHz). This is especially important on 136kHz, where strong signals are present around the image frequency. Sensitivity on both bands was around 1 microvolt for 10dB SNR with a CW bandwidth of 300Hz; this is not particularly high, but is quite adequate if a transmitting-type antenna is used, or a preamplifier or preselector such as the one above.

In order to prevent low frequency noise generated by the PC and its power supply from getting into the sound card audio input, it was important to maintain isolation between the audio output ground and the RF input ground of the SoftRock circuit. The RF ground was connected to the metal case housing the SoftRock board and input filter, and the audio output and DC supply ground connections were insulated from the case. It was also necessary to use separate DC supplies for the SoftRock and preamplifier or transmitter to prevent ground loops. Connecting RF and Audio grounds together within the case resulted in a 30 - 40dB increase in noise level.

Home made receivers

Because of the stringent requirements of a receiver for 136kHz, it is not worth building one from scratch unless you have considerable expertise in this area. Nevertheless, a basic receiver can be constructed for fun or for occasional portable use. IK2PII's 136kHz direct conversion receiver is described at [14]. For more serious applications, IK2PII has designed a receiver with an audio output at 2,500Hz specifically for QRSS use. The final selectivity is achieved in the QRSS software. Full details can be found at [15].

There are few very close-in strong signals at 500kHz, so it is more viable to use a simple receiver. G3WCB's direct conversion receiver (**Fig 2.9)** was conceived as a 'weekender' project and is designed to combine portability with low power consumption (60mA at 12V) and reasonable performance. Stability is good enough for CW, and possibly for QRSS3.

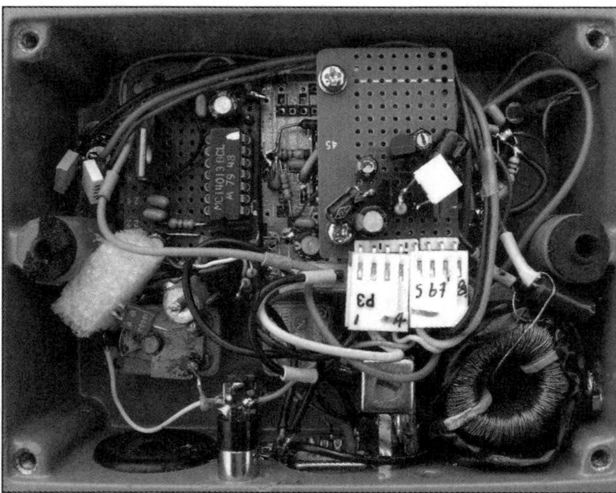

G3WCB's D1131 direct conversion receiver for 500kHz

The VXO uses a 1 MHz Murata ceramic resonator X1 (RS part 656-158). 501 - 504 kHz can be covered in two switched bands. Link LK-1 on the reset line of the CD4013 divider inhibits the 501 kHz output when it is removed. This can be used to mute the RX, while leaving the VXO running for better stability.

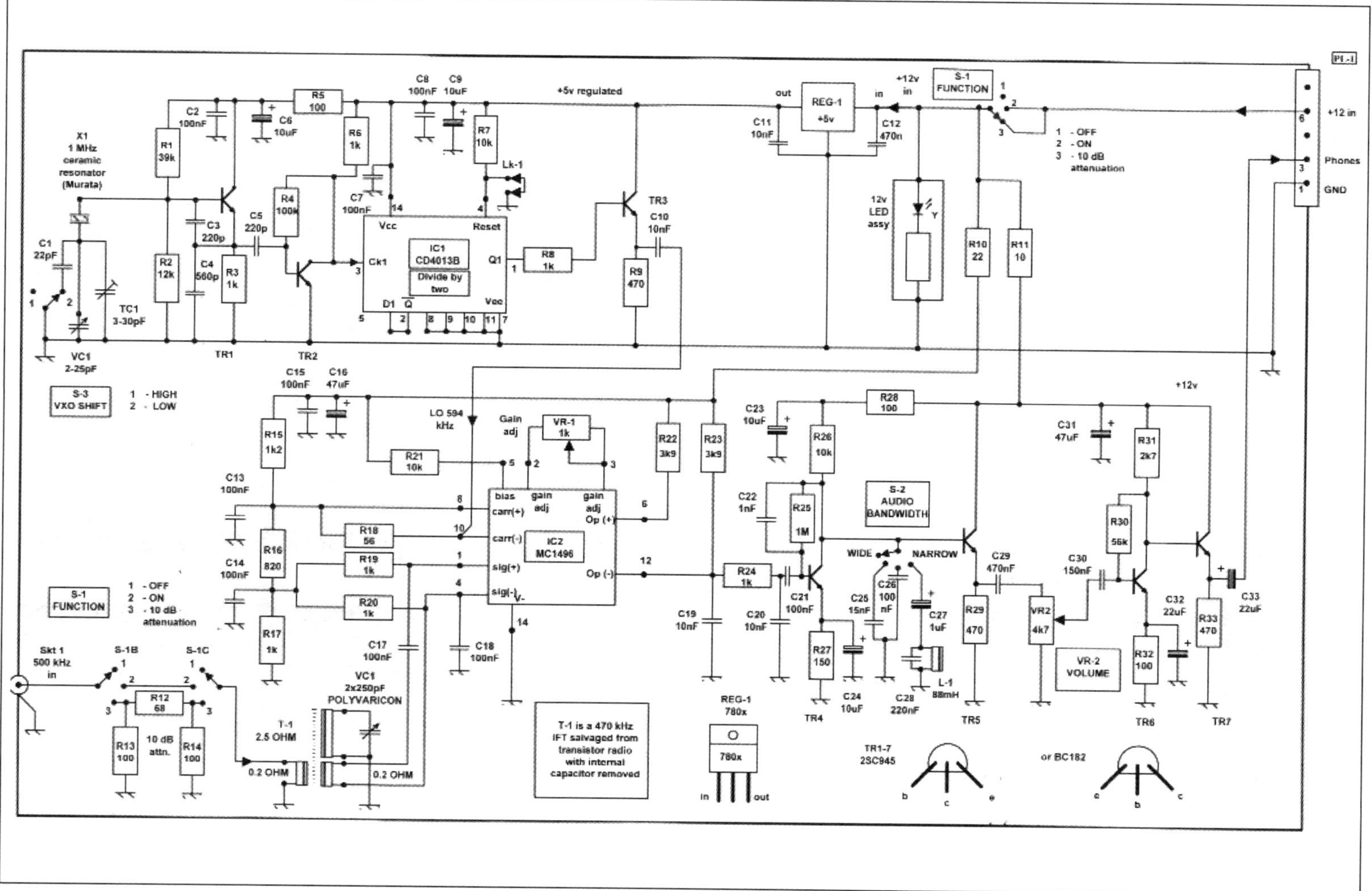

Fig 2.9: Direct conversion receiver covering 501 - 504kHz

The divider could be keyed via this link to enable the VXO to drive a transmitter.

BC182 transistors are used for all stages, but 2SC945 transistors also work. TR5 should be a low-noise device with a high Hfe for best performance, as the bulk of the RX audio gain and noise contribution comes from this stage.

Avoid using disc ceramic caps for the audio stages, as they can be microphonic. T-1 is a salvaged 470 kHz IFT with the internal capacitor removed and VC-1 is a 350 pF Polyvaricon capacitor, both from a scrapped portable radio.

The inductor in the collector of TR5 is a 88mH toroid tuned with a 220nF polyester capacitor. It is switched in and out by S-2. S-2 also allows capacitors to be switched in to tailor the high-frequency response of the audio stages.

With a good pair of earphones (eg Sennheiser HD48011) it is just possible to detect a CW signal of -123 dBm, or about 0.3 micro-volt on 501kHz. With a simple tuned pre-amp (single J-310) this improves to -141 dBm. The noise level on 500 kHz at the G3WCB location is about -100 dBm, with local UK 500 kHz amateur signals averaging around -70 dBm, so the pre-amp is not essential, but the extra selectivity reduces the amount of broadcast band breakthrough.

References

[1] TS-850 mods at *http://www.radiomods.co.nz/kenwood/kenwoodts850.html.* Note that the modification is simpler than described on this web site, as at Stage 9 it is not necessary to remove the RF board. Simply solder a jumper on the track side of the board. [Note that any mods to commercial radios are done at your own risk]

[2] Low pass filter. *http://www.g0mrf.freeserve.co.uk/lpf.htm*

[3] Receiver mods for LF use. *http://www.amrad.org/projects/lf/rx/index.htm*

[4] Selective Level Meter MV61 Used as a Receiver for VLF and LF *http://www.qru.de/MV61.htm.*
Also, Frequency Selective Voltmeters and their Uses in the Radio Hobby *http://www.qru.de/selective%20level%20meters.html*

[5] The PA0LQ Audio CW Filter. *http://www.alg.demon.co.uk/radio/136 /af_filter.htm*

[6] RS Components web pages and on-line catalogue: *http://rswww.com*

[7] 'Rocky' SDR software by VE3NEA at *http://www.dxatlas.com/Rocky/*

[8] 'Spectrum Lab' and other radio-related software can be downloaded via DL4YHF's web pages: *http://freenet_homepage.de/dl4yhf/*

[9] 'Winrad' SDR software and other radio-related software can be downloaded from I2PHD's Weaksignals site: *http://www.weaksignals.com*

[10] Radio Communication Handbook, 9th edition, 2007, RSGB

[11] *http://www.rfspace.com/sdriq.html*

[12] *http://sundry.i2phd.com/sdriq_on_LF.htm*

[13] *http://www.softrockradio.org*

[14] IK2PII's direct conversion receiver. *http://www.qsl.net/ik2pii/lf/ dcrx136.htm*

[15] 136kHz One Knob QRSS Receiver. *http://www.qsl.net/ik2pii/lf/ okqrssrx.htm*

3

Antennas and matching

In this chapter:

- A tiny bit of theory
- Antenna options
- Marconi design considerations
- Danger high voltage!
- Using an existing antenna
- Ground systems
- Purpose-built antennas
- Marconi loading and matching
- Transmitting loops
- Why use 50 ohms on LF?
- Antenna supports

THIS CHAPTER DEALS WITH the special requirements of transmitting antennas, all of which can be used for reception. Antennas designed specifically for receiving are covered in the next chapter.

Mathematics have, by and large, been kept to a minimum; the main emphasis being on practical considerations. Those wishing to investigate the 'why' rather than the 'how' should read references [1], [2] and [3].

As discussed earlier, the ideal antenna for the 136kHz band would be a vertical 550 metres high tuned against an extensive earth mat around 1km across. Even at 500kHz, you would need to use a 150m high tower. In practice, even commercial LF stations do not often use full sized antennas. A compromise is reached by shortening the element length, bending it to reduce its height, and compensating for the 'lost wire' by adding a loading coil.

For a typical amateur installation, the degree of compromise is considerable. This gives rise to several problems, the greatest of which is a reduction in efficiency to a fraction of 1% on 136kHz and only a few percent at 500kHz. Others include the need for a large loading coil and the presence (at least on 136kHz) of very high antenna voltages at quite low transmitter powers.

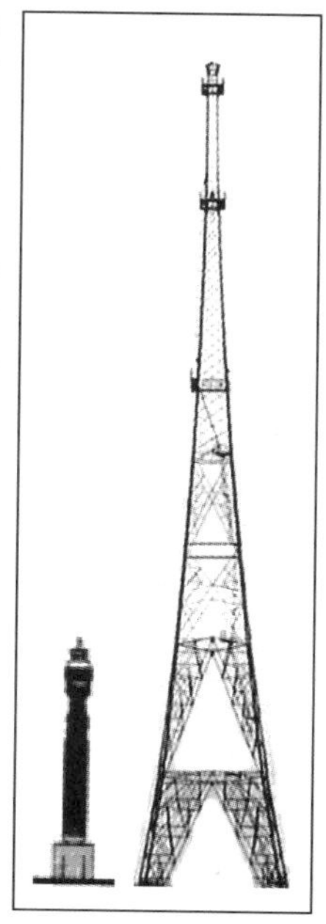

A full-sized vertical for 136kHz would be nearly three times as high as London's BT tower

A tiny bit of theory

The effective radiated power (ERP) radiated by an antenna is determined by the product of its radiation resistance, the square of the antenna current, and the directivity (ie the gain resulting from the directional pattern of the antenna):

$$P_{ERP} = r_{RAD} \times I^2 \times D$$

We have control over two of these at LF: the radiation resistance of the antenna and the current passing through it. The radiation resistance is related to the antenna's size and shape, whilst the current is a function of the applied RF power and the total resistance. Unfortunately, the radiation resistance is not the

See the chapter on Measurement and Calculations for the maths behind low frequency antennas, including how to calculate ERP.

only resistance consuming the transmitter power, there are also the loss resistances. These losses occur within the antenna and its matching system, and in the environment of the antenna (the ground system, objects near the antenna). On HF these loss resistances are often negligible as they are small compared to the radiation resistance, but at LF this is certainly not the case.

For most amateur antennas the radiation resistance on the 136kHz band is in the range of one to a few hundred milliohms (yes, thousandths of an ohm!), while loss resistances are in the range of 30 to 200 ohms. This means that, dependent on the antenna and its environment, about 99% to 99.99% of the transmitter power is not radiated but absorbed in the loss resistances. This is why it is actually quite difficult for the average amateur station to reach the UK licence limit of one watt effective radiated power.

Typical radiation resistance rises to somewhere between a few tens of milliohms and an ohm or two at 500kHz and losses fall to about half of the 136kHz figure. This results in an efficiency improvement of 20-30 times that on the lower band. Because of this, it is relatively easy to achieve the 100mW ERP limit in the experimental licences.

For those who like maths, the formula for calculating the radiation resistance of a monopole is given in the measurements chapter. The formulas for caculating antenna efficiency and hence ERP can also be found in that chapter. Being able to estimate ERP is an essential part of the experimental permit for transmitting at 500kHz.

At a distance, the electric and magnetic fields produced by any antenna are the same for a given effective radiated power. Close to a loop antenna, however, the magnetic field is relatively large, while the electric field near a vertical monopole predominates.

Antenna options

Those with very large gardens may think in terms of a loaded horizontal dipole for 136kHz. Unfortunately, the effective height would be so low as to render such an antenna totally ineffective. There are two practical options: a loop or a

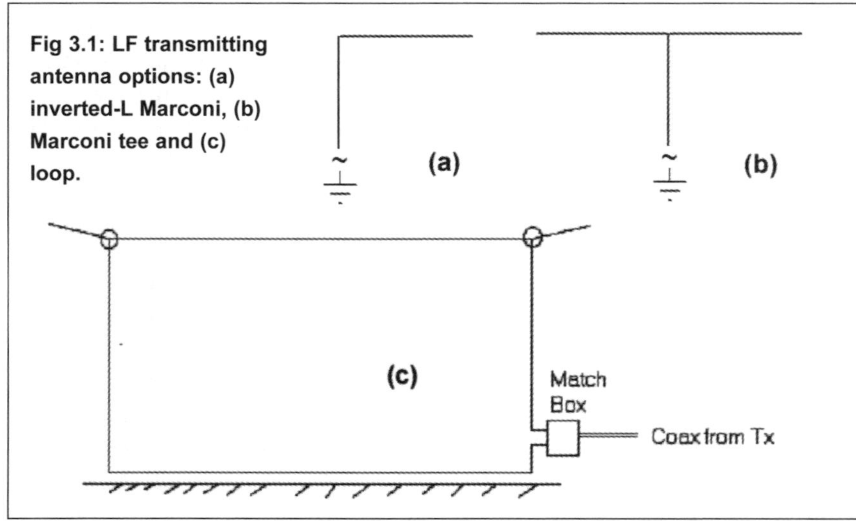

Fig 3.1: LF transmitting antenna options: (a) inverted-L Marconi, (b) Marconi tee and (c) loop.

Marconi (vertical) (**Fig 3.1**). Experiments by UK amateurs have shown the Marconi to have some advantages, but the loop continues to have its devotees, especially in the USA.

An LF transmitting loop comprises a single turn of low-loss wire (there is no advantage in a multi-turn system) with as large an area as possible, with its lowest point a metre or so above ground (**Fig 3.1c**). The loop must be tuned to resonance and matched to the feeder or transmitter. Its chief advantage is that, as described above, it is much less affected by lossy nearby objects, eg trees and houses, than a Marconi and it does not require a good ground. The loop has a figure-of-eight directional pattern; this is a disadvantage for transmission due to the deep nulls in the transmitted signal at right angles to the loop.

The classic Marconi is a vertical monopole with the top part bent over to form a capacity hat. Typical designs for HF and MF use are the 'T' and the inverted 'L'. These work fine at LF, though any shape of top section will work so long as it has sufficient capacity to ground. An efficient ground system must be provided.

Design considerations of an LF Marconi

The formula for calculating effective radiated power (ERP) is dealt with in detail in the measurements chapter. For the purposes of the design of a vertical antenna it is important to note that it includes on the top line the term h_{eff}^2. This means that the ERP is directly proportional to the square of the effective height of the antenna. So doubling the effective height will increase your radiated power by four times and any increase in h_{eff} will be useful.

So what is effective height and how does it differ from the actual height? If you consider the current distribution on a short vertical (and all amateur LF antennas can be considered to be short), it can be seen that the current is at a maximum at the bottom - usually the feedpoint - reducing approximately linearly to zero at the top (**Fig 3.2**). The average current is half of the maximum current. The effective height is therefore considered to be half of the total height.

If a horizontal capacity hat is added, as in the inverted-L, the effective height will be increased from this 50% figure, by an amount determined by the size of the capacitance. Note that the effective height will always be between 50% and 100% of the height of the vertical section. A very large amount of horizontal wire will bring the effective height close to 100%. Any part of the capacity hat that is lower than the top of the vertical section will tend to reduce the effective height.

A bonus to having a substantial capacity hat is that it reduces the amount of inductive loading needed to bring the antenna to resonance, ie the loading coil can have fewer turns and hence less loss.

The vertical section should be as vertical as possible because any horizontal component will have a capacity to ground which will detract from the effective height. There is no need for multiple wires in the vertical section. The

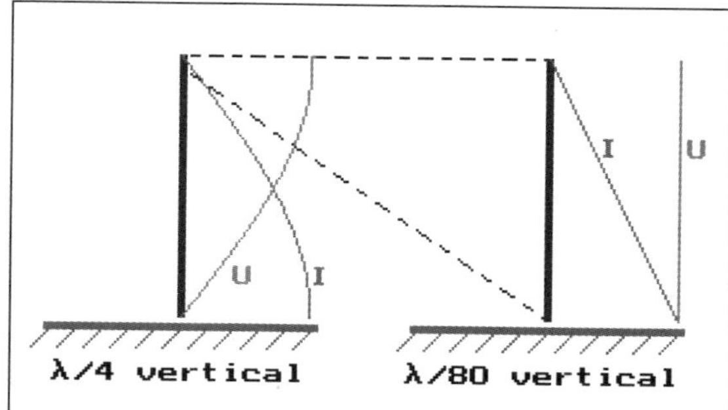

Fig 3.2: Current and voltage distribution on a full-sized, and very short, Marconi antenna

> **The Golden Rule of short Marconis:**
>
> *Get as much wire in the air as you can, as high as possible*

vertical wire should also be as far away as possible from other vertical items such as house wiring and trees.

It is often necessary to run the vertical wire close to the pole or tower that supports it. In this case, unless the pole is very well insulated from ground and other supports (walls, guy wires) losses can be reduced by grounding it. You may think that this will 'short out' the vertical wire, but in fact it simply provides a low-loss capacitance to earth instead of dissipating power in the lossy return to earth. If in doubt, try it and see for yourself.

In general terms, the capacity hat should comprise as many wires as possible, as far apart as possible and covering as much ground as possible.

Without getting into too much detail, the key physical factor is that there is a logarithmic variation of capacitance with both diameter of wire and height of wire above ground level. A calculation for doubling the wire diameter from 1mm to 2mm results in an increase of capacitance of only some 7%. The height above ground also only has a minor effect. The practical implication is that the wire diameter used and the height above ground are not critical factors in determining the net capacitance. The length of the top loading wire is the main factor.

Results of capacitance calculations based on reference values of 1mm diameter wire and a T antenna (**Fig 3.3**) with a height of 10 metres above ground are:

* vertical downlead approximately 6 picofarads per metre of wire
* top loading approximately 5 picofarads per metre of wire

We shall use these figures in a later chapter to calculate the approximate radiated power from a Marconi antenna.

Further calculations were carried out to explore the impact of running two same diameter parallel wires, rather than a single wire. The reference condition again being wire of 1 mm diameter at 10 metres above ground. The following results were obtained:

* 2 wires separated by 1 mm increases capacitance by about 4%
* 2 wires separated by 10 mm increases capacitance by about 19%
* 2 wires separated by 100 mm increases capacitance by about 39%
* 2 wires separated by 1 metre increases capacitance by about 68%
* 2 widely separated wires increases capacitance by up to 100%, ie double the capacitance of a single wire, as one would expect.

The results indicate how proximity effect limits the realisable net capacitance for closer spaced wires. However, despite proximity effect, it is generally the case that two wires are better than one when it comes to increasing the net capacitance. Note that doubling the wire diameter results in four times the surface area and happens to result in 7% more capacitance, whereas two same diameter wires that are nearly touching involve two times the surface area and happen to have a 4% increase in capacitance. Note also that doubling the wire diameter gives a weight increase of four times, so in terms of mechanical support and sag of wires in an antenna, two separate wires again are generally better than a single thicker wire. It is clear that multiple wires are the answer to arranging useful top loading. It is

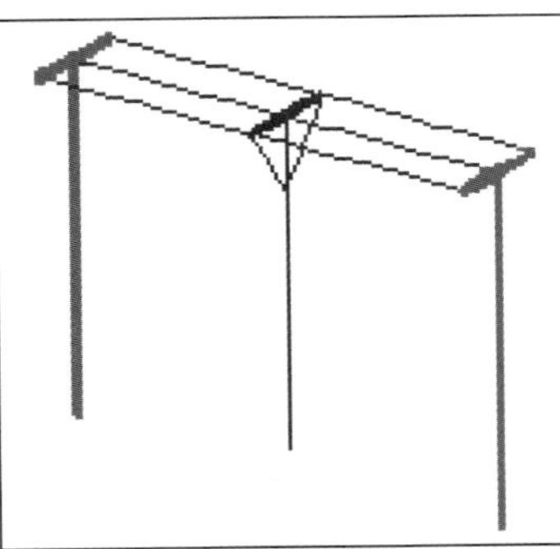

Fig 3.3: Multiple wire tee antenna

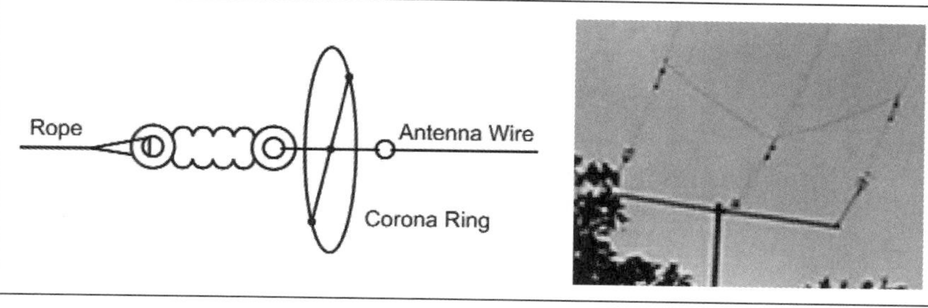

Fig 3.4: Two ways of reducing corona discharge from wire ends: (left) A ring termination, and (right) ends joined together. The photograph shows the far end of a three-wire capacity hat. Note the two sets of insulators on each wire

also clear that this is already known to the designers of commercial LF beacon antennas, as T antennas are extensively used, with typically two or three parallel wires in the top loading, with spacing of a metre or so.

In practice, the wires need not be the same length or in a symmetrical pattern. It is tempting to increase capacitance by bringing the ends of the capacity hat down towards the ground as is done with full-sized HF antennas such as the inverted-vee. However, the effective height, and therefore the efficiency, of a short LF antenna is considerably reduced if the capacity hat droops too much. The wires should not run too close to lossy objects such as trees and buildings. In fact it can be useful to prune the trees and large shrubs in your garden before erecting the antenna.

Danger, high voltage!

Extremely high voltages - tens of kilovolts - can be expected on an LF Marconi tuned to 136kHz, even with transmitter powers of a few tens of watts. For this reason, never allow any part of an LF antenna to touch trees, walls, window frames or even plastic guttering. Not only will this cause large losses, but there is also a significant risk of fire as several LF experimenters have already found out. Note that, contrary to what you might think, a small antenna will have higher voltages on it than a large one.

At 500kHz, the smaller power levels and greater antenna efficiency reduce voltages to a few hundred volts, but care must still be taken.

Very high antenna voltages can produce an effect known as 'corona discharge' in which tiny sparks emit from wires, even through insulation. Corona eats away at plastic items such as cable ties. It is tempting to rely on nylon rope as an end-insulator, but this will invariably lead to the rope melting and the wire falling down. Instead, use good quality insulators. If two insulators are used in series, join them with short lengths of wire, not plastic. Even after taking these precautions, it is important to reduce the corona as the sparks are a form of power loss. Corona discharge is far worse at sharp points, such as the ends of wires or right angle bends. Losses can be reduced by ensuring that all bends are gradual. Wire ends can be protected by forming them into a small loop. Corona on a multi-wire top section can be reduced by joining the ends together. **Fig 3.4** illustrates these methods.

A plastic dustbin can be used as a waterproof housing for the main part of the loading coil at the foot of the mast

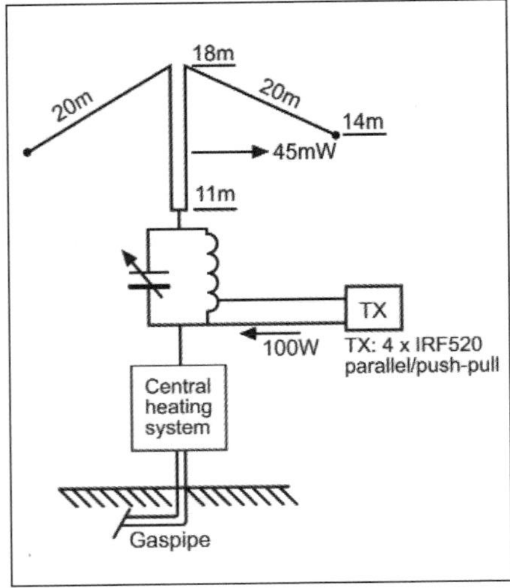

Fig 3.5: This is how PA0SE uses his 40 metre dipole as an LF antenna. Note that his variable capacitor is a vacuum type - an air-spaced component would certainly flash over. A variable inductor is more often used

Precautions against high voltage flash-over should extend to all parts of the antenna system, including the loading coil and any tuning mechanism. It is especially important to pay attention to any part of the antenna that passes through the window or wall of a shed or the house. A common problem is how to run an LF antenna wire through a window frame from the 'shack' to the outside world. Often the loading coil is located in the shack for ease of tuning and to keep it out of the weather. The voltage on the antenna system is far higher after the loading coil, so a preferable arrangement is to mount the coil in a weatherproof box such as a plastic dustbin outside the shack (see photograph). The wire between the coil and the transmitter then has a much reduced voltage on it.

Any part of the antenna system that can be touched should have clear warning signs, but this is no substitute for making the antenna inaccessible to humans and animals.

Using an existing antenna

With care, an existing MF, HF (or even VHF) antenna installation can be pressed into service as an 136kHz/500kHz antenna, usually by strapping the feeder to form a vertical element and using the MF/HF antenna as a capacity hat (**Fig 3.5**). The system should, of course be tuned against a ground system (see later).

An ideal set-up would be a dipole for 1.8MHz, with the shack directly underneath its centre. However, smaller antennas will work, especially if they are at a good height. It is possible to modify feeder runs when the shack is not in the ideal position.

As described above, the vertical section - in this case the dipole's coaxial feeder - should be predominantly vertical and clear of any nearby objects. It may well be necessary to divide your coax run into the vertical bit that goes to the antenna and the horizontal bit that runs from the shack. Adding a connector at this point will make it simple to change from the LF Marconi configuration back to the HF arrangement

A box should be installed at the foot of the vertical section, to contain the loading coil and any matching device. This will need an enclosure at least 0.5m cube, but preferably larger. A dustbin or small shed is ideal. In the intense RF fields near the loading coil and antenna feeder, objects such as plants, trees or masonry may cause significant RF losses. If the loading coil enclosure cannot be positioned away from these, an enclosure lined with (or made of) metal which is earthed can improve efficiency by screening the coil from the lossy materials.

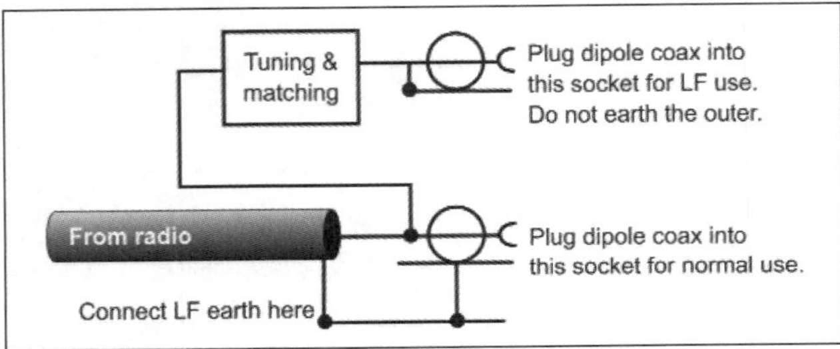

Fig 3.6: Simple method of switching a dipole for 160, 80 or 40m between use as a dipole and use as a Marconi for 136kHz and/or 500kHz, by using coax sockets

Do not be tempted to install a switch to change the antenna configuration from HF to LF. The LF antenna will have very high voltages on it when transmitting and these can cause flash-overs that may damage your HF radio. It is preferable to do the change-over by moving coax plugs (**Fig 3.6**).

The horizontal section of an HF dipole may already be suitable if it is well engineered, but it is important to check that it does not droop too much, that it does not touch or even run too close to trees or walls, and that the insulators are of high quality. Making improvements in these areas may also boost the performance of the antenna when used on the bands they were originally intended for.

An 160m or HF ground-plane vertical or inverted-L can be pressed into service for LF using a similar technique.

An entirely horizontal wire will not be effective at LF. However, if a long-wire antenna can be contrived to have some vertical component, perhaps by introducing a slope or moving the feedpoint to ground level, it can work surprisingly well.

It may be possible to use an HF, or even VHF, beam antenna if the mast is well insulated from the ground, or the tower can be used as the support for a sloper for LF.

Ground systems

A vital part of a Marconi antenna is the ground system, which forms the return path for the antenna current to the transmitter output.

The ground system can be as simple as a single earth rod driven into the ground, or as complex as hundreds of radial wires. Commercial low frequency stations use hundreds of kilometres of wire spread out over a radius of several hundred metres.

How easy it is to provide an efficient ground connection, and indeed the efficiency of the antenna itself, will depend on the conductivity of the soil beneath the antenna and extending for some kilometres away from the station. Sea water is ideal and proximity to the sea can be a great advantage. Clay can be useful, whilst sand and rock tend to be poor. **Fig 3.7** gives an idea of how the soil conductivity varies with geography.

Amateur LF stations have been operated from all types of terrain, so do not be discouraged. Poorer soils just need a bit more work and some ingenuity.

The most basic earth connection is a single metal stake driven a metre or so into the ground. The current density is highest at the bottom of the vertical section, so the earth stake should be as close

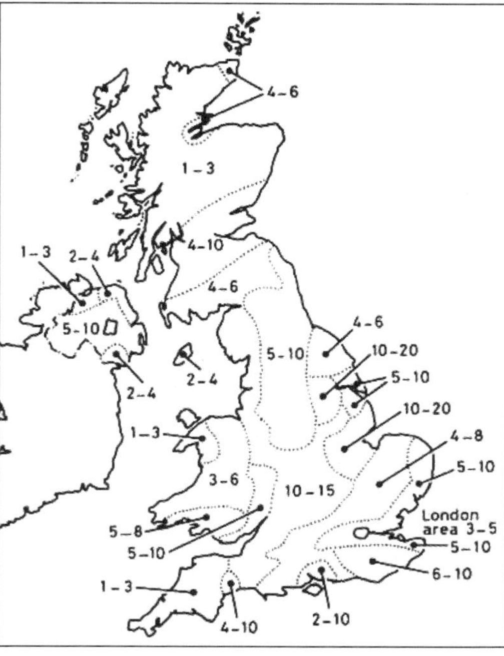

Fig 3.7: Rough ground conductivity map of the UK (figures quoted are for 1.5MHz). Conductivity is moderate to good in central and southeast England, poor in London, west and northwest. Urban areas tend to be of lower conductivity than farmland and rural areas

> **WARNING**
>
> Many modern houses in the UK have an electricity safety earth system known as Protective Multiple Earthing (PME). Under some fault circumstances this could pose a risk to amateur stations. It is recommended that your RF earth is bonded to the PME bonding point using cable of at least $10mm^2$ in accordance with IEE wiring regulations. A leaflet on this subject, endorsed by the Electricity Association, is available from the RSGB's EMC Committee.

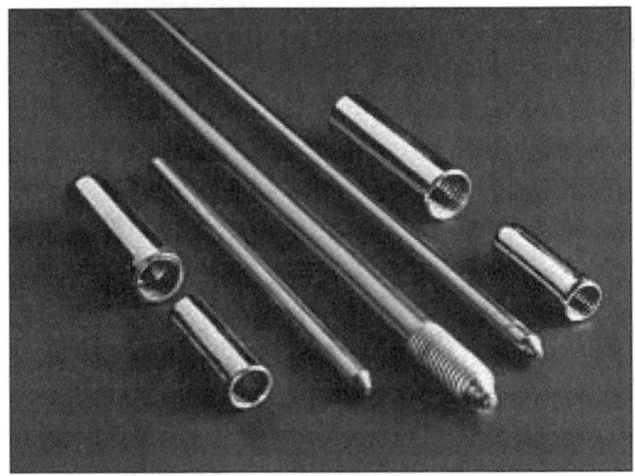

Purpose designed earth rods *[photo: www.conexmetals.com]*

as possible to this point. This simple arrangement will get your station on the air, but should not be regarded as optimum.

In practice, successful LF earth systems include a mixture of earth stakes, radials and any other earthed items such as water pipes and even tin roofs.

When using a Marconi antenna on the 1.8MHz, radial wires, sometimes raised above ground, are often used in preference to earth stakes. This is still an option on 136kHz, but any radials will be a much smaller fraction of a wavelength and hence much less efficient.

Earth stakes should be a metre or two long. Copper water piping is cheap and easily obtainable but it is soft and will eventually bend rather than go any deeper. Purpose-designed earth rods are now available from big hardware stores.

Radial wires should be as long as possible and can be run along the surface of the ground, or just below it. There seems little agreement on whether the wire should be bare, ie in direct contact with the soil, or insulated.

As a general rule of thumb, an LF earth system should comprise as many elements (stakes, radials, water pipes) as possible, but this is not the entire answer. Firstly, the efficiency of the earth system is not directly proportional to the number of elements involved, and the results obtained from the second set of radials will be rather less than the first set, and so on. A point will be reached where adding further elements to the ground system produces little or no improvement. Increasing efficiency further will then require improvements to other parts of the antenna system.

Secondly, it has been found that not every additional earthing element improves the situation. This may be because the reactances inherent in each element act against each other. So when building your earth system, it is useful to bring each separate element to a connection strip, so that the effect of each one, or a combination of elements can be tested. Measuring the RF current flowing into each earthing element will show which are the most effective.

> **WARNING**
>
> Before driving an earth stake into the ground, it is vital to make sure you avoid any buried services, such as water, drains, telephone, cable TV, gas or electricity.

Suitable current meters are described in the measurements chapter. A sophisticated method of measuring ground loss, and some experimental results, can be found on G3NYK's web site [4].

Although a good earth is important for a Marconi antenna, do not spend too much effort on it because the other losses in the system can be much higher. Time and energy are better spent getting more wire in the air, and higher.

Purpose-built antennas for small gardens

When designing an LF antenna from scratch, there are two important considerations: height and ground coverage.

Ideally the garden should be clear of RF absorbers such as trees and shrubs, the antenna should be well away from the house and you should have several poles or towers around the periphery of the garden, plus one in the centre supporting the vertical wire. However, in practice, every system will involve some kind of compromise, often a great deal of compromise.

Try not to compromise too much on height. As discussed above, the effective height has a square law influence on the ERP, so try to make the vertical section as high as possible whilst avoiding too much droop on the horizontal sections.

The top section, or capacity hat, can be any shape, but the most popular and practical are the L and T.

The key to success is to cover as much new ground as possible but the arrangement chosen will depend on the environment, ie how many high supports exist or can be erected, how much real estate is available and, importantly, what the neighbours will tolerate. Remember that any new antenna system may require planning permission.

A multi-wire top section may use parallel wires in the classic L or T configuration (**Fig 3.8**), or simply as much wire as can be strung between tall trees on the site (**Fig 3.9**). As detailed above, the wires should be as far apart as possible; the closer they are, the less benefit is achieved. It can be useful to join the ends of multiple wires. This may add a little to the capacitance, particularly if

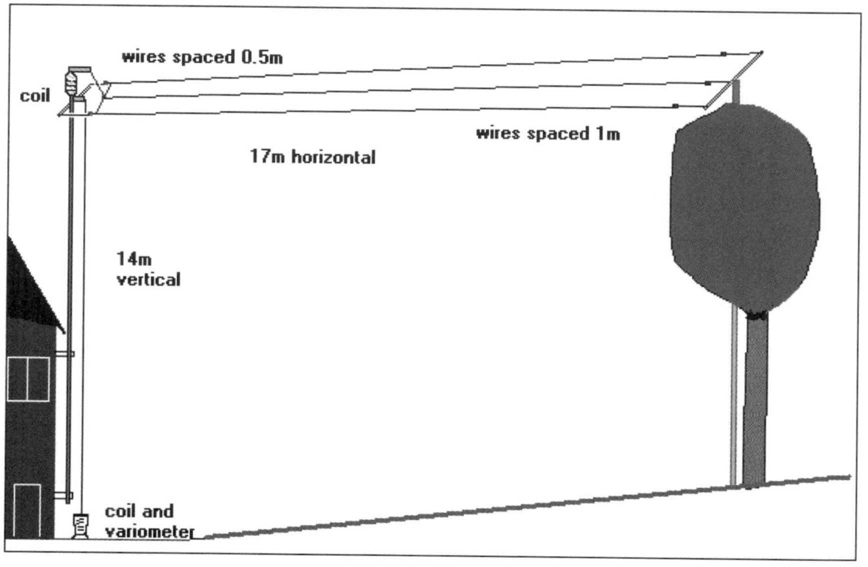

Fig 3.8: The suburban LF antenna system of G3XDV, using a house-mounted mast, and another strapped to a tall tree. The antenna uses both top and bottom inductive loading plus three top wires. This set-up has been used to make a transatlantic contact

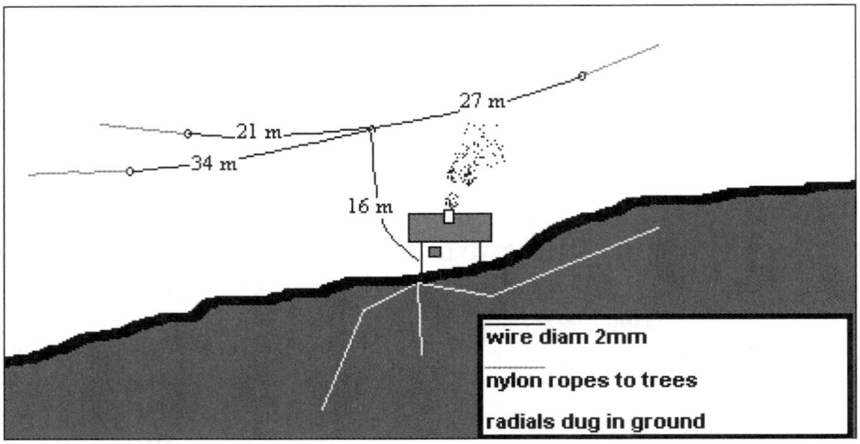

Fig 3.9: A larger set-up at OK1FIG's summer house has a top section of different lengths of wire going to a variety of handy supports. This arrangement led OK1FIG being heard at world-record distances

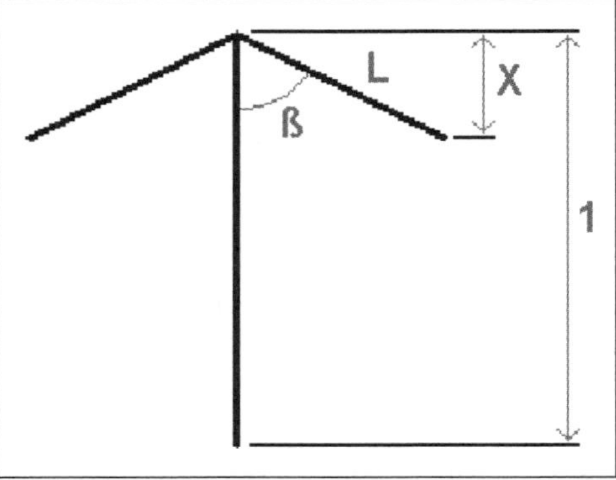

Fig 3.10: An umbrella antenna has several short top wires bent downwards to make a capacity hat. This illustration comes from [1] where a formula can be found for optimising this type of antenna

the wires are spaced far apart, but will mainly reduce corona discharge. Joining the ends may also help to keep most of the antenna aloft if one of the supports breaks.

Other capacity hat configuration used by commercial LF stations such as non-directional beacons (NDBs) is the umbrella (**Fig 3.10**). It's main advantage is that it requires only one mast, and the top wires can be part of the guying arrangement. Although this is less efficient, it may be possible to compensate by increasing the RF power.

A spiral top section (**Fig 3.11**) has been tried with some success as it combines capacitance with some extra inductance, but it is quite difficult to engineer.

Are more short wires preferable to one longer wire? This comes back to the aim of as much capacitance as possible without sacrificing too much height. A single very long top wire can be extremely effective, especially if it is at a good height (15m or more), but a similar effect can be achieved by many shorter wires. It is really a matter of what is the most convenient and if you have the resources for one long and many short wires - go for them all!

If you have the option of planning where to put the vertical section, rather than this being dictated by circumstances, it should be as far as possible from other vertical structures, including trees, masts and house wiring. The top wires must not touch any part of a tree - this will lead to losses, unpredictable performance and (on 136kHz) fires. Instead, keep all wires a few metres away from trees if at all possible. Similarly, avoid running wires above tall shrubs - or cut the shrubs first.

Loading and matching a Marconi

Any practical low bands vertical will be very much shorter than the length needed to be self-resonant. The resultant capacitive reactance must be compensated for by the addition of a series inductance, known as a loading coil. Depending on the antenna's size, and the frequency in use, this inductance can range from

0.1mH to more than 4mH. In addition, some kind of tuning mechanism will be required.

For receiving, almost any coil of the appropriate inductance will serve to resonate the antenna. However, a coil used for transmitting must be able to withstand the high current and voltage involved, as well as have the lowest possible losses. It must also be kept out of the rain.

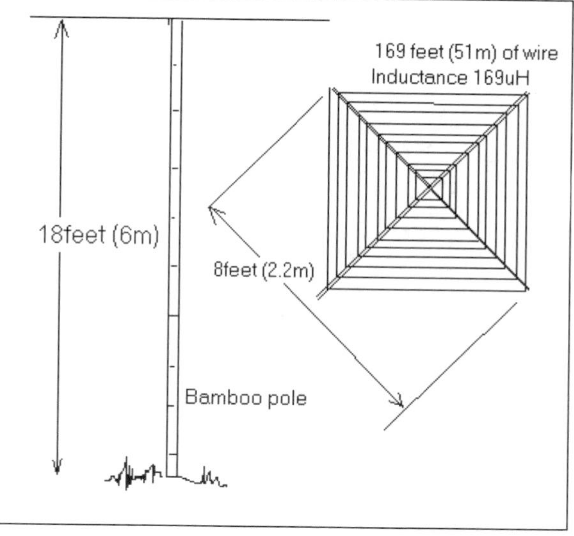

Fig 3.11: A spiral top has elements of inductive as well as capacitive loading

The loading coil is a critical part of any LF antenna system. It must be home-constructed because nothing suitable is available off the shelf. For this reason, there are as many different types of loading coil as there are LF stations.

To start with, a coil former must be found. This normally entails a visit to the local DiY store. The former must be made of a material with low RF loss - if in doubt, cut off a small piece and cook it in a microwave oven, together with a cup of water (important). If the material gets hot, don't use it. In general, expect light coloured material to be less of a problem than darker.

The coil former is typically between 50 and 500mm in diameter and 200-500mm long. The actual dimensions will vary, depending on the thickness of the wire used and the inductance required. The sides of the former must be parallel - don't be tempted to use something tapering like a bucket as the turns will eventually move. It is not essential for the former to have a circular cross-section.

Formers that have been successfully used include drain piping (or several pipes), rolled up plastic fencing, compost bins, fizzy drink bottles and plastic

Two examples of loading coils for 136kHz: (left) a thing of beauty from CT1DRP is wound with aluminium wire and the integral variometer can be clearly seen, whilst (right) a wheelie-bin coil, tapped every ten turns proved useful for the DF2BC/P lighthouse expedition

YU7AR's variometer tuned inductor

boxes. The variety is illustrated on these pages.

Losses in the loading coil reduce the power that can be radiated, so care must be taken in construction. You should also take into account the fact that the coil may have several tens of kilovolts on it. The 'goodness' of an inductor is called its 'Q'. A typical LF loading coil will have an unloaded Q of 100 to 400, depending on the construction and wire type used.

Factors affecting the Q include the coil's size and shape, the type of wire used and the spacing between the wires. The optimum shape is a width to diameter ratio of 2.5, although a more commonly used ratio is 1, probably for practical constructional reasons. The optimum spacing between wires is the width of one wire. In practice, this can be approximated to by using plastic covered wire, so that the insulation on adjacent wires keeps them about one wire apart. Wire of about 1mm to 1.5mm diameter is popular. Enamelled wire can be used, so long as the insulation is thick enough to withstand the voltage between adjacent turns.

Because the AC current flows only on the outer part of the wire in the coil, RF losses are greater than the DC resistance (the skin effect). A typical 136kHz inductor may have RF losses of 10 ohms or more, which in a well engineered system may be significant, so it can pay to use Litz wire. This is specially designed multi-stranded wire that has each of its wires insulated from the other. It is quite expensive and difficult to obtain, but worth grabbing if some becomes available. An inefficient system, which has significant earth losses for instance, may not benefit greatly from a few ohms reduction in inductor losses. However, the golden rule with developing your LF station (or any other for that matter) is to reduce losses whenever you can, an ohm at a time, improving your signal a fraction of a decibel at a time - the fractions will all eventually add up to a big signal.

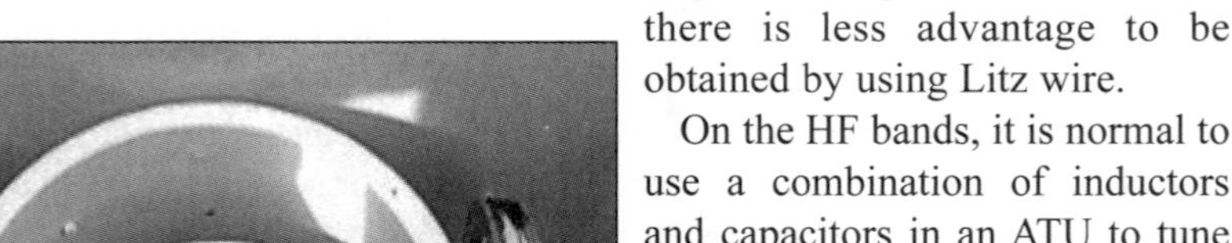

Because of the smaller value of inductance required for operation on 500kHz, there is less advantage to be obtained by using Litz wire.

GW4ALG's variometer is remotely tuned by this belt drive

On the HF bands, it is normal to use a combination of inductors and capacitors in an ATU to tune out any reactance. Unfortunately, the voltages at LF are so huge that any capacitor is likely to flash over, except when using very low power with a very efficient antenna on 500kHz.

Under most practical conditions, any tuning must be carried out in the inductance itself - a variable inductor is required. A crude, but simple, way of producing a variable inductor is to make 'taps' on the coil every few turns. This is certainly an excellent method if you have little idea of the inductance required to tune the antenna.

Fine tuning can be done by sliding ferrite material in and out of the inductor. Beware, though, that ferrites vary considerably and many get very hot in this application, with attendant losses. Broadcast radio ferrite rods are often unsuitable for 136kHz, whilst pieces of ferrite from demolished switch-mode power supplies can be effective. Take care not to put your fingers anywhere near a loading coil carrying RF - use a long plastic rod to insert the ferrite.

Loading coil, variometer and matching transformer built by GM4SLV for 500kHz use. It is all mounted in a five gallon beermaking bin

A better and more conventional method of varying inductance is to make another, smaller coil that rotates inside the larger one. Depending on its position, a portion of the inductance of the small coil either adds or subtracts from that of the large coil. This is known as a variometer.

The inductors described below have a wide range of inductance and are ideal for experimental purpose, such as when a new station or new antenna is being set up, or for portable use. The basic principles can be used when graduating to a system that requires much less adjustment, such as that used in an established station. It is well worth keeping the multi-purpose inductor, however, for any future experiments or for giving to someone new to the band.

When the antenna has been finalised, another coil can be constructed with a fixed inductance slightly less than is needed. Then a smaller inductance, with a variometer coil, can be placed in series with the large one and used for fine tuning within the amateur band. It is often convenient to place the large inductor outside, beneath the antenna, and to house the variometer coil in the shack. Alternatively, a remotely tuned variometer may be constructed.

You may wonder why an antenna needs fine tuning in a band that is only the width of an SSB transmission. An efficient LF antenna is likely to have a high enough Q to have a 3dB bandwidth of only 1kHz or so. Furthermore, the antenna's capacitance will change with the seasons and the weather, due to changing losses in the soil and adjacent objects (eg trees).

Spreading the inductance

It is possible to make an improvement to a very short Marconi, ie one with relatively little top capacitance, by moving most of the inductance to the top of the vertical section (**Fig 3.12**). This reduces the voltage on the downlead, and in turn reduces the losses to nearby objects such as trees and houses. Theoretically an improvement of about 3dB can be achieved. However, because there is less of the antenna beyond the elevated coil, more inductance is required with consequent resistive losses. Mounting the coil may also present difficulties. A light

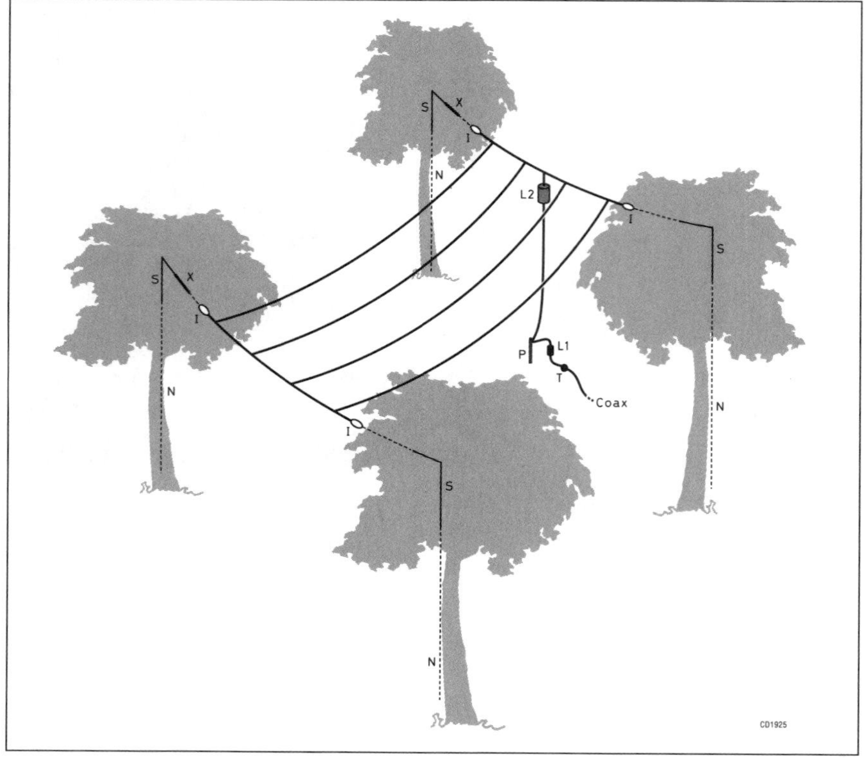

Fig 3.12: ON7YD's antenna uses four trees as supports. He reduces losses in the trees by mounting most of the loading coil at the top of the vertical section

A pressurised drinks bottle makes a very light-weight inductor for mounting on top of the mast

weight inductor is shown in the photograph. It is wound on a two litre fizzy drink bottle. To make the bottle firm enough to wind the coil, first remove the screw cap, then place it in a freezer for a few hours. Remove it from the freezer and immediately replace the cap. The cold air expands to make the bottle feel solid. Elevated inductors have been found to have a diminishing effect with increasing capacity hat size.

An alternative which has been used successfully, is to spread the inductance along the entire length of the antenna by helically winding it. The engineering problems have not made this a popular option.

Matching Vertical Antennas

In principle, you could use the same matching networks used for HF antenna matching, such as the pi- or T networks, to match vertical antennas at 136kHz or 500kHz. But in practice it is found that the component values, particularly for capacitors, are impracticably large, and for 136kHz require very high ratings due to the high antenna voltage. The two most popular LF/MF antenna matching circuits are shown in **Fig 3.13**.

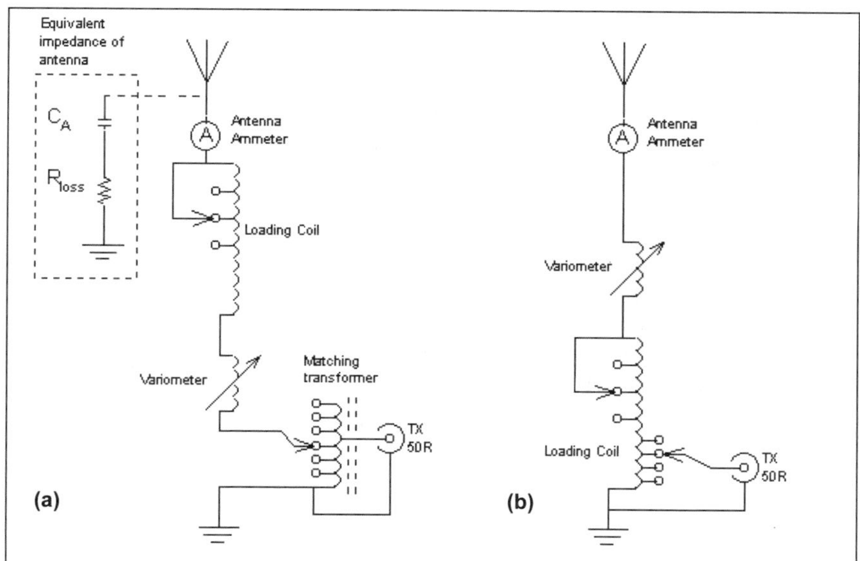

Fig 3.13: (a) LF antenna tuner; (b) Alternative antenna tuner circuit

In **Fig 3.13(a)**, a series loading coil has an inductive reactance that cancels out the capacitance, C_{ant}, of the antenna. The resistive component of the impedance (practically equal to the loss resistance) is then matched to 50 ohms, or other value of transmitter output impedance, using a ferrite-cored transformer. The capacitance of back garden amateur antennas, typically hundreds of picofarads, corresponds to a loading inductance of a few millihenrys at 136kHz, and a few hundred microhenrys at 500kHz. For most antennas, R_{loss} is between perhaps 10 and 200 ohms, requiring transformer turns ratios between about 1:2 and 2:1 to match to 50 ohms.

One design of 136kHz matching transformer, satisfactory at power levels up to 1kW, uses an ETD49 transformer core in 3C90 ferrite material, wound with 32 turns of 1.5mm enamelled copper wire, tapped every two turns. A much smaller transformer can be used at 500kHz. For power levels up to 20 watts or so, a Fair-Rite 22mm diameter, 43 material toroid core (5943007601) wound with 25 turns of 0.6mm wire, and again with taps every two turns, is suitable. The 50-ohm transmitter output is connected at the 16 turn tapping point, and the 'cold' end of the loading coil connected to the tap that gives optimum matching.

Because the antenna reactance is much larger than the resistance, the loading inductor must be capable of fine adjustment to obtain resonance accurately. As described above, coarse tuning is achieved by changing the coil tapping point, and a variometer allows fine tuning over a narrow range. This matching arrangement is very straightforward to use, since the adjustment of antenna resonance and resistance loading are almost completely independent.

More information on using ferrite materials at low frequencies can be found in Appendix 2.

Another popular matching network uses a tapped loading coil as shown in **Fig 3.13(b)**. The low potential end of the coil is equipped with closely-spaced taps, so the loading coil also performs the function of the matching transformer. Although this is physically simpler than Fig 3.13(a), the electrical behaviour of this circuit is more complicated.

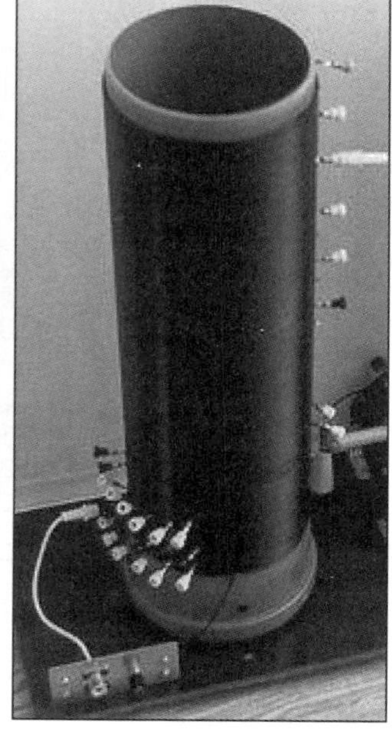

(above): Antenna tuners at M0BMU using the circuit in Fig 3.13 (a) - 136kHz (left), 500kHz (right)

OK1FIG's multi-tapped loading coil is used for tuning as well as matching as in Fig 13.3(b)

The primary and secondary of the transformer are not tightly coupled, so the transformer impedance ratio will not closely correspond to the turns ratio and the adjustment of the antenna to resonance and selection of the impedance-matching tap will be somewhat interdependent. However, it is not difficult to find a suitable tapping point by trial and error, and this will not often then need to be changed.

The range of antenna loss resistance that can be matched using the tapped loading coil depends on the coil geometry. In general, if the coil has a relatively small diameter and coarse winding pitch (ie it is wound with thick wire), the maximum value of R_{loss} that can be matched is quite low. If the coil has large diameter and fine winding pitch, much higher R_{loss} can be matched. However, the coil is then less suitable for low resistance antennas, because the required tap is only a few turns from the grounded end of the coil, giving very coarse steps in matching adjustment.

The graphs in **Fig 3.14** show examples of the range of antenna loss resistance that can be matched with coil diameters of 100mm, 150mm and 200mm, and various winding pitches. A Microsoft Excel spreadsheet is available for calculating similar curves for any coil diameter and winding pitch [5]

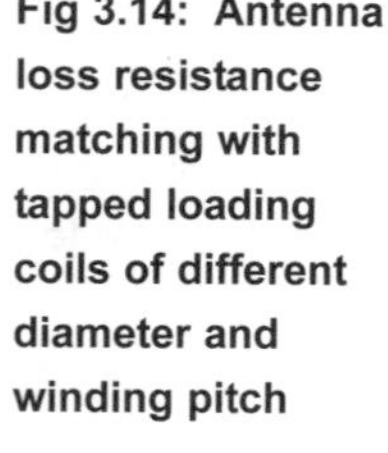

Fig 3.14: Antenna loss resistance matching with tapped loading coils of different diameter and winding pitch

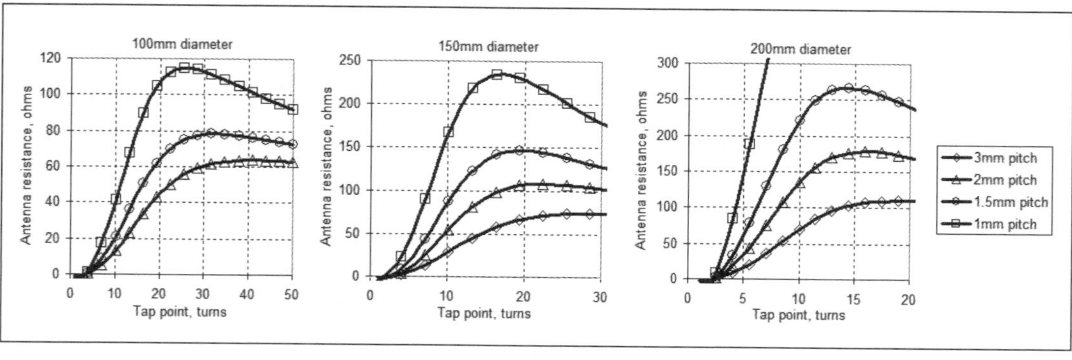

Sometimes it is desirable to isolate the radio earth from the mains safety earth, and this can be achieved when using either matching method shown above, albeit at the expense of some 'copper' loss in the windings. In Fig 3.13(a) a separate primary winding can be used instead of the auto-transformer method. When using the Fig 3.13(b) arrangement, a few turns of wire can be wound round the earthy end of the coil, but the number of turns must be determined by experimentation and this can be very fiddly to get right.

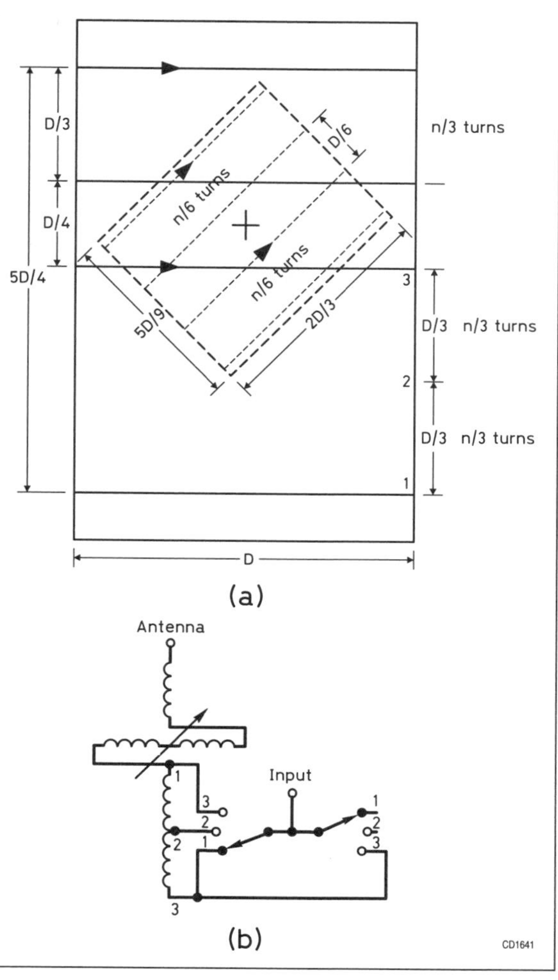

Fig 3.15: G3LNP's variometer design allows a very wide range of inductance adjustable with no gaps

Practical inductors for 136kHz

Each of these inductors is variable with a maximum of 3 to 4mH which should be enough to match most LF antennas. If more inductance is needed, a fixed coil can be added in series with the variable one.

Tapped coil: A typical tapped inductor comprises 200 turns of 1.5mm (16SWG) plastic insulated wire wound on a 150m diameter former. The taps are at 100, 50, 25, 12, 6, 5, 4, 3, 2, and 1 turn, giving adjustment over a very wide range, whilst being capable of fine tuning.

The photograph shows OK1FIG's loading coil which uses this type of design. He uses the lower turns for coupling to the transmitter, tapped for adjustment of the matching.

Tuning and matching are achieved by selecting taps with 4mm sockets and banana plugs. It is important to make sure the transmitter is switched off when making adjustments. For a more permanent arrangement, the 4mm sockets can be replaced with soldered connections.

Wide range variometer: The construction method of a coil built by G3LNP is shown in **Fig 3.15**. The coil has an inductance range of 6:1 in three stages without gaps and is intended to be used with a separate toroidal matching transformer (see above).

Taps 1, 2, and 3 provide respectively 2L/3 to L, L/3 to 2L/3 and L/5 to L/3 where L is the total inductance. Unused turns below tap 2 can be left open whilst unused turns below tap 3 should be short-circuited to minimise both voltage stress and losses.

The inductor typically has a total of 150 - 200 turns of 1.5mm diameter (16-17SWG) wire in a single layer. The number of turns chosen will depend on how large your antenna is, but it does no harm to have too many. The former is 200mm diameter and about 250mm long, but this is not critical - it depends largely on what is available.

Fig 3.16 shows the construction. The turns are divided between the outer main coil and the inner variometer coil. Each coil is split to allow space for the rotating mechanism. Construction is straightforward using 6mm shafts running in bushes salvaged from old volume controls and doubling as terminations for the flexible "pigtails" forming inner to outer coil connections. These mechanics are compatible with standard insulated shaft couplers and control knobs.

The important considerations are to make sure all the windings have the same direction and that rotation is restricted to 180 degrees. It is advisable to use a working tap which puts the inner coil in the additive inductance position to minimise losses.

Use the formula below to calculate the turns (n) on the larger coil for maximum inductance L (ignore the small coil):

$$\mathbf{n = \sqrt{(50L/D)}}$$

where D is diameter of outer coil in inches and L is in μH. The distribution of the turns (in terms of n) is shown in Fig 3.15.

Practical inductors for 500kHz

All of the information above can be used to design loading coils and variometers for use at 500kHz. In general, they will have lower inductance which means fewer turns. They also do not need to cope with such high power levels, especially voltage, so the engineering is easier.

Tuning up

A Marconi antenna can be tuned up roughly by optimising the received signal. If possible, choose a constant ground-wave signal in or close to the band. DCF39 on 138.830kHz is useful for this (use this only during daylight as sky-wave interference can produce slow fading). Unfortunately, there are few signals close to 500kHz, but aeronautical beacons some 100kHz below the band [6], or broadcast stations at the lower end of the medium wave band [7] can be a start. An alternative is to ask a fairly local station to transmit a beacon for you.

Then, using the largest taps first, vary the taps on the loading coil. When the strongest signal is received, alter the variometer position (or the fine tuning taps) to peak it. It may be necessary to make further adjustments to the taps so that the variometer tunes correctly. If the antenna fails completely to tune, make sure the earth is connected. If all else fails, tune your receiver to beacon on a lower or higher frequency and see if resonance can be obtained there.

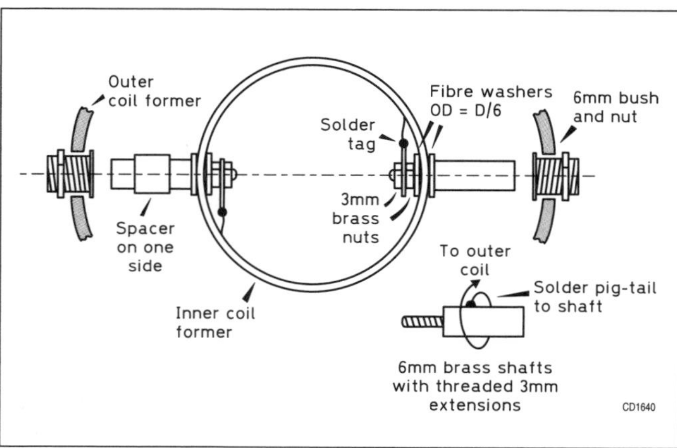

Fig 3.16: Detail of G3LNP's inner coil bearings. Note that this degree of engineering is not essential

> **WARNING**
>
> Antenna tuning circuits carry very high voltages that can burn, as well as high currents that can cause injury or death. Always make sure that the transmitter is off - and cannot be keyed by anyone else - before touching tuner components, eg to change coil taps. Rapid changes in impedance may lead to the destruction of the power amplifier transistors.

Once resonance is achieved, apply a little in-band RF, perhaps from your driver, and measure the antenna current using one of the methods described in the measurements chapter. Note that such tests should be carried out in a part of the band that avoids interference with other operators (usually at the lower frequency end of the allocation - but don't be afraid to ask) and that you should send a callsign at 15 minute intervals. If you cannot avoid the middle of the band, perhaps because your transmitter is crystal controlled, make sure you send callsigns often and listen periodically for any calls.

ON6ND shows off his well-engineered coil with its variometer and current meter

Having re-peaked the antenna tuning, now is the time to tackle the matching. Having turned the transmitter off, adjust the matching (coil taps, link winding size or matching transformer taps). Key the transmitter again and re-tune the antenna, noting whether the new matching setting is an improvement. Continue this until an optimum setting is found.

Gradually increase the amount of power applied to the antenna, monitoring the antenna current. If a sudden jump in current occurs (upwards or downwards), it is probable that something is breaking down, possibly flashing over. Carefully examine any visible parts of the antenna and its matching system and repair any problems. If flash-over is suspected, but no evidence can be seen, try testing the antenna after dark when any sparks will be more easily visible. Corona discharge is sometimes only very faintly visible, and may be easier to detect by the hissing sound it makes. Take great care not to damage your transmitter whilst doing this. If all is well, you will have an amp or more (somewhat less on 500kHz) going into your antenna and a stable system that can be adjusted either side of its present tuning and matching.

Transmitting loops

An alternative to the Marconi vertical is a vertical loop of wire, often rectangular in shape with the lowest part a metre or so off the ground. **Fig 3.17** gives the basic arrangement. The loop has the advantage that it works well in locations where there are many vertical objects, such as trees, which would adversely affect a Marconi. It has the disadvantage that it is directional, with nulls of some 20dB at right angles to the plane of the loop.

Like the Marconi, the loop requires careful engineering in order to be efficient. The main difference is that Marconis have lots of volts and loops have lots

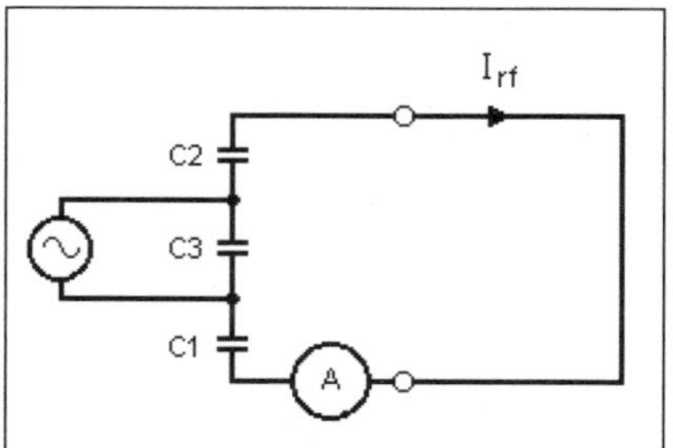

Fig 3.17: Schematic of a typical LF loop antenna, showing a balanced capacitive potential divider feed

of current - perhaps tens of amperes on the 136kHz band. As with any other small antenna, the efficiency is determined by the ratio of the radiation resistance to the loss resistance. The main consideration is to make the loop as large as possible, and to keep the loop resistance as low as possible.

The radiation resistance depends on the loop area, not the shape, but some shapes require more wire (and hence resistive loss) than others. GW4ALG found a triangular shape convenient (**Fig 3.18**). A circular loop needs least wire and a square needs less than a rectangle. In practice, a rectangular loop is most often constructed as this will give the largest loop for the real estate and height available.

The calculations for evaluating your own loop can be found in the Measurement and Calculations chapter of this book. As a starting point a practical antenna used by G3YMC on 136kHz is described below.

At 500kHz, a loop antenna should be competitive in efficiency with a vertical; however, at the time of writing, loop antennas do not appear to have been tried on this band.

The main advantage of transmitting loops is that the loop voltages are much lower than for the vertical, resulting in lower dielectric losses in objects around the antenna. This makes a loop a good choice for wooded surroundings, where many trees close to the antenna would lead to very poor efficiency with a vertical. This seems to be a common situation in North America, where several LF loop antennas have been constructed using branches of tall trees to support the loop element. Loops also do not rely on a low resistance ground connection, so may be an improvement where there is very dry or rocky soil. A disadvantage is that stronger antenna supports are required to support the thick loop conductor.

Feeding, tuning and matching

As an LF loop is very small compared with the wavelength, the polarisation is vertical and independent of the feedpoint, ie it can be fed at any convenient point.

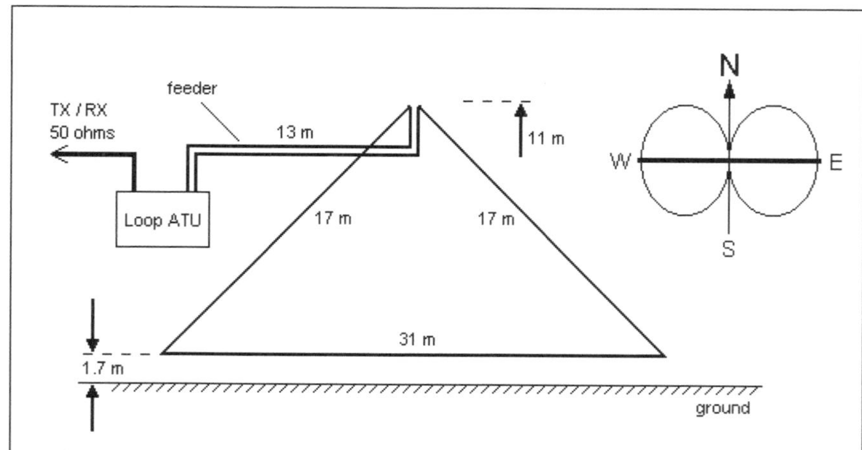

Fig 3.18: GW4ALG's loop antenna is a quite different shape

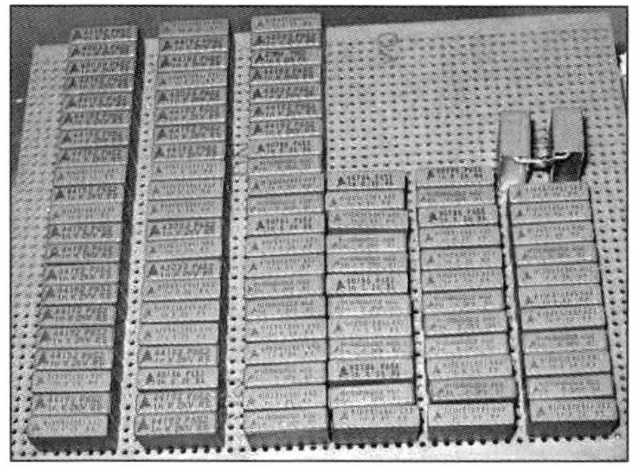

100 capacitors connected in series/parallel to match G3YXM's 136kHz loop antenna [9]

The loop can be considered to be an inductance which must be brought to resonance with a capacitor. The capacitors used for tuning, and perhaps matching too, are required to carry high currents and voltages, so must be of good quality to keep losses down. Metallised polypropylene 'pulse' type capacitors have low losses in this frequency range, and are available in large capacitances and voltage ratings of 2500V or more. The limiting factor with loop tuning capacitors is often internal heating due to the RF current rather than the breakdown voltage. In large polypropylene capacitors, currents of a few amps are allowable, and loop voltages may reach a few kilovolts with transmitter powers typically employed at 136kHz, so series-parallel combinations of capacitors will often be needed. Suitable transmitting mica or ceramic capacitors with suitable ratings are occasionally available surplus, but are very expensive when bought new.

Components need not be so highly rated if the loop is used exclusively at 500kHz. More information on capacitors and their sources are in Appendix 2.

Matching a loop antenna normally uses one of the circuits shown in **Fig 3.19**. **Fig 3.19(a)** uses a step-down transformer to match the loop R_{loss} to the 50 ohm transmitter output, and a series capacitance to resonate the loop inductance L_{ant}. $L_{an}t$ in henrys is given approximately by the formula:

$$L_{ant} = 2\times10^{-7} P \cdot \text{Log}_e\left(\frac{3440A}{dP}\right)$$

where P is the overall length of the loop perimeter (m), A is the loop area (m^2), and d is the conductor diameter (mm). C_{tune} is therefore:

$$C_{tune} = \left(\frac{1}{2\pi f\sqrt{L_{ant}}}\right)^2$$

C_{tune} is often divided into two series capacitors as shown, to make the loop voltages approximately balanced with respect to ground. The required transformer turns ratio is $\sqrt{R_{load}}/R_{loss}$.

An alternative matching scheme uses a capacitive matching network, **Fig 3.19(b)**. The values of C1 and C2 are:

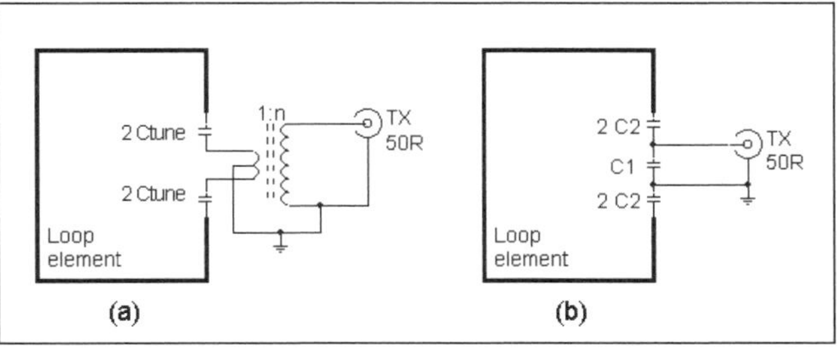

Fig 3.19: Methods of feeding a loop antenna: (a) Toroidal transformer similar to that used for feeding a Marconi, and (b) a capacitive potential divider

$$C_1 = \frac{\sqrt{\dfrac{R_{load} - R_{loss}}{R_{loss}}}}{2\pi f R_{load}}, \quad C_2 = \frac{1}{2\pi f \left(2\pi f L_{ant} - \sqrt{R_{loss}\left(R_{load} - R_{loss}\right)}\right)}$$

GYMC's loop antenna

The loop used by G3YMC (**Fig 3.20**) was the result of site restrictions that made a Marconi difficult to implement [8]. The location is in a typical suburban estate with terraced houses on all sides and a back garden of 15m x 7m. It is not practical to use the front of the house so scope for antennas is limited. A loop antenna seemed the ideal answer. It was decided to use the whole of the garden for the antenna, which allowed a loop with a wire length of 45m, and an area of 100m^2. The first loop erected used ordinary 19/0.76 wire. However, the resistance of 45m of this is about 1.2 ohms, and it rapidly became apparent from the reports received (or lack of them) that the efficiency was very poor at about 0.001% with a radiated power of a few hundred microwatts.

The wire was then replaced with heavy duty loudspeaker cable with the pairs connected in parallel, to give an effective wire cross-section of 5mm^2 and a measured DC resistance of less than 0.1 ohms. In fact the effective resistance at 136kHz was rather higher due to skin effect and other considerations. Measurements showed that this was in fact 0.65 ohms.

The loop is a rather dog-legged construction. One end is supported by a 10m pole by the house, the other end is at only 5m, since rear guying of a pole there is not possible. The wire is run in a sort of rhombus between these points, with the lower sides running along the garden fence about 0.3m above ground. The loop is fed at one corner at ground level, via a matching box screwed to the wall of the house. The dimensions in **Fig 3.20** are given as a guide only.

The calculations on the loop revealed the following:

* loop area 100m^2
* radiation resistance 13.5 micro-ohms
* effective loop series resistance 0.65 ohms
* efficiency 0.002%
* radiated power for 35W input 0.7mW
* Loop inductance 70µH

The loop is matched to the transmitter by the capacitive divider method shown in Fig 3.18c. In this case the capacitor on the transmitter feed (C1) is

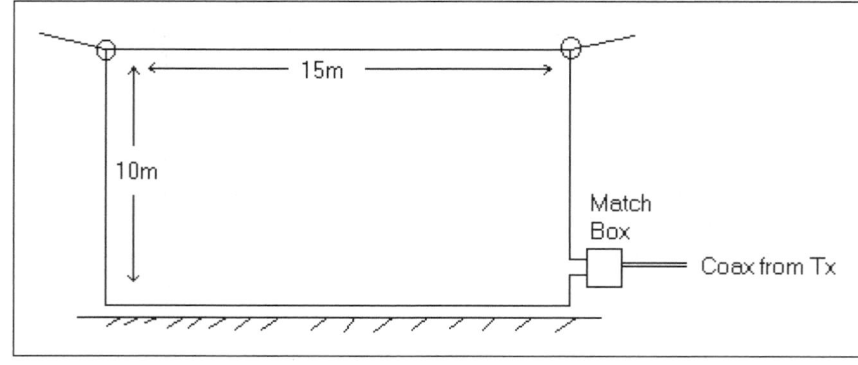

Fig 3.20: G3YMC's rectangular loop antenna for 136kHz which helped him work five countries on CW with just 35W RF input

200nF and the tuning capacitor (C2) is 22nF. G3YMC used polypropylene capacitors from the Philips 376 series which are available in various voltage ratings up to 2kV. Philips 378 series capacitors may also be suitable, but the 376 has a much better specification for handling pulse currents. Initial use of Wima metallised polyester capacitors for the parallel component were somewhat disappointing as these soon went lossy and overheated. Surprisingly significant is that the change in temperature between early morning and mid day results in a resonance change of some 200Hz HF; in the cold winter mornings there is appreciable shift LF.

The bandwidth of the loop is quite small, and it is only possible to move the transmit frequency by some 100Hz either side of resonance before retuning is necessary. Tuning is carried out with several small switched capacitors inside the matching box selected with miniature toggle switches. If you put up a loop and find it is quite broad there is something wrong with it.

Measuring the current in the loop wire with a thermocouple ammeter was found to give a good guide to loop performance and enabled the actual value of the series resistance to be confirmed. Due to the magnitude of the current, which can be quite high, the test was performed at a reduced power level of 5W. At this power level a current of 2.6A was measured in the loop. The loss resistance can be calculated directly using Ohms Law and works out at 0.66 ohms (allowing for the DC resistance of the meter). It was encouraging that this agreed so closely with the computer simulations.

Note the magnitude of the current. At G3YMC's normal 35W it is nearly 8A. If the power were to be increased to 400W, a hefty 26A would flow. It is clear that there will be significant heating of the matching capacitors at this level and use of suitable capacitors is most important.

Comparisons between received signals on the loop and a 60ft longwire antenna showed stations in the line of the loop to be typically 10-15dB better on the loop than on the other antenna. However stations in the null are some 10-15dB better on the longwire. This suggests the null is around 30dB.

The loop offers an antenna for small sites where large antennas are out of the question and the ground resistance is poor.

Why use 50Ω on LF?

Unlike amateur HF and VHF/UHF equipment, low frequency transmitters and antennas may not have impedances of exactly 50 ohms. It is, however, convenient to use this impedance for cabling, and to transform up or down as appropriate. This makes matching easier, allows the use of conventional test gear and reduces cable losses which can be significant if mis-matched, even at low frequencies.

Antenna supports

In striving to achieve the required height for an efficient low frequency antenna, all manner of supports have been used, including an apartment block, a lighthouse and a church tower.

A more practical alternative, is a tall tree. Trees make useful supports, cause no problems with the neighbours and do not require planning permission. However, they can absorb quite a lot of the RF, especially in summer. It is interesting to note that LF antennas near trees show a marked change in resonance during spring and autumn. They also tend to move when it is windy, so some method must be used to avoid the antenna or the tree branch breaking. For instance, bungee cables, used for securing items on car roofs, can be placed in series with the antenna wire and/or the rope that goes over the tree branch.

A catapault or bow and arrow can be used to propel an object over a high branch, attached to a monofilament line. This can be used to haul up a much thicker rope attached to the antenna. Alternatively a pole can be erected using the tree trunk as a support.

One method of using a tree as a support is to strap a pole to the trunk

In the absence of enough tall buildings or trees, one or more masts must be erected. Note that this may require planning permission. In general, the mast should be at the maximum practical height. It may be possible to use a mast that can be raised and lowered when required, either telescopically or folded over.

Should the mast be insulated from the ground? Well, ideally it should, and it could then be used as part of the antenna. This is often used by commercial LF stations, but it is quite difficult to engineer, bearing in mind the large voltages present on short verticals. A more practical solution is to earth the mast and ensure that any antenna wires are a few metres away from it. The worst option is to have a mast that has resistance to earth, say via brackets fixed to a wall or through a concrete base, as this will dissipate RF in a way that varies from day to day. If you are in doubt, earth it.

Care needs to be taken with guy wires. If they are insulated from ground, capacitive coupling to the antenna element can result in high RF voltages being present on the guy wire, representing a hazard for anyone coming into contact with them. This also applies to other conducting objects, such as ladders, garden furniture etc. This can be avoided by grounding them, however this may allow significant RF current to flow in the guys, which will act as a partial screen around the antenna generally reducing the effective height. Insulating rope used instead of wire for guys is one possible solution.

G3LDO's fold over 16m mast

Masts made of an insulating material may be a useful option. Telescopic fibreglass masts can be purchased [10] and they are suitable for portable use though rather too flexible for a permanent installation. Roach poles used by fishermen may also be employed in an LF antenna.

A helium filled balloon can make a useful temporary support for a vertical wire. Several 400mm balloons, of the type used for children's parties, can be used in a bunch (**Fig 3.21**). This is an option for anyone unable to erect a permanent high mast, though obviously it is only available on a windless day. The lower part of the antenna is supported conventionally on a pole. This allows the balloons to carry less wire, reduces the possibility of the wire tangling in nearby objects and keeps the high voltages away from the ground. GW4ALG used this method to make many DX contacts, including a record-breaking one with OH1TN, from his tiny garden.

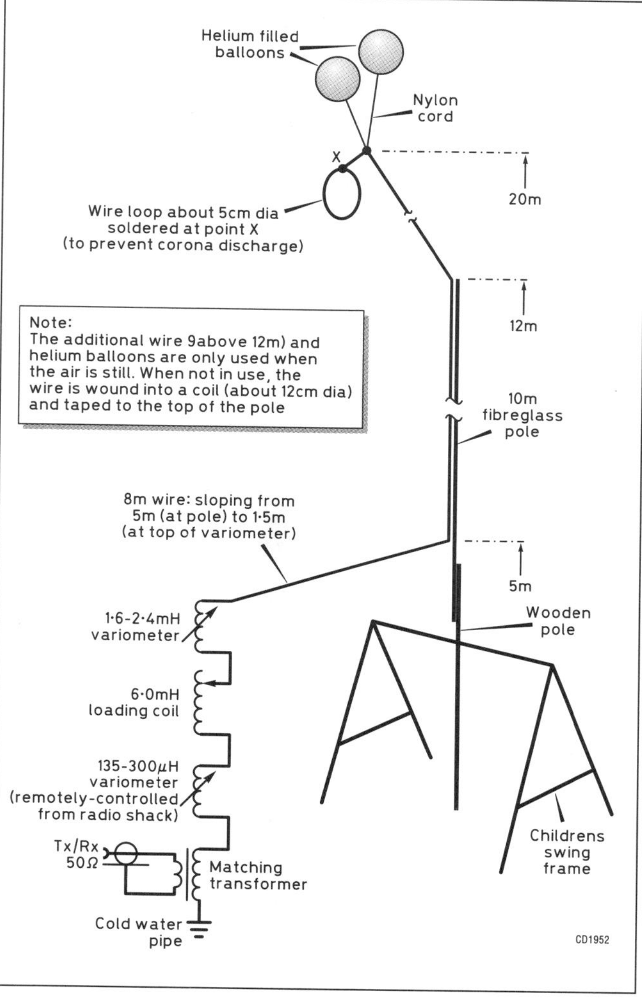

Fig 3.21: GW4ALG used this method to raise his antenna to 20m on calm days. The nylon cord is essential as any RF close to the balloon will burst it!

Portable operation at LF is more difficult than from a fixed station, because it can take a long time to raise the antenna to a decent height. Kite supported antennas have been used with great success [11, 12], although some skill in flying a kite must be acquired before using it to support an antenna. The wire can either be trailed beneath the kite, or more usefully can be made part of, or replace, the supporting 'string'. Given the right kite and good wind conditions, a 60m vertical wire (the maximum kite height allowed in the UK) can be supported in a stable way for hours. Safety is an important issue and no part of the kite should be able to touch an overhead wire. Furthermore, when transmitting, the wire will carry harmful voltages and must not be anywhere near members of the public. There are additional height regulations when operating close to an airfield.

References

[1] ON7YD's antenna pages. *http://www.qsl.net/on7yd/136ant.htm*

[2] 'Radiation from an antenna', P Dodd, G3LDO. *http://web.ukonline.co.uk/g3ldo/Basic_EM.htm*

[3] *Radio Communication Handbook*, RSGB.

[4] REF-NYK: G3NYK on earth loss: http://*www.btinternet.com/~alan.melia/aelossbr.htm*

[5] *http://www.wireless.org.uk/tap_coil.xls*

[6] List of Non Directional Beacons: *http://www.xs4all.nl/~cisquet/NDB.htm*

[7] European medium-wave broadcasters list: *http://mysite.wanadoo-members.co.uk/freq_find/AM_153_954.pdf*

[8] G3YMC's loop page. *http://www.btinternet.com/~dsergeant/loops.htm*

[9] *http://www.wireless.org.uk/loopy.htm*

[10] Moonraker, Unit 12, Cranfield Road Units, Cranfield Road, Woburn Sands, Bucks MK17 8UR. Tel: 01908 281705. *http://www.moonrakerukltd.com/*

[11] G3XDV's portable operation using a kite. *http://homepage.ntlworld.com/mike.dennison/index/lf/gw3xdv/october99.htm*

[12] G3YXM' portable operation using a kite. *http://www.wireless.org.uk/136gm.htm*

4

Receive antennas

In this chapter:

- Why use a receive antenna?
- Positioning a receive antenna
- Noise on feeders
- Practical loop antennas
- Active whip antennas

BECAUSE A RECEIVE-ONLY antenna does not require the complexity and sheer scale of one used for transmitting, some people will want simply to receive on LF and not transmit at all. There is a great deal of pleasure to be had in optimising a low frequency receiving station and then giving DX stations reports or contributing to the experimental data being compiled on propagation. Any of the antennas described here are suitable for serious receiving.

Those equipped for transmitting will find that their antenna will work well as a general purpose receive antenna. It may, however, pick up local electrical noise which is particularly prevalent on these frequencies, and will certainly have no controllable directivity. So it is often useful to supplement the main station antenna by having one solely for receiving.

It is often the case that local noise originates outside the amateur's home, propagating along mains or telecomms cables, via which it is coupled to the antenna. Re-positioning the antenna can reduce the noise level, but this is not often an option with a large transmitting-type antenna. The best approach under these conditions is to locate a separate, compact, receiving antenna where noise pick-up is minimised. With suitable design, quite small antennas can provide a signal-to-noise ratio limited only by the external band noise, so there is no compromise in receiving sensitivity.

Dedicated receiving antennas for the LF and MF ranges can be classified as whips and loops (**Fig 4.1**). A whip is just a small vertical antenna, and responds primarily to the electric field (E-field) component of a radio wave. A loop develops a signal at its terminals primarily due to induction by the magnetic

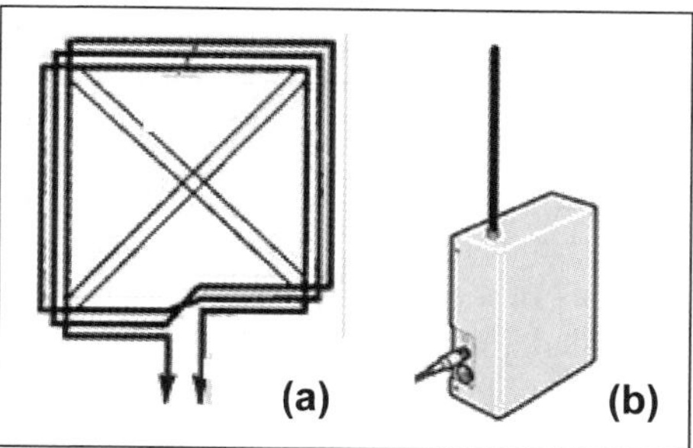

Fig 4.1: Some low frequency receiving antennas: (a) loop, and (b) active whip

field component (H-field) component of the radio wave. At a particular location, the fields generated by local noise sources may be chiefly E- or H-field, so using the appropriate type of receiving antenna can give a substantial reduction in noise. However, the nature of RF fields is such that both E- and H- fields are always present to some extent even if one dominates the other, so neither type of antenna is a 'miracle cure' for all noise problems. But experimentation with the type and position of the receive antenna often yields major reception improvements.

A whip antenna is omnidirectional. A loop has a figure-of-eight directional pattern, with two deep nulls at right angles to the plane of the loop, and maximum reception along the plane of the loop. This can be a disadvantage if the loop is fixed and the wanted station is in the null, but small loops can be rotated by hand or using a rotator suitable for a VHF antenna. On the other hand, the directional characteristic can be extremely useful in nulling out interference from man-made sources, either local (for instance switch-mode power supplies which can be a problem on both 136kHz and 500kHz) or distant (for instance Loran on 136kHz), provided there is a considerable difference in direction between wanted signal and unwanted noise. The E-field produced at a location by a received signal varies considerably due to the local screening effects of buildings, trees, etc. near the receiving antenna, so the signal level at the output of a whip antenna is strongly affected by its location. The H-field is much less affected, so loops can operate well when tucked away in a confined location. This also makes loops a better choice when repeatable signal level measurements are wanted, for example when making field strength measurements.

A whip antenna can actually be a self-supporting whip, or a short wire element. It may be tuned in the same way as a transmitting antenna, or, for example, using the preselector circuit shown in the Receivers chapter. Alternatively, active whip antennas (sometimes called 'E-field probes') are un-tuned, but use a high-impedance buffer amplifier to match the whip element to the low-impedance receiver input. Active whips give wide-band reception, and can be very small - often the whip element is around 1m long. Due to their wide-band nature, the buffer amplifier must be well designed to avoid intermodulation, especially if located close to broadcast stations. A popular active whip design by PA0RDT is described later in this chapter. The signal level at the output of an active whip is quite sensitive to its location; when the whip is at ground level, output will be much lower than when elevated to a position where it is not screened by surrounding buildings, trees, etc. This loss in signal level can be compensated for by increasing the size of the whip element. Being essentially vertical antennas, both tuned and active whips require a good ground connection.

Several varieties of loop antennas exist, including tuned loops, active loops and also 'terminated' loops. For many years, tuned loop 'frame' antennas have been used by medium wave DXers, and these can also be effective for LF/MF amateur use. A typical design for 136kHz uses a square wooden frame with about 1 metre sides, wound with around 30 turns and tuned with the paralleled sections of a 500pF + 500pF variable capacitor. A tap at 1 or 2 turns from the grounded side of the winding matches the loop to a low-impedance receiver input. For 500kHz reception, about 15 turns can be used instead. The signal output from a loop like this is a small fraction of a microvolt, and a preamplifier

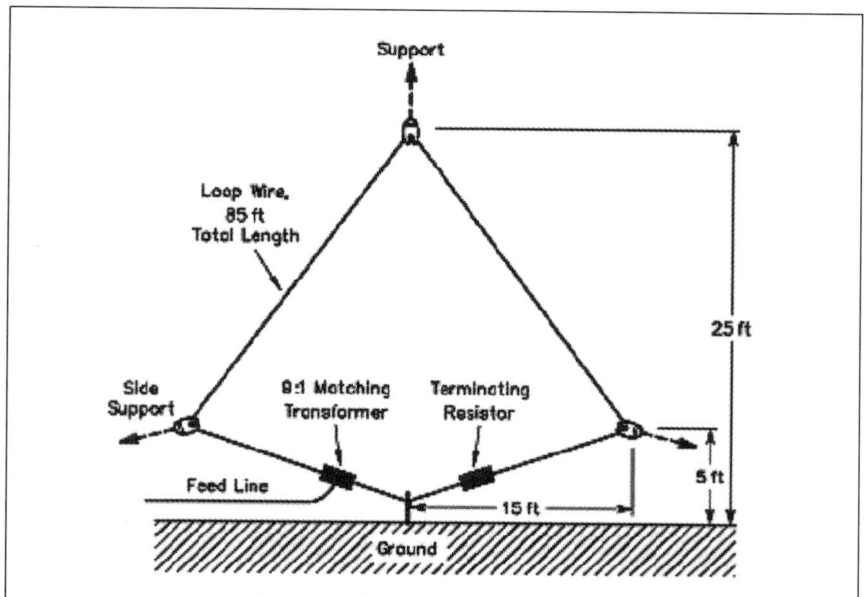

Fig 4.2: The K9AY EWE antenna has an omnidirectional response

(such as those shown in this chapter and Chapter 2) will be needed for all but the most sensitive receivers. Some amateurs have built much larger loops; the signal output is roughly proportional to the area of the loop, so a larger loop with an area of several square metres can eliminate the need for a preamplifier. However, it is more difficult to position a large loop to minimise noise pick-up. The tuned loop has a high Q, and is quite effective in filtering out unwanted signals. The drawback of this is that the bandwidth of the loop is very narrow and it will frequently require re-tuning, which is somewhat awkward when the antenna is some distance from the shack. It is possible to make the loop tunable from the receiver end of the feeder; see the 'Lazy Loop' later in this chapter.

Un-tuned active loops can be made to have a very uniform response over a wide bandwidth; they are widely used professionally for measuring field strength for this reason. Active loops suitable for the LF/MF range are commercially available, for example the Wellbrook Communications LFL1010 [1].

Several types of un-tuned "terminated loop" antennas have been developed, the best known being the K9AY (**Fig 4.2**) and 'EWE' antennas [2]. These use a relatively large wire element simultaneously as a loop and a vertical antenna, with a terminating impedance that combines both signal components at the receiver input to give a unidirectional (cardioid) pattern. These antennas have been mostly used by amateurs on 160m and the lower HF bands, but are also capable of excellent results at 136kHz and 500kHz. They do however require a fairly large area of ground in a noise-free location for good results.

Positioning a receive antenna

The most important thing in achieving effective noise reduction using a dedicated receiving antenna is to find the optimum position for the receive antenna. Whip antennas usually give best signal-to-noise ratio when clear of surrounding obstructions and as high up as possible, preferably on a mast of some sort. This will also tend to keep the antenna as far as possible from mains noise sources,

LF tuned loop antenna

which tend to generate greatest noise levels inside and near buildings. Whips are vulnerable to picking up noise from other resonant antennas; if a whip is fairly close to the main LF/MF transmitting antenna, the main antenna loading coil should be open-circuited while receiving, for instance using a relay.

Loop antennas are particularly prone to picking up the magnetic fields generated by noise on mains cables so should also be kept as far from mains wiring as possible. However, the noise level will often change greatly over distances of only a few metres, so moving the loop around within the available area will often locate a 'sweet spot' where noise levels are low. The directional property of the loop may often be used to null a local noise source; the apparent direction of the null on the local noise may also change over a short distance, so in some cases it will be desirable to have two or more loops in different positions to receive signals from different directions. A loop positioned near the feed point of the main transmitting antenna may pick up noise due to the magnetic field around the loading coil and downlead; this can also be prevented by using a relay to open-circuit the loading coil.

As can be seen from these remarks, all types of receiving antenna perform best outdoors; indoor receiving antennas almost always give disappointing results in this frequency range. If an indoor antenna is unavoidable, it will again be worthwhile experimenting with different locations inside the building, or even within the same room, since positions further from mains wiring and noisy appliances will usually have significantly less noise.

Noise on feeders

A problem that may affect any type of antenna used for reception is noise currents flowing along the outer braid of coaxial feeders. Since the receiver end of the cable is normally connected to mains earth, the feeder provides an alternative path for mains noise currents to flow through, particularly if there is an additional RF ground at the antenna end (a 'ground loop'). Noise currents flowing along the feeder will in turn induce noise in the receiving antenna. The best way to check for this problem is to monitor the noise level with a battery-operated receiver, making sure that no connection exists between the mains ground and the antenna and receiver.

Loop antennas do not depend on an earth connection for operation, so keeping the loop and feeder insulated from ground will minimise the amount of noise current present on the feeder. In at least one case, a high noise level in a loop antenna was caused by long grass coming into contact with the loop and creat-

Fig 4.3: Example of a well-constructed LF loop by PA0SE

Fig 4.4: Preamp with 50-ohm input suitable for loop antennas

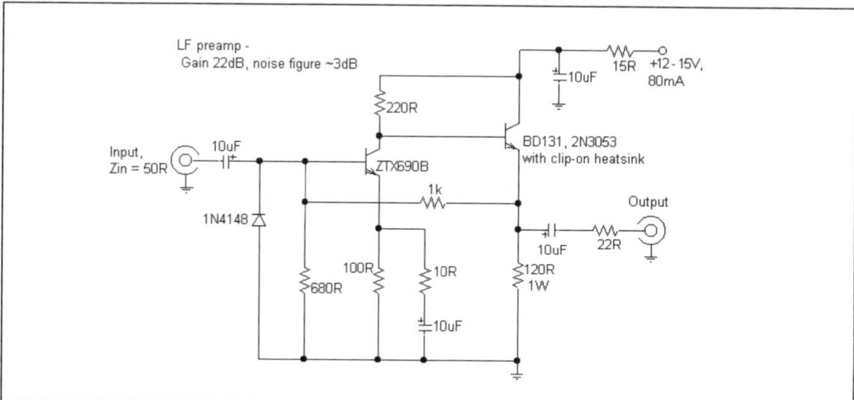

ing a conductive path for noise currents. Vertical antennas, including receiving whips, require a ground connection, preferably as close as possible to the antenna. The level of noise current in the feeder can be greatly reduced by inserting a 1:1 ratio RF isolating transformer into the feeder, breaking the connection between mains and RF ground, while still allowing signals to pass along the feeder normally.

The PA0RDT Mini-Whip design includes such an isolating transformer in the DC power feed unit at the receiver end of the feeder. A similar result can be achieved with a transmitting antenna by using a matching transformer with separate primary and secondary windings to isolate the feeder at the antenna end.

Practical loop antennas

Traditional tuned loop antennas are shown in **Fig 4.3**, and can consist of about 30 turns of wire wound onto a wooden cross-shaped frame, typically about 1m^2, tuned by a variable capacitor. The receiver input is fed via a low impedance tap two turns from the grounded end of the winding. The output of the loop is small, and a low-noise preamplifier will normally be required, such as the one shown in **Fig 4.4**.

The Q of the loop is typically 100 or more, so re-tuning will be required even within the narrow low frequency bands. This selectivity is very useful in reducing intermodulation due to strong out-of-band signals. A number of amateurs have used much larger tuned loops for reception, which achieve higher output signal levels and so can dispense with the preamplifier, at the expense of being more bulky.

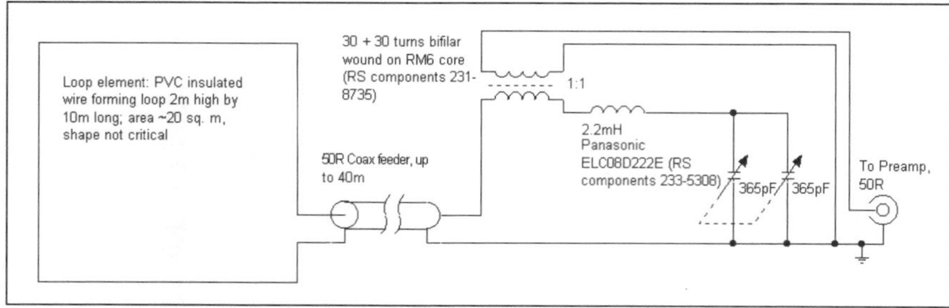

Fig 4.5 'Lazy loop' and tuning arrangement

M0BMU 'Lazy Loop'

An alternative is the 'lazy loop' of **Fig 4.5**. This uses a large single-turn loop, the area of which is around 10 - 20m^2. The shape is not at all important, and it can be normal insulated wire slung from bushes or fence posts, etc, hence the name! The loop can be fed through a coax feeder, allowing it to be positioned remote from the shack to reduce noise.

The other great advantage of this system is that the critical tuning components are nice and dry in the shack, no remote control, no waterproofing of the amplifier, just twiddle and go! It also gives a useful amount of front end selectivity. This tuning arrangement is not optimum from the point of view of minimising losses, but due to the large loop area the signal-to-noise ratio is more than adequate. It is also possible to use somewhat smaller, multi-turn loops.

Again, a low-noise preamp, such as the one in Fig 4.4 will be required. The preamp has an input impedance of 50 ohms, and with a 50 ohm load gives 22dB gain. The noise figure is roughly 3dB, which is low enough for most things, and has quite good strong signal performance - it can cope with 100mV RMS input without clipping, so the receiver will almost always be overloaded before the preamp. Other pre-amplifiers can be found in the Receivers chapter.

The output impedance is more or less that of the 22 ohm resistor, which ensures stability with reactive loads, so it is not fussy about what load it is connected to. The bandwidth with the transistors shown is about 5MHz, but it is really meant for the LF/VLF range. TR1 can also be a ZTX650 with similar results, also a 2N4401 or 2N2222 are OK but with 1 or 2dB more noise. A BD135, BFY52 or 2N3053 work well for TR2 - this runs quite warm so a clip-on heatsink is desirable. Extra filtering of the 12V will be required if there is significant noise on the supply.

The preamp has been used with several different types of antenna, but the one shown in Fig 4.5 is quite useful. It is a fairly large single turn loop, which is series tuned by an inductor and variable capacitor. The inductor should be reasonably high Q - I used two 1mH ferrite cored chokes (RS components 233-5291), with a Q of about 80. The transformer allows one side of the tuning capacitor to be grounded - almost any high-permeability ferrite core should work OK. The tuning part is located in the shack, and connected to the loop with coax; this can be quite long, since it effectively just increases the inductance of the loop, which in any case is much smaller than the 2mH tuning inductance.

The area of the loop required depends on how 'deaf' the receiver is. If sensitivity is inadequate, a bigger loop can be put up. The area is the important factor which decides the signal level; height and shape are not critical. This means it only takes a few minutes to put up, and can use any available supports - the original loop was just slung between a fence post and the branches of a bush, with no additional insulation. A wire thrown over a small tree also worked fine - hence the 'Lazy' title. It could also be useful as a receiving antenna for portable operation.

Of course, the antenna should be mounted as far as possible from noise sources, such as mains wiring. If one end is made moveable, the loop can be turned to null out QRM. The tuning inductance can be changed to cover different frequency ranges, including 500kHz.

M0BMU's one metre square bandpass loop

Bandpass loops

The need to frequently re-tune a high Q loop is something of a drawback; the Q can be reduced by adding resistive loading, but unfortunately this also reduces the signal level available to the receiver. An alternative approach to increasing loop bandwidth is to combine the tuned circuit formed by the loop with other capacitors and inductors to form a bandpass filter. This results in a wider bandwidth, while at the same time improving rejection of out-of-band signals. Two such bandpass loops are shown in **Fig 4.6(a) and (b)**.

The $1m^2$ loop system uses a loop consisting of 10 turns of $1mm^2$ PVC insulated stranded wire, divided into two windings of five turns each. The windings

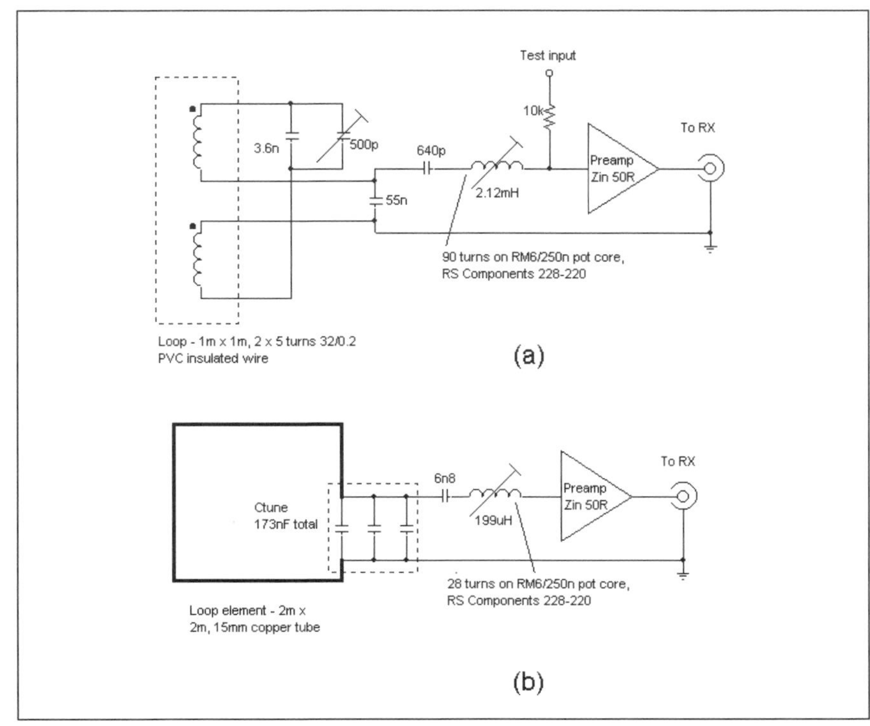

Fig 4.6: (a) $1m^2$ Bandpass loop. (b) 2m x 2m Bandpass loop. Values can be scaled to operate at 500kHz

The 2m x 2m bandpass loop

are taped together in a bundle and supported on a cross-shaped wooden frame. The loop inductance is resonated by a total capacitance of approximately 3.6nF, and coupled through the 55nF capacitor to a second, series-tuned circuit of 640pF/2.12mH. Output is taken from the series tuned circuit to a preamplifier. The two coupled tuned circuits give a flat pass-band about 4kHz wide centered on 137kHz. The response of the antenna is -40dB down at 115kHz and 160kHz, giving good rejection of LF broadcast stations and Loran at 100kHz. The preamplifier has an input impedance of 50 ohms, and uses the circuit shown in Fig 4.4. The 2.12mH inductor is wound on an RM6/250n adjustable pot core; the capacitors should be low-loss types such as silver-mica, polystyrene or polypropylene. To align this antenna, inject a signal at 137kHz between ground and the 10k resistor, and temporarily disconnect one of the loop windings. Monitor the preamp output on a receiver, and tune the 2.12mH pot core for a minimum signal. Then reconnect the loop, and tune the 500pF trimmer for maximum signal.

The 2m x 2m loop uses a single-turn element made from copper water pipe; this is easier to weatherproof compared to a multi-turn winding, and self-supporting. The loop element has 7.9uH inductance, and is tuned by a total of approximately 173nF, made up from smaller-value polypropylene capacitors connected in parallel. This feeds the same 50 ohm preamp through a series tuned circuit made up of 6.8nF/199uH. The bandwidth of this larger loop is about 26kHz at the 3dB points. The tuning is less critical than for the smaller loop, and it is sufficient to adjust the loop tuning capacitance and the series-tuned circuit separately for resonance at 137kHz, before connecting them together.

Both these loop designs are capable of providing ample signal to noise ratio even under quiet band conditions. The noise level at the preamp output is around 1uV in 300Hz bandwidth, so a receiver with reasonably good LF sensitivity is required; some amateur-type receivers with poor LF sensitivity may require additional preamplification. A more detailed description of these antennas can be found in [3]. Of course, the loops can be re-tuned for use at 500kHz if required.

A smaller loop

G3YXM used the preamp in Fig 4.4 with a smaller, multi-turn loop mounted on a rotator. The loop was supported on a 'crucifix' made from two 2m aluminium poles, one vertical and one horizontal, bolted together at the centre. The wire was wound round four self-tapping screws sticking out near the ends of the poles. He used five turns which seemed to give the best sensitivity on 136kHz. He reported: "The interesting thing is that the loop behaves differently from the main aerial especially at night. Sometimes signals can be much better on the loop, although orientation is critical. I recently worked OH1TN with 100% copy on the loop, whereas if I listened on the main wire he was a very difficult copy - and it wasn't local noise that made the difference. The loop does seem to be able to pick out the best mode of propagation sometimes."

G3YXM's loop antenna

Active whip antennas

Quite short wire or whip antennas provide adequate signal to noise ratio at LF when matched to the receiver input by a high impedance buffer amplifier. The response of the resulting Active Whip antenna, or E-field antenna, is broadband, and can extend from the VLF range to the VHF range, depending on the amplifier used. The preamplifier is located at the base of the antenna, and its DC supply is usually fed up the coax. The whip element is often around 1 - 2m long, and the small size makes the antenna easy to site in an electrically quiet location. As with the loop antennas, it is important to experiment with the antenna location to find a site that has a low noise level. Since all signals over a wide frequency range are presented to the buffer amplifier input, good dynamic range is important, and overload problems may occur if there are high-power broadcast stations nearby.

Unlike loop receiving antennas, the signal output level from an active whip depends strongly on its position, partly due to the screening effect of surrounding buildings and other objects, and partly on the height of the whip element above the ground plane. Greater output will be obtained if the whip is mounted on a mast, or on the roof of a building, rather than at ground level.

The PA0RDT Mini-Whip Antenna

The PA0RDT-Mini-Whip© was designed by Roelof Bakker, PA0RDT, and has been built and used successfully for LF and MF reception by numerous amateurs. Good receive performance extends from 10kHz to over 20MHz. The compact size of this antenna also makes it very suitable for portable operation.

The Mini-Whip 'whip' element is in fact a small piece of copper-clad board. The shape is not important provided capacitance to ground is similar, and other whip element construction can also be used, eg a small metal box with the preamp inside. Tests were performed to optimise the size of the whip element, and the design achieves good sensitivity while maintaining maximum overall output at about -20dBm to prevent receiver overload. The buffer amplifier is optimised for good strong-signal performance. Second order output intercept has been measured by AA7U as being greater than +70dBm, and third order intercept greater than +30dBm.

Power is fed from a 12 - 15V DC supply to the Mini-Whip via the power feed unit and the coaxial feed line, which can be up to 100m long. The power feed unit includes an RF isolating transformer, which reduces noise due to ground loops, but this is not always essential.

The buffer amplifier is constructed 'dead bug' style on the ground plane half of the board next to the whip element, which is formed by the other half of the

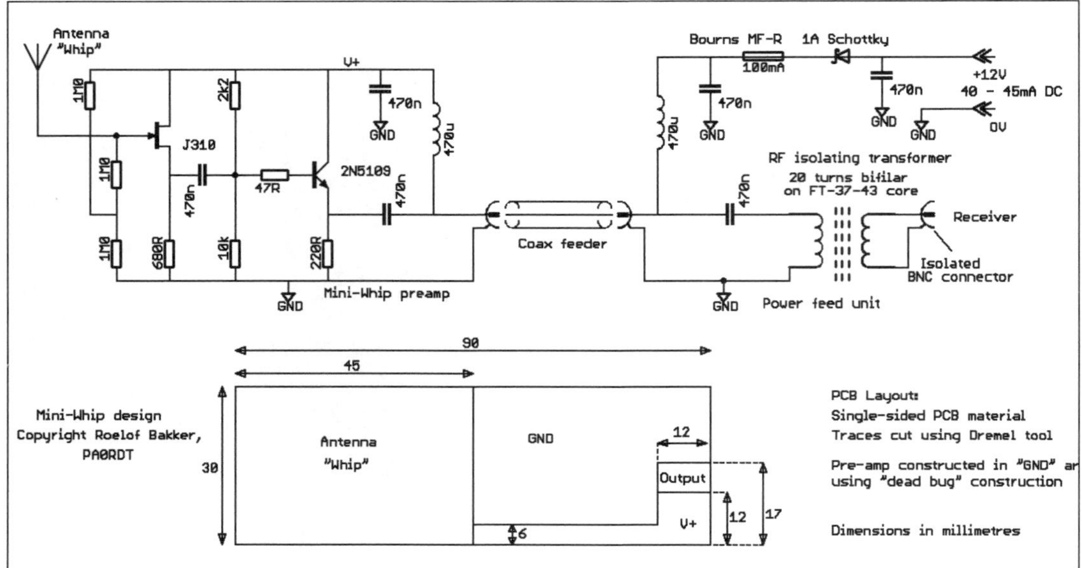

Fig. 4.7 The PA0RDT-Mini-Whip©

board (see **Fig 4.7**). The complete circuit board is mounted inside a 100mm long section of 40mm plastic drain pipe, with two end-caps. One end-cap carries an insulated BNC connector to which the circuit board is soldered.

PA0RDT notes that the electric field from most interference sources is largely confined within the building. For best results therefore, the Mini-Whip should be mounted on a non-conducting pole in a position well clear of buildings. Grounding the outer braid of the coaxial feeder to a ground rod installed close to the point where the feeder enters the shack also helps to reduce interference generated by noise currents flowing on the feeder.

A more detailed article can be found at [4]. A ready-made Mini-Whip can also be purchased from PA0RDT [5].

References

[1] *http://www.wellbrook.uk.com*

[2] *http://www.hard-core-dx.com/nordicdx/antenna/loop/k9ay/*

[3] *http://www.wireless.org.uk/bploop.pdf*

[4] *http://www.veron.nl/afd/voorne_putten/Lezing/pa0rdt/pa0rdt-Mini-WhipGeneralDescription%5B1%5D.pdf*

[5] E-mail: *roelof@ndb.demon.nl*

5

Generating a signal

In this chapter:

- VFOs
- Crystals and VXOs
- Dividing a VFO
- Transverter
- Direct Digital Synthesis

ANY LOW FREQUENCY transmitter must start with a signal source. Because the allocations at 136kHz and 500kHz are so narrow, CW operation can be carried out with a crystal controlled transmitter, but being restricted to a single frequency is a serious practical limitation. Most operators use some form of variable oscillator, especially if they intend using both CW and QRSS which have centres of activity in different parts of the bands. The choice of oscillator depends on the frequency stability required and the need to set its frequency accurately. CW needs a much less stable and accurate signal source than, say, QRSS120 which must stay within 0.05Hz for hours at a time.

VFOs

Very few LF stations use conventional signal frequency VFOs, but GW4ALG used the one in **Fig 5.1** as part of his Marathon 136kHz QRP LF transmitter project [1]. The 50pF tuning capacitor provides a tuning range of 10kHz, more

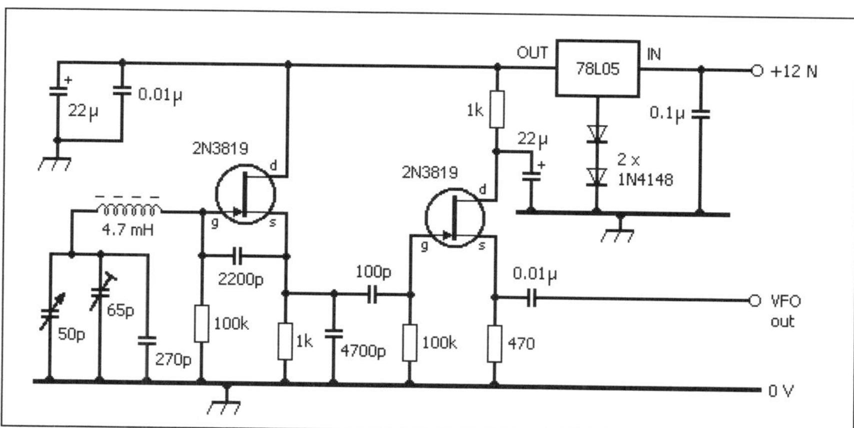

Fig 5.1: 136kHz VFO built by GW4ALG

than enough to cover the entire amateur band. 4.7mH RF chokes work very well in this circuit. The VFO drives a very effective FET buffer which presents the VFO signal to the driver stages.

Crystals and VXOs

The simplest way to generate a signal is by using a crystal oscillator, though a signal frequency crystal for 136kHz is likely to be expensive and difficult to obtain. Several 500kHz operators have taken advantage of surplus 500kHz frequency standard crystals, 'grinding' them to move the frequency above 501kHz (see the G3XAQ transmitter in a later chapter). The frequency can be pulled further by a VXO circuit but only over a small range, eg 100Hz.

A more useful variable frequency signal source uses two HF crystal oscillators roughly 136kHz (or 500kHz) apart. These can be old crystals, in the 4MHz to 15MHz region, salvaged from your junk box - perhaps from an old VHF transceiver, found at a rally, or purchased new for a few pounds. One crystal oscillator is pulled in frequency by a series capacitor (sometimes an inductor is included, but this may reduce stability) to achieve a VXO with a range of 2kHz or so - a much greater amount than achievable using a low frequency crystal. The two crystal oscillators are mixed and filtered to produce an output covering most of the band. This approach is suitable for CW and QRSS3 which is used for Europe-wide contacts, but it may be have inadequate stability for longer dot lengths of QRSS (eg 60 or 120 second dot period used only for intercontinental DX working) and some data modes. Examples of this technique for 136kHz and 500kHz can be found in the Transmitters chapter.

Another variation on crystal control is to divide the frequency of an HF crystal oscillator using a digital divider chip. An example is shown in **Fig 5.2**, where the 8738.89kHz crystal frequency is divided by 64 by the 74HCT4060 IC to

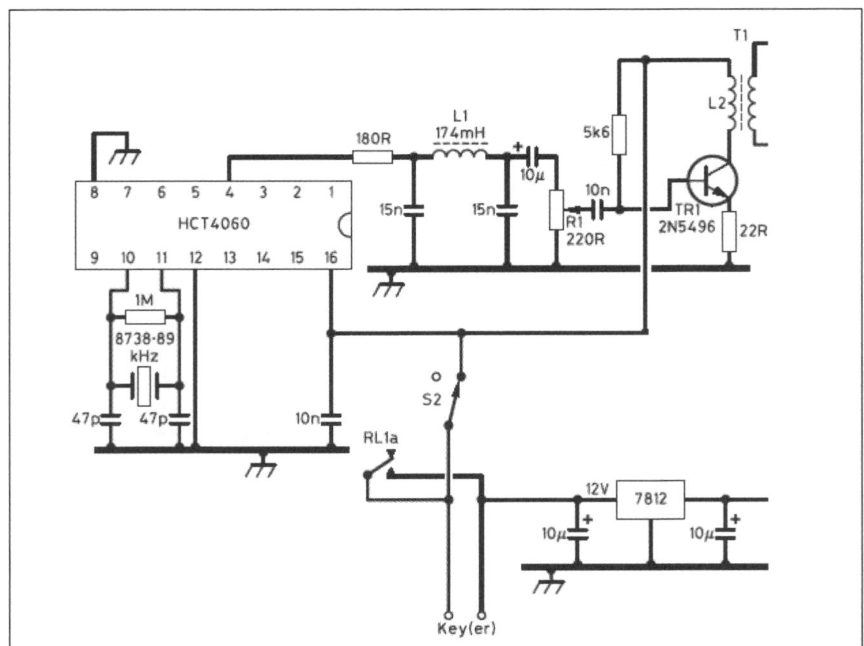

Fig 5.2: Part of a transmitter designed by PA0SE. The 4060 chip divides the crystal to the 136kHz band

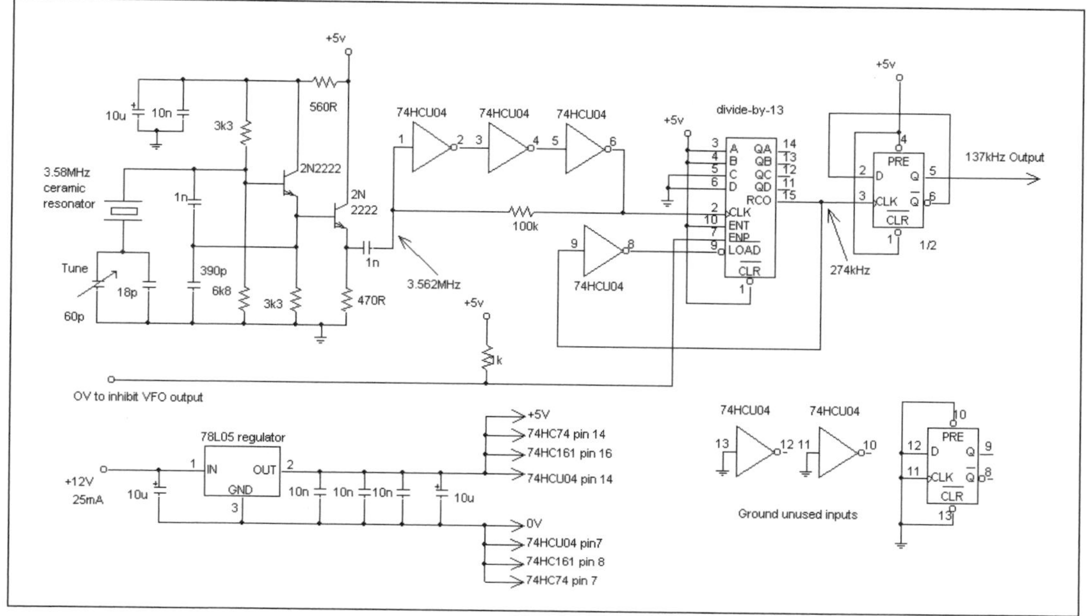

obtain output at 136.545kHz. The output frequency is fixed, but the stability is excellent, since any drift at the HF crystal frequency is also divided by 64.

An extension of this method is to divide a ceramic resonator oscillator to provide a variable oscillator with good stability and coverage of the complete band (**Fig 5.3**) A 500kHz version can be found in the Transmitters chapter.

Fig 5.3: 137 kilohertz ceramic resonator VFO

Dividing a VFO

An HF VFO can be fed into a divider to produce a stable and variable source. The one in **Fig 5.4** was built by PA0SE as a replacement for the crystal in Fig 5.3(a).

The VFO has a frequency range of 8684.8 .to. 8819.2 kHz. This is divided down to by 64 in the HC 4060 to give a frequency range to the input to the PA of 135.7 to 137.8kHz. The consequence of this approach is that the frequency stability is excellent because the small amount of VFO drift is divided by 64 on 136 kHz.

To achieve the desired tuning range, the total capacitance C2 + C3 = 32.06 x C1. To achieve the desired output frequency, the inductance L1 = 322uH/(C2 + C3). In

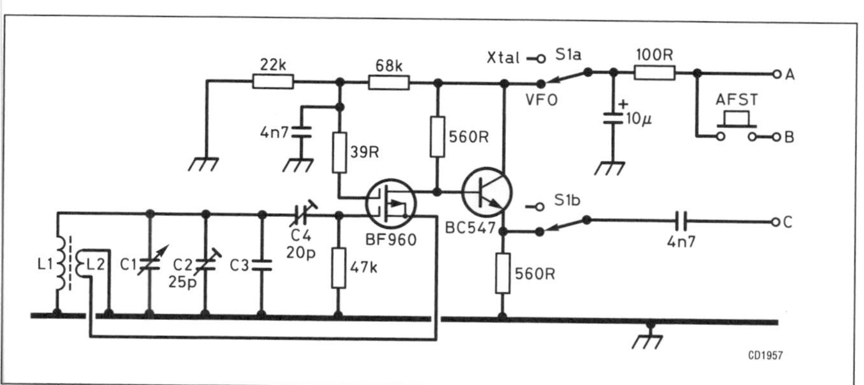

Fig 5.4: PA0SE's 9MHz VFO is divided to produce a very stable signal

this case, C1 has a range of 16.5pF, making C2 + C3 529pF, and L1 0.609uH (11 turns on a Micrometals T-68-6 toroid core). C3 is made up of paralleled smaller capacitors (silver-mica or polystyrene types). C2 is an air trimmer of 25 pF maximum. L2 is 1 turn wound in the same direction as L1. Starting from the earthed end both turns go in the same direction through the centre of the toroid. The signal level from the VFO is set by C4. Switch S1 selects VFO or crystal control. The TUNE push button connects the supply voltage to the HC4060 and VFO only. This results in a weak signal on the transmit frequency for zero beating on to a received signal.

An HF transmitter can be used as a VFO, with a digital frequency divider to obtain low frequency output. This can give excellent stability and full band coverage. It may also be possible to generate narrow-band FSK using the transmitter in SSB mode. It is convenient to choose a frequency division ratio of 10:1 or 100:1, so that the rig frequency display provides the correct readout (but with the decimal point moved). Most current HF transceivers inhibit transmission outside the amateur bands, but in many cases simple modifications extend the tuning range to convenient frequencies such as 13.600MHz or 5.020MHz (modification details for many rigs are available from the manufacturers and user web sites). The HF rig power output should be kept low, and connected to a suitable dummy load and attenuator to terminate the transmitter output and provide the correct level to drive the divider. Some transceivers have a 'transverter output' that can be used.

Transverter

If your HF transceiver has good stability (see receivers chapter) and a milliwatt level output, it can be transverted down to 136kHz or 500kHz. Apart from being able to tune the entire band, this will enable the transceiver keying circuits to be used. Furthermore, any data mode capability can be used at LF provided the transmitter is sufficiently linear.

The transverter described here was built by G3YMC for use on 136kHz, and converts to and from his FT101ZD tuned to the 10MHz amateur band. This band was chosen primarily because 10MHz computer crystals are cheap and readily available, and the performance of some amateur transceivers is rather better on this band than on the more commonly used 28MHz band.

No originality is claimed for the design. It was built up using published circuits in the *ARRL Handbook* and elsewhere, modified ad hoc for the application. The circuit is described in blocks, with all components shown but no detail is given on the inductors and transformers except for general guidelines. It is intended as an experimenter's unit rather than something available off the shelf.

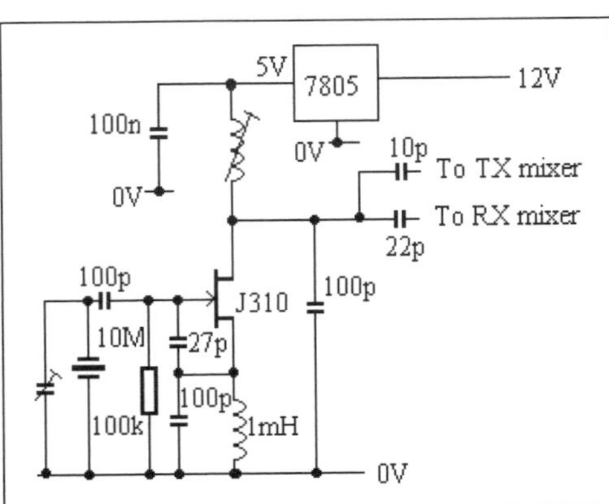

Fig 5.5: The 10MHz oscillator forms the heart of G3YMC's transverter

A 10MHz JFET crystal oscillator is used. This is a conventional circuit (**Fig 5.5**) and outputs a reference to the receive and transmit mixers. A trimmer

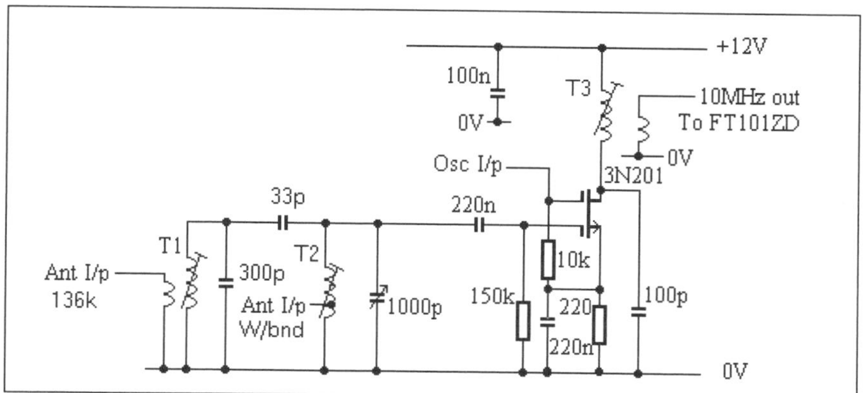

Fig 5.6: The receive converter of G3YMC's LF transverter

capacitor can be used to set the frequency accurately. The oscillator is powered from a stabilised 5V rail provided by a 7805 regulator to ensure stability. The two output capacitors may be adjusted in value to obtain the correct injection levels.

The receive converter (**Fig 5.6**) uses a dual gate mosfet mixer preceded by an FET preamp. Input from the antenna is applied to a fixed tuned stage, T1. This transformer uses a cut down long-wave ferrite rod from a scrap radio and resonates in the 136 band with a parallel capacitor of around 300pF. This is top capacitive coupled to a second tuned stage (using a pot core) which can be tuned from 65-180kHz with a dual 500pF variable capacitor. An input is provided here for a wideband reception antenna, but at lower intermodulation performance.

A 3N201 dual gate mosfet is used as the receive mixer, with the oscillator injection applied to G2. This is conventional with the drain resonated to 10MHz by T3, wound on a quarter inch former.

The transmit section of the transverter consists of a mixer, low level driver stage, mosfet power stage and output matching and filtering. The transmit mixer is mounted in the same box as the receive converter; the other stages are in a separate box.

A 10MHz drive signal is taken from the low power output socket of the HF transceiver and fed to the transmit mixer (**Fig 5.7**) where it is terminated in 50 ohms and attenuated to a suitable level for applying to the gate of a dual gate mosfet. An injection signal is applied to the second gate from the crystal oscillator. The drain is connected to a parallel tuned circuit at 136kHz, whose out-

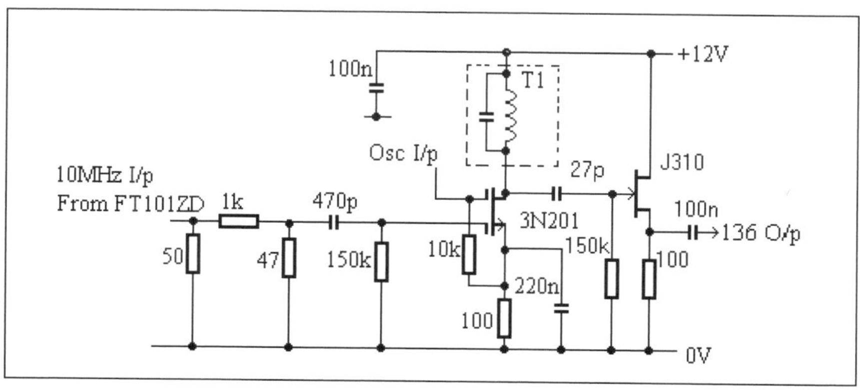

Fig 5.7: The transmit mixer

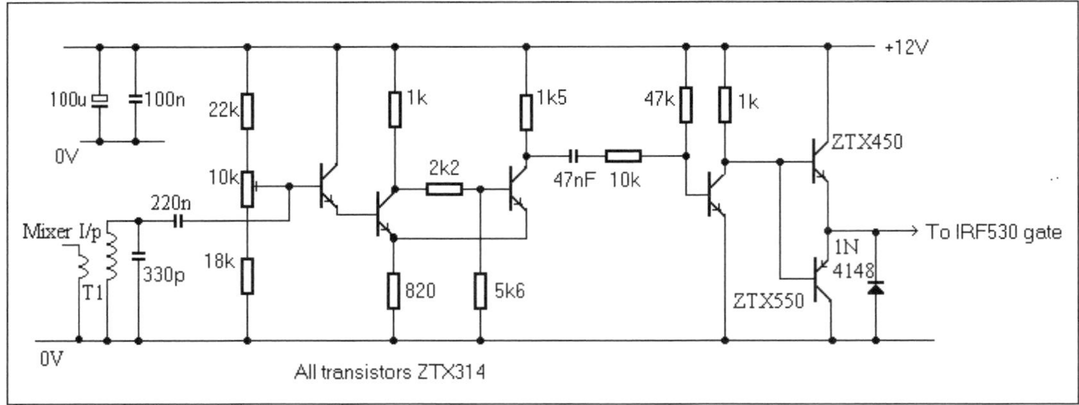

Fig 5.8: Transmit driver of the transverter

put is buffered by an FET source follower and fed to the transmit driver stage (**Fig 5.8**).

The low level input from the transmit mixer is passed through a 136kHz tuned stage and then fed into a Schmitt trigger to produce an approximately square waveform. Fine adjustment of the Schmitt threshold 10k potentiometer allows the mark-space ratio to be optimised. The drive is buffered by dual emitter followers and applied to the gate of the power mosfet. These low level stages are powered by a 12V rail derived from the 24V PA rail via a 7812 regulator.

The output amplifier (**Fig 5.9**) consists of a single IRF530 mosfet run off a 24V supply. The current taken and the output power is determined by the impedance matching, which transforms the 50 ohm load impedance to around 3 ohms at the drain of the FET.

T2 and T3 are bifilar wound transformers on 3C85 ferrite rings [Note: 3C85 has now been discontinued. 3C90 is a suitable substitute - see Appendix 2 for details], each transformer being configured for an impedance transformation of 4:1. Harmonics are reduced by a low pass filter. The inductors are 13 turns of wire on a 25mm ferrite ring.

The transmitter has an output of around 35 watts into a resistive load. When using a real antenna the output may be different. A power supply of 24V at 4A maximum is recommended.

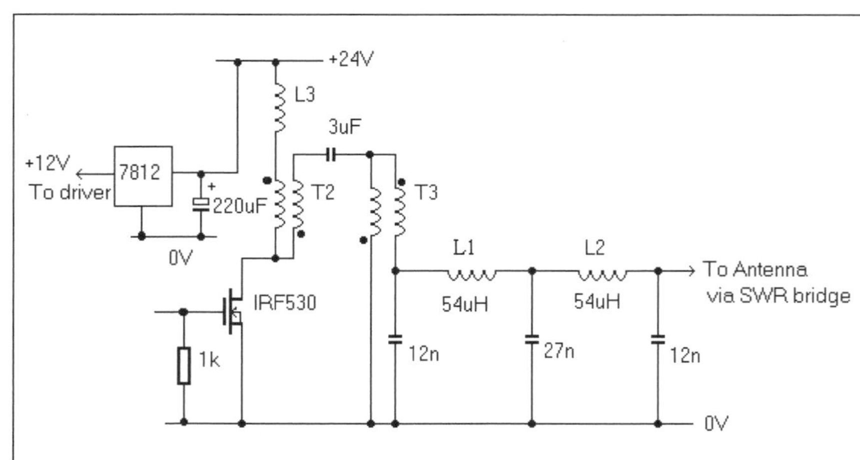

Fig 5.9: Transverter power amplifier and low pass filter

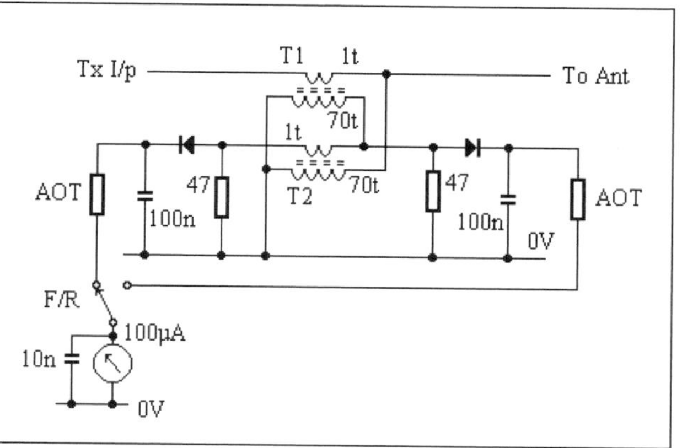

Fig 5.10: SWR monitor for the G3YMC transverter

The simple SWR/Power meter shown in **Fig 5.10** can be used as a tuning aid. The value of the AOT resistors depends on the sensitivity of the meter, and is typically about 10kohms - adjust for full scale deflection in the forward direction. T1 and T2 are wound on the same 3C90 toroids as used in the transmitter. The diodes should be point contact or germanium ones with low forward voltage drop (eg OA91).

Direct Digital synthesis

The most sophisticated way to generate a signal at LF is Direct Digital Synthesis (DDS). A sine wave is produced from a crystal oscillator reference by entirely digital means. The DDS provides the accuracy and stability of the crystal reference, together with high tuning resolution. The main limitation of the DDS, that the output frequency is restricted to less than half the reference frequency, is not a problem for LF/MF signal generation. The DDS must be carefully designed to avoid noise sidebands and spurious emissions. Further information on this technique is contained in [2].

It is beyond the scope of this book to describe how to build your own direct digital synthesiser, but there are several circuits and kits available. Most use software stored on a chip, which relies on the constructor being equipped to do the programming or being prepared to buy the programmed chip. All require skill and experience. [3, 4]

ZL1BPU's LF DDS/exciter, is not difficult to construct and has many useful facilities, including: resolution of better than 0.1Hz; high stability; support for CW, FSK, Hell and MFSK; beacon mode, sweep generator and RF output up to 1W. Full details, including how to buy the software can be seen at [5].

References

[1] GW4ALG's 'Marathon' LF QRP project. *http://www.alg.demon.co.uk/radio/136/qrptx.htm*

[2] *Radio Communication Handbook*, RSGB.

[3] Build a PIC Controlled DDS VFO, 0 to 6MHz, by Johan Bodin, SM6LKM. *http://home4.swipnet.se/~w-41522/minidds/minidds.html*

[4] A software based DDS for 137kHz. *http://wireless.org.uk/swdds.htm*

[5] ZL1BPU's DDS/exciter. *http://www.qsl.net/zl1bpu/MICRO/EXCITER/Index.htm*

6

Transmitters

In this chapter:

- □ Commercial options
- □ Beginner's 136kHz Tx
- □ 136kHz low pass filter
- □ Class D transmitters
- □ Class D design example
- □ G3YXM 136kHz1kW Tx
- □ G0MRF 136kHz 300W Tx
- □ G3XAQ 500kHz ECL82 Tx
- □ M0BMU 500kHz Class D Tx
- □ G3YMC 500kHz VXO Tx
- □ 500kHz low pass filter
- □ Power supplies

BECAUSE OF THE extremely low antenna efficiencies, 136kHz is not a band for low power transmitters. Typically, it can take several hundred watts (perhaps over 1kW) of RF to reach the 1W ERP licence limit. The exact figure depends on the size of antenna used, but a transmitter delivering over 100 watts is desirable.

Experiments with QRSS have shown that it is possible to achieve ranges of several hundred kilometres whilst running only a few watts of RF (tens of milliwatts ERP) and can be a good way to start. However, for CW and long haul contacts much more power must be used.

The 136kHz band in the UK (and many other countries) has a limit on effective radiated power (ERP) and not on transmitter power, it is possible to compensate for an inefficient antenna simply by increasing the RF fed to it. In practice, however, the higher voltages on smaller antennas eventually lead to a practical limit on the amount of power that can be used. So the first step that should be taken is to make the antenna as efficient as possible (see antennas chapter).

Life is somewhat easier for those operating solely on 500kHz because practical antennas are more efficient, and the ERP limit for experimenters is lower. It is possible to reach 100mW ERP using a transmitter power of a few watts or perhaps tens of watts.

Commercial options

There is little off the shelf equipment for transmitting on LF. Most operators build their own equipment, and they often report this to be part of the challenge, enjoyment and satisfaction. Although some data modes require linear amplification, most LF transmitters use high efficiency non-linear output stages.

The one commercial transmitter made for the 136kHz amateur band was 'The First' from Ropex which sold for just under £200. It was ready built, ran up to 130W of crystal controlled CW from a 12V supply and included keying and

Ex-Decca Navigation LF transmitter, showing the three transmitter modules at the top. Most of the chassis space is occupied by the tank circuits

antenna changeover circuits. Very few were made, but one may occasionally be available secondhand.

Some surplus equipment for 136kHz may be found on the second-hand market, though very few commercial users have transmit allocations in this region. The most popular was built by Racal Decca for the Decca Navigation System [1] that was scrapped at the end of the 20th century. The transmitter units, which operated in the 70 -130kHz region, are on very bulky steel frames designed for rack-mounting, but are metered and well protected. They can run up to 1.2kW and require two power sources, 24V at 2 amps, and between 50 and 80 volts at up to 25 amps. Some of them work with almost no modification, whilst others - the lower frequency versions - require a small amount of tweaking. Help on this can be obtained from other users of the band (see chapter on sources of information). The Decca units contain only the driver and output stages and must be fed from a 136kHz signal source, such as a DDS or crystal oscillator - see previous chapter.

The BK Electronics 300W audio amplifier is capable of 100W or so at 136kHz

A few audio amplifiers work at 136kHz. Hi-fi amplifier units with onboard mains power units are available from BK Electronics [2] giving a few hundred watts of audio. These amplifiers can provide 100W or so at 136kHz and at less than £100 they make a useful starting point for those unwilling to build their first LF transmitter from scratch, but who are still prepared to do a few modifications to make the equipment work way beyond its design frequency.

The Hafler P3000 audio amplifier has been used in the USA. It runs up to 300 watts and its bandwidth is specified as 300kHz. This makes it suitable for linear operation on 136kHz, and therefore ideal for data modes, though it is rather expensive at around £500. A data sheet can be found at [3] and the experiences of W1TAG, whose 136kHz beacon WD1XES is frequently received in Europe, is at [4].

Although there is some old marine equipment available for 500kHz, the low power requirements of operating at this frequency make it simple to build your own transmitter.

Home made transmitters for 136kHz

A simple LF transmitter is shown below. In addition a transverter capable of 35W output was detailed in the previous chapter. For more useful power levels more complex designs are required. Some experimenters have built valve amplifiers [5] but most LF signals come from transistor amplifiers using power mosfets in Class D (or E) push-pull, sometimes with several transistors in parallel. Several are described later in this chapter. Although some experience is required, there is always support for the constructor, both from the original designers and from those amateurs who have already built the circuits.

If higher power is required, two power amplifiers can be 'paralleled' using a Wilkinson Combiner. A combiner used by the VA7LF Group for their trans-Pacific tests is described at [6].

A beginner's transmitter

This small low power transmitter, designed by Peter Schnoor, DF3LP, uses a simple VXO/mixer to produce a variable, but stable, CW signal on 136kHz. Depending on the pi-filter components used and voltage for the final stage, this transmitter should be capable of 100 watts output.

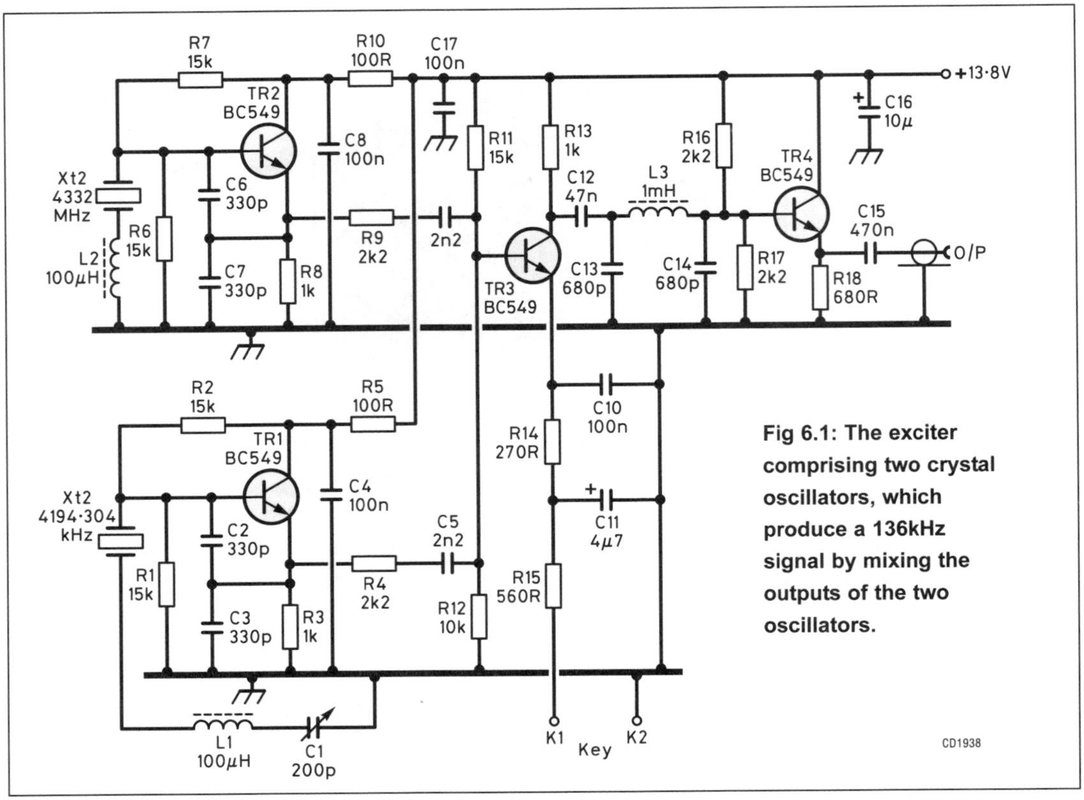

Fig 6.1: The exciter comprising two crystal oscillators, which produce a 136kHz signal by mixing the outputs of the two oscillators.

The exciter (**Fig 6.1**) comprises two crystal oscillators, which produce a 136kHz signal by mixing the outputs of the two oscillators. One of the oscillators is a VXO, which gives a frequency variation of about 2.5kHz on the 136kHz band.

The conversion product is filtered and amplified by an emitter follower, a square wave pre-driver and the switching stage to drive the power amplifier: see **Fig 6.2**. This power amplifier does not make use of any output transformer since ferrite toroids for 100-200kHz are not always available. The prototype was built from junk box components in two to three hours.

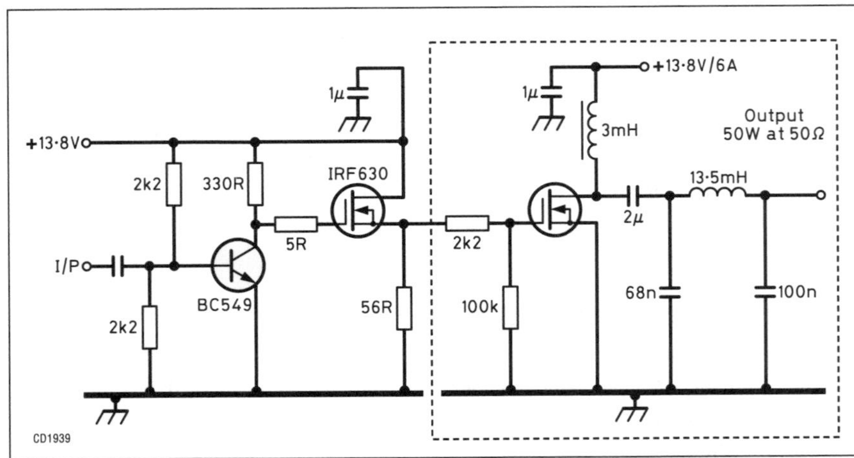

Fig 6.2: Driver and power amplifier of the DF3LP 100W transmitter

The components of the exciter and the two driver stages are soldered directly to the copper side of a simple PC board shown in **Fig 6.3**. The power amplifier stage was built separately from the exciter and drivers using 'ugly construction'.

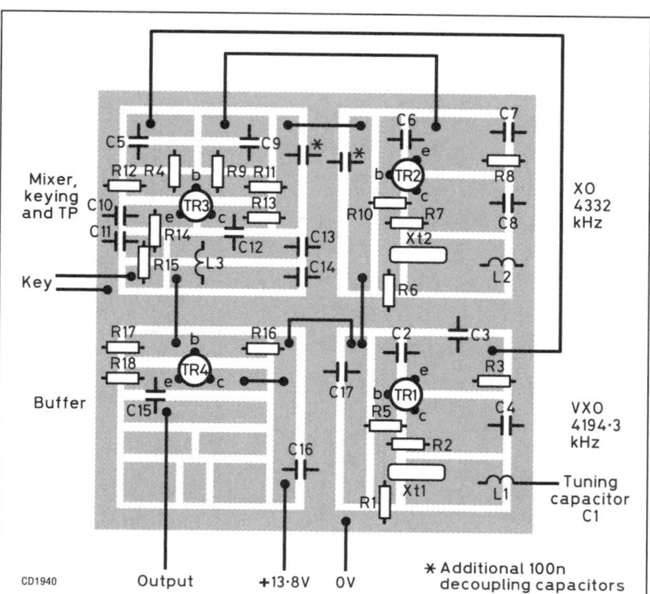

Fig 6.3: PC-Board for the exciter and driver stages

The pi-filter coil is air wound using 23 turns of 2.5mm enamelled wire, on a 45mm former. Use only high grade 400 volt polypropylene capacitors for the output filtering (see Appendix 2).

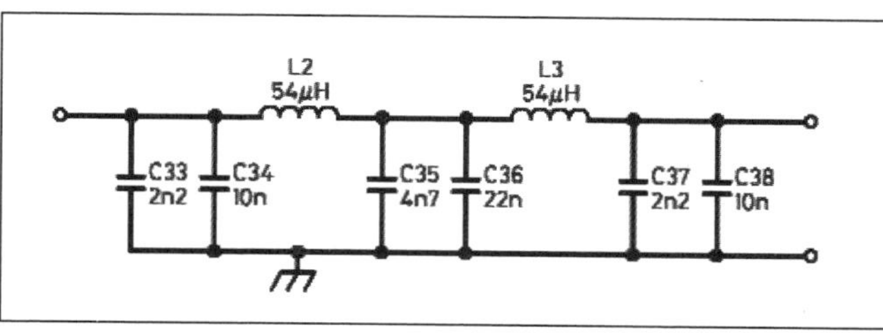

Fig 6.4: This low pass filter makes a useful stand-alone project as it can be used with any 136kHz project

The output from the filter is not a clean sine wave so an additional pi network low pass filter, such as the one described below, is recommended.

An IRF630 can be used for the final stage but the IRF640 is much better since its on-resistance is lower. This small amplifier will give more power by using a higher voltage; an IRF840 is recommended.

136kHz low pass filter

The output from a simple LF transmitter can be high in harmonics, so it must be followed by a low pass filter.

The filter shown in **Fig 6.4** can be built as a stand-alone project so that it can be added to any experimental transmitter you may build.

The inductor is 59 turns of 0.8mm enamelled wire on a T157-2 powdered iron toroid. High voltage poly-propylene capacitors with a working voltage of 400 to 1000 volts must be used.

Class D transmitters

LF transmitters are usually required to produce between 100W and a few kilowatts of output. Most LF operators are currently using class D switching-mode output stages; these can achieve very good efficiency, which considerably simplifies cooling problems associated with high-power linear amplifiers. These

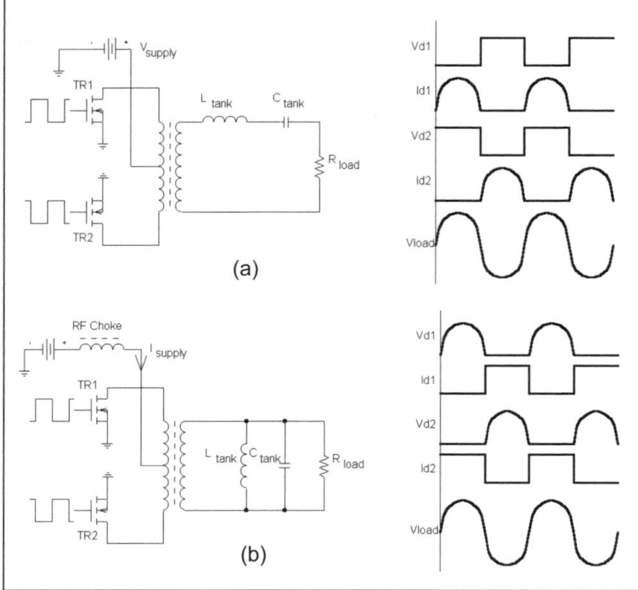

Fig 6.5: (a) Voltage-switching class-D amplifier, and (b) Current-switching class-D amplifier with MOSFET drain waveforms

circuits are also well suited to inexpensive power mosfets and other components intended for switch-mode power supplies operating in a similar frequency range. Switching mode circuits are, however, more difficult to key or modulate satisfactorily. Fortunately, most LF operation uses simple on-off keying of the transmitter, or frequency-shift keying.

Class-D amplifiers fall into two distinct types: voltage-switching, **Fig 6.5(a)**; or current-switching, **Fig 6.5(b)**. In each case, the load is connected to the output stage via a resonant tank circuit.

The voltage-switching type has a series-tuned tank circuit; the switching mosfets develop a square-wave voltage at the input side of the series tank circuit. However the tank circuit ensures the current flowing in the load is almost a pure sine wave.

The current-switching type has a parallel-tuned tank circuit; the supply to the output devices is a constant current which is applied to the tank circuit in alternate directions depending on which MOSFET is switched on. The resulting square wave current applied to the tank circuit again results in an almost sinusoidal voltage across the load.

Since a constant-current DC supply is not very practical, a constant voltage supply is used with a series RF choke. Provided the impedance of the choke is much greater than the load resistance, the supply current is almost constant. The major advantage of class D is that the MOSFETs are either fully 'on', in which case the only power loss is due to the MOSFET 'on' resistance, $r_{DS(on)}$, or fully off, with essentially zero power dissipation. In practice, there are additional losses, but these are small compared to linear amplifiers, and efficiency can exceed 90%.

In many amateur circuits, the tank circuit is replaced by a low-Q low-pass filter, **Fig 6.6**. This circuit is 'quasi-parallel resonant'; it provides a resistive load

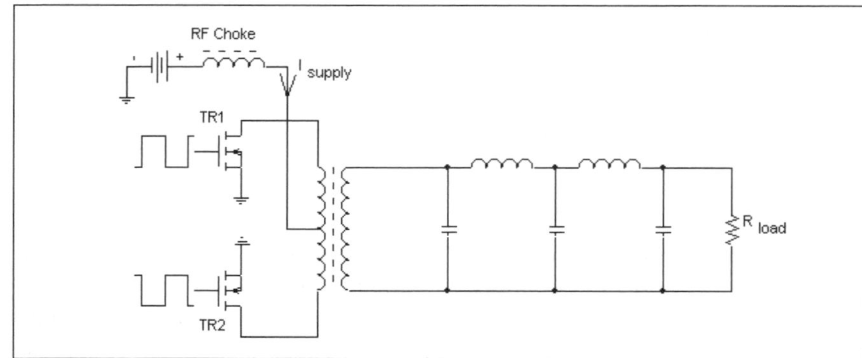

Fig 6.6: Practical form of Class D output stage

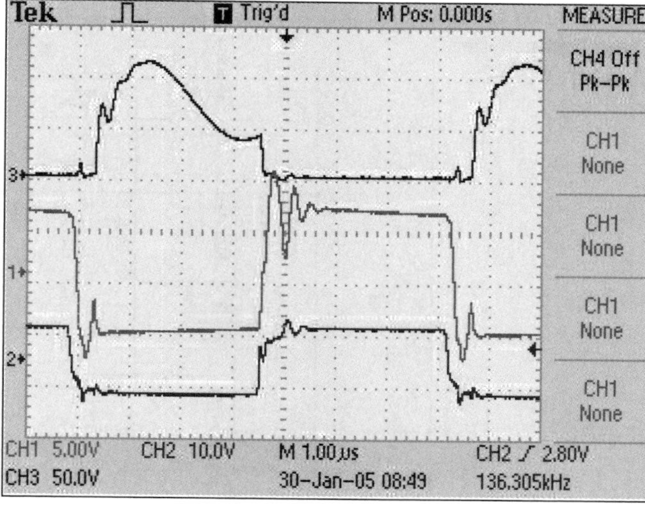

Fig 6.7: Class D waveforms. Upper trace, drain voltage; middle trace, drain current; lower trace, gate drive voltage

at the output frequency, but a low shunt impedance at the harmonics. The low Q leads to non-ideal class D operation in that the voltage waveform is not a perfect sine wave, but has the advantages that smaller inductors and capacitors are required, tolerances are less critical, and better rejection of higher harmonics is provided by the multiple filter sections. The voltage and current waveforms of a real-world class D output stage using this circuit are shown in **Fig 6.7** Compared to the idealised waveforms, some high frequency 'ringing' is visible. This is due to stray capacitance and inductance which inevitably exists in the circuit, and is undesirable since it causes increased losses, as well as the potential for generating high - order harmonics. It is therefore important to minimise stray reactance, two important causes of which are the parasitic capacitance of the mosfets themselves, and the leakage inductance of the output transformer. Adding damping RC 'snubber' networks can also usefully reduce the level of ringing.

As with other types of amplifier, the output power of class D amplifiers is defined by the supply voltage V_{cc}, output transformer turns ration n and load impedance R_L. For the voltage switching amplifier:

$$P_L = \frac{8n^2V_{cc}^2}{\pi^2 R_L}$$

While for the current-switching class D:

$$P_L = \frac{\pi^2 n^2 V_{cc}^2}{8R_L}$$

These formulas assume losses in the circuit are negligible; in practice, some losses do occur but since they are small, the results given by the formulae are reasonably accurate.

Class D PA design example

The design process for a class D transmitter output stage is best illustrated by an example. The following design is for a LF transmitter with about 200W output, using a current-switching class D circuit. This is a modest power level for 136kHz, but the principles discussed have been applied equally well to designs with 1kW or more output using this circuit configuration, which is probably the most popular in use at present. The complete circuit is shown in **Fig 6.8**.

The first design decision is what DC supply voltage to use, since the power supply is normally the most expensive and bulky part. In this case 13.8 volts was selected; it can use the standard DC supply found in many amateur shacks. The DC input power required will be about 10% greater than the RF output due

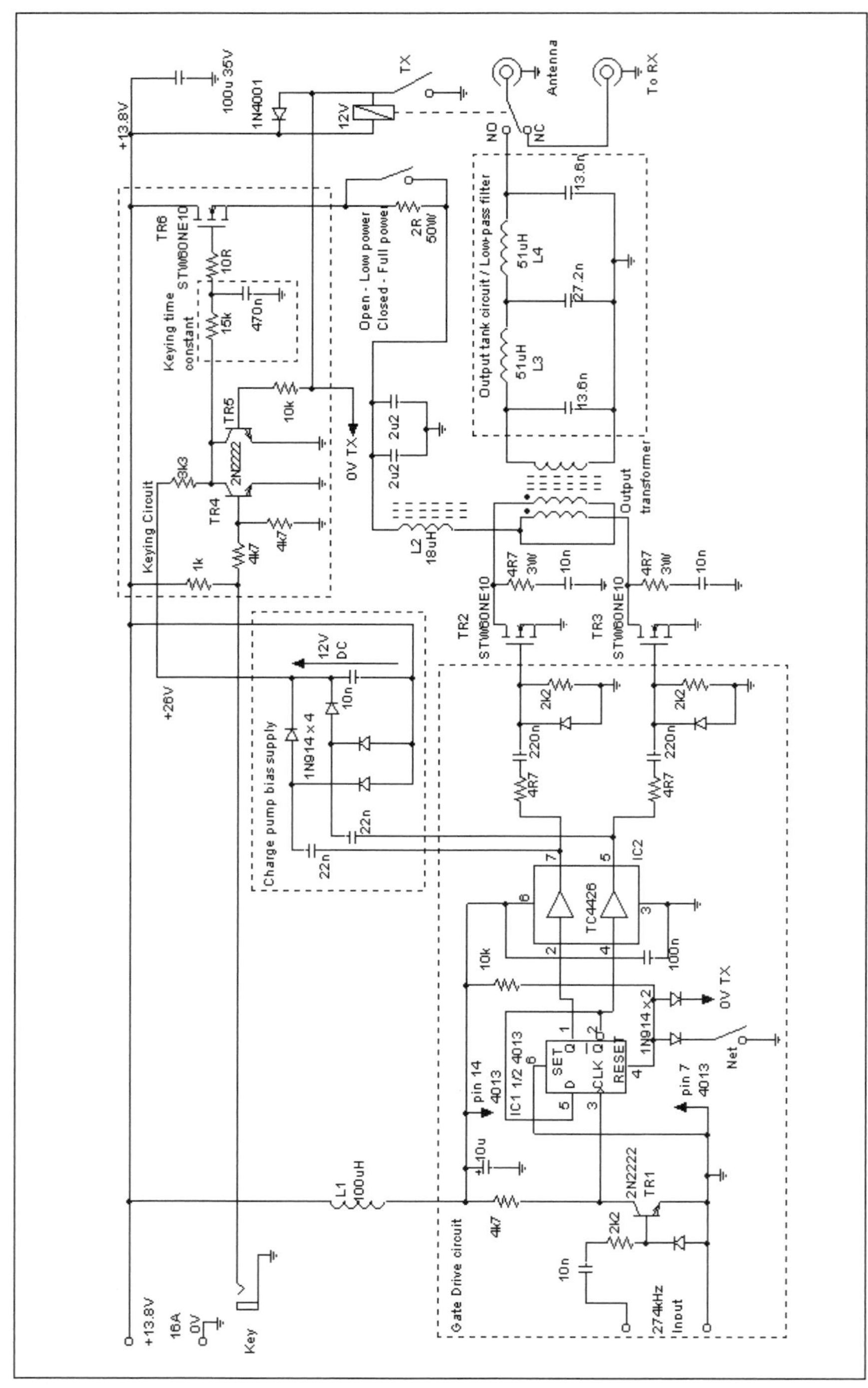

Fig 6.8: 200W Class D transmitter circuit

to losses, so the expected supply current will be 220W / 13.8V = 16A, a level that most 13.8V supplies can readily deliver. For higher power designs, 40 to 60V is often a good compromise, since the problem of large DC and RF currents is then reduced. It is perfectly possible to use an 'off line' directly rectified AC mains supply with no bulky mains transformer, as has been done by G4JNT [7];

note that design for electrical safety is absolutely critical in this case. Inexpensive switching MOSFETs are available suitable for any of these supply voltages.

In the ideal push-pull current switching circuit, the peak MOSFET drain-source voltage will theoretically be π times the DC supply voltage, in practice about four times the 13.8VDC supply is likely. MOSFETs should be selected so that only a few percent of the DC input power will be dissipated in their 'on' resistance, $r_{DS(on)}$. This condition also ensures the mosfet will have adequate drain current rating. STW60NE10 devices were used for TR2, TR3, with BVDS of 100V, and a typical $r_{DS(on)}$ of 0.016 ohms, leading to about 4W dissipation due to the 'on' resistance and 16A supply current ($I^2 \times r_{DS(on)}$).

Additional dissipation occurs during the transient period where the device is switching 'on' or 'off'. This can be determined from measurement of circuit waveforms, but can be assumed to be similar to that due to $r_{DS(on)}$. In normal operation therefore, each mosfet will only dissipate a few watts; however with a severe mismatch, power dissipation can be much higher, especially without DC supply current limiting. For a robust design, the MOSFETs and their heatsink should be able to dissipate of the order of 50% of the total DC input power, at least during a short overload period. The STW60NE10 devices have a TO-247 package and can dissipate 90W each at a case temperature of 100 degrees C, which is adequate.

The output transformer is the most important part of the design. It is normally wound on a core using the same ferrite grades that are used for switch-mode power supplies. These may be large toroidal cores, pot cores, or 'E' cores with plastic bobbins.

Several manufacturers produce suitable materials; these include Ferroxcube (Philips) 3C8, 3C85, 3C90, Siemens N27, N87, Neosid F44, and Fair-Rite #77 grades. All these ferrites have permeability around 2000, and have reasonably low loss at 137kHz. They are available in a variety of forms, such as EE, EC, and ETD styles, and sizes; a designation such as ETD49 means an ETD style core that is 49mm wide. A good selection of different core types is available from component distributors [8, 9] at reasonably low cost.

Transformer design is a complex topic in its own right, but a simplified procedure usually gives satisfactory results for amateur purposes, as follows.

Given the supply voltage and load impedance (usually 50 ohms), the turns ratio of the output transformer determines the output power. Rearranging the formula for current-switching class D given in the previous section gives:

$$n = \sqrt{\frac{8P_L R_L}{\pi^2 V_{cc}^2}}$$

For V_{cc} = 13.8V, R_L = 50 ohms, and P_L = 220 ohms, this gives n = 1:6.8. Next, a suitable sized core is chosen. As a guide, using the types of ferrite listed above, an ETD34 core is suitable for powers up to 250 watts, an ETD44 core for 500 watts, and an ETD49 for up to 1kW. Similar sizes in different styles have similar power handling. If in doubt, use a bigger core!

The number of turns N in the secondary winding can then be determined. N must be large enough to keep the peak magnetic flux B_{peak} to a value well below the saturation level at the expected output voltage level, V_{RMS}:

$$B_{peak} = \frac{V_{RMS}}{4.44fNA_e}, \quad V_{RMS} = \sqrt{P_L R_L}$$

Where A_e is the effective area of the core in m^2. The number of turns must also be large enough so that the inductance of the winding has a large reactance compared to the load impedance. A value of X_L about 5 - 10 times the load impedance is desirable. An ETD34 core and bobbin of 3C85 ferrite material was available, which according to the manufacturer's data has A_e of 97.1mm2 (97.1 x 10^{-6} m^2), and A_L of 2500nH/T^2. A suitable maximum value of B_{peak} for power-grade ferrite materials is around 0.15 tesla. For 220W output, V_{RMS} is 105V A few trials using the formulas resulted in n = 14 turns, B_{peak} = 0.127T and L = 490uH, X_L = 422 ohms, which meets the criteria given.

Two turn primary windings result in a turns ratio of 1:7, close enough in practice to the 1:6.8 design value. The primary windings were 4 x 2 turns, quadrifilar wound of 1mm enamelled copper wire, using two windings in parallel for each half of the primary winding. The secondary of 14 turns, 0.8mm enamelled copper was wound on top of the primaries, and insulated from them with polyester tape.

The DC feed choke L2 must be capable of handling the full DC supply current without saturation and also have a high reactance at 137kHz compared to the load impedance at the transformer primary, which is (50Ω / 7^2), about 1Ω. A reactance of 10Ω or greater is adequate, requiring at least 12uH. A high Q is not required, since only a small RF current flows in the choke. The 18uH choke used a Micrometals T-106-26 iron dust core. Iron dust cores of similar types to this can often be salvaged from defunct PC switch-mode PSUs. The winding used 2 x 17 turns in parallel of $1mm^2$ enamelled copper wire. An air-cored inductor would also be feasible, if more bulky.

The output filter consists of two identical cascaded pi-sections. The filter should provide a resistive load at the 137kHz output frequency, but a low capacitive reactance at harmonics. This can be achieved by designing the pi-sections as low-Q matching networks, with equal source and load resistances. This yields a circuit with two equal capacitors. The standard pi-section design formulae can be used, modified for $R_{in} = R_{out} = R$:

$$X_C = \frac{R}{Q}, \quad X_L = \frac{2QR}{Q^2+1}$$

$$C = \frac{1}{2\pi f X_C}, \quad L = \frac{X_L}{2\pi f}$$

Most designers select Q between 0.5 and 1. Metallized polypropylene capacitors are a good choice, since they have low losses at 137kHz, and are available with large values and high voltage ratings. The DC voltage rating should be several times larger than the RMS RF voltage present; the main limitation is the heating effect of the RF current causing internal heating of the capacitor. Several 6.8nF, 1kV polypropylene capacitors were available, so C = 2 x 6.8nF = 13.6nF was used. This has reactance of 85.4Ω at 137kHz, forcing Q = 0.585, and giving XL = 43.6Ω, L = 50.6uH. The inductors must have low loss at 137kHz to avoid excessive heating. Micrometals T130-2 iron dust cores were used, wound with 68 turns of 0.7mm enamelled wire. It is a good idea to check the capacitance and inductance of the filter components using an LCR meter or bridge. However, the main effect of small errors is only to slightly alter the output power from the circuit, without greatly affecting the efficiency.

The drive signal applied to the class D output stage is a 50% duty cycle square wave. The 137kHz gate drive signal is obtained from a 274kHz input using a D-type flip-flop in a divide-by-two configuration, guaranteeing an accurate 50% duty cycle. When the circuit is switched to receive, the flip-flop is disabled by pulling the reset input high, preventing a 137kHz signal leaking to the receiver input and causing interference. For netting the transmitter, the 'net' switch enables the flip-flop.

The MOSFETs require zero or negative gate voltage to switch the transistor fully off, and +10 to +15 volts to bias them fully on. The mosfet gates behave essentially as capacitors, requiring transient charging and discharging currents as the drive voltage switches on and off, but drawing no current while the gate voltage remains stable. In order to achieve fast mosfet switching, a TC4426 gate driver IC is used. These driver ICs accept a TTL-compatible logic level input signal, and are designed to produce peak output currents of 1 amp or more which charge and discharge the mosfet gate in a fraction of a microsecond. A disadvantage of using a flip-flop to generate the drive signal is that if the input signal is lost one mosfet will remain switched on and act as a virtual short across the supply. To avoid this, the gate driver is capacitively coupled to the mosfets; the shunt diodes perform a DC restoration function, making the full positive peak voltage available to drive the gate. If drive is lost, the gates discharge through the 2.2kΩ resistors, switching both mosfets off. The 4.7Ω resistors in series with the gate drivers help to reduce ringing.

Each mosfet has a series RC damping network from drain to source, reducing high frequency 'ringing' superimposed on the drain waveform. The component values are best determined experimentally, since they depend on the individual circuit. A good starting point is to make the capacitor about five times larger than the mosfet output capacitance. A resistance between 2Ω and 20Ω is usually effective. Effectiveness is best checked by examining the mosfet drain waveforms with an oscilloscope, and compromising between minimising high-frequency ringing and excessive power dissipation in the resistors. Larger capacitors and smaller resistors normally result in reduced ringing, but increased dissipation. These components should be appropriate for high frequency use; in this circuit, 4.7Ω, 3W metal film resistors, and 10nF, 250V polypropylene capacitors were satisfactory.

The transmitter is keyed using series mosfet TR6. The mosfet should have low $r_{DS(on)}$ to minimise loss when switched on. A third STW60NE10 was used, although since the maximum voltage applied to this device is the 13.8V DC supply, a lower voltage device could be used instead. During the rise and fall of the keying waveform, dissipation in the keying mosfet peaks at about 25% of the maximum DC input, 55W in this case. However, when the mosfet is fully on, it dissipates only a few watts due to $r_{DS(on)}$, and when fully off dissipation is practically zero. Therefore the average power dissipated is small, under 10W in this circuit, provided it is not keyed very rapidly.

In order to bias this mosfet fully on, a voltage around 10V higher than the 13.8V DC rail must be applied to the gate. Only a few milliamps of bias is required; a small auxiliary DC supply could be used in a mains-powered transmitter, but in this case the bias voltage was obtained by rectifying the capacitively-coupled gate drive waveform using a charge-pump circuit. The bias is controlled by the key input via transistor TR4, and the keying waveform is shaped by the RC time constant to give around 10ms rise and fall times. TR5 maintains the keying 'off' when the circuit is switched to receive. The 15V zener across the mosfet gate and source limits the gate voltage to prevent damage. The output power of a class D transmitter can be varied either by changing the supply voltage, or by having multiple taps on the output winding; both these techniques are used in the G0MRF and G3YXM designs described later. In this design, a resistor can be switched in series with the DC supply, reducing the supply voltage to the output stage to around 4V, and RF output to 18W, for tuning-up purposes. The 2Ω wirewound resistor dissipates nearly 40W in low power mode, so greatly reduces efficiency, but does make it very difficult to damage the PA due to its inherent current limiting, useful when using a battery supply or when initially testing the circuit.

Construction of this type of transmitter is reasonably non-critical. The low-power parts of the transmitter can be assembled using 'veroboard' or similar, but the gate driver IC must have a 0.1uF ceramic decoupling capacitor directly across the supply pins due to the large transient currents present. Also for this reason, the gate leads, and the ground return from the mosfet sources should be kept very short (<30mm).

The mosfets, output transformer, keying circuit and DC feed carry heavy currents, so connections should be as short as possible and use thick wire (at least 2.5mm^2). The RC damping components should be mounted directly across the mosfet drain and source pins, and the connections to the output transformer kept short. The circuit described above was assembled on an aluminium plate about 160 x 200 x 3mm, which provided ample heatsinking for the three mosfets when air was allowed to circulate freely. In an enclosed box, a fan would probably be desirable.

Testing a class D circuit should start by checking operation of the gate-drive circuit, ensuring that complementary 12Vp-p square waves are present at the mosfet gates at the correct frequency. A dummy load is almost obligatory for testing LF transmitters (see the Measurement and Calculation chapter). If possible, apply a reduced DC supply voltage to the output stage (but not to the gate drive circuit!), or use a series resistor to reduce the supply voltage, as included in this circuit. An oscilloscope is the ideal tool to check the correct waveforms are present. A useful check is the efficiency; the ratio of RF output power to DC input power should be well over 80% if the circuit is working correctly.

G3YXM 136kHz 1kW transmitter

G3YXM set out to design a transmitter that is reasonably small, produces around 1kW RF output, and will withstand antenna mis-match and other mishaps. The description here is an abridged version of the original article available via G3YXM's web pages [10]. The circuit is shown in **Fig 6.9** and the major components are listed in **Table 6.1**.

An input signal at 1.36MHz from the VFO (**Fig 6.10**), or from a crystal oscillator and further divider, is divided by ten, the output at IC4 being a symmetrical

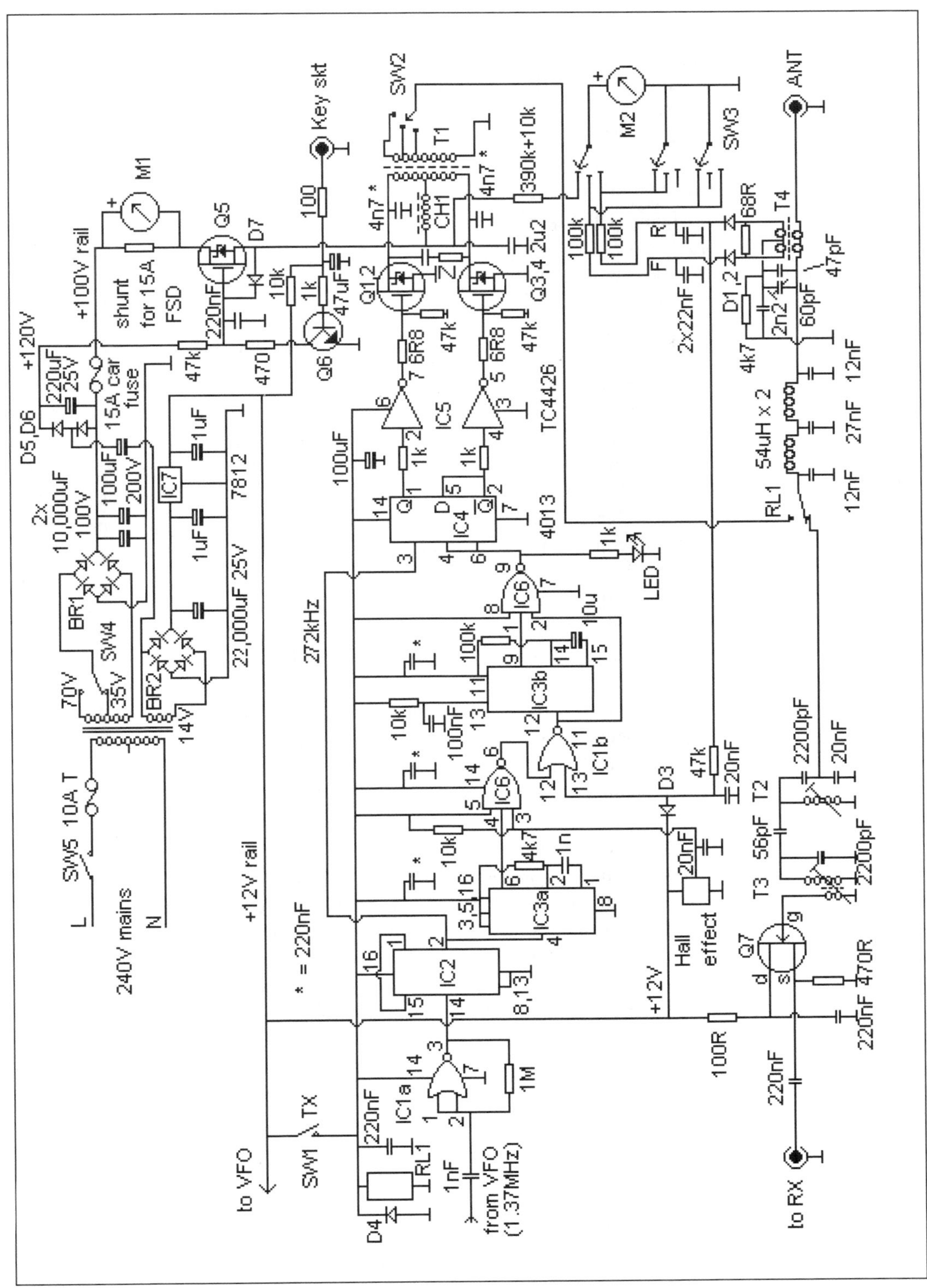

Fig 6.9: G3YXM one kilowatt transmitter

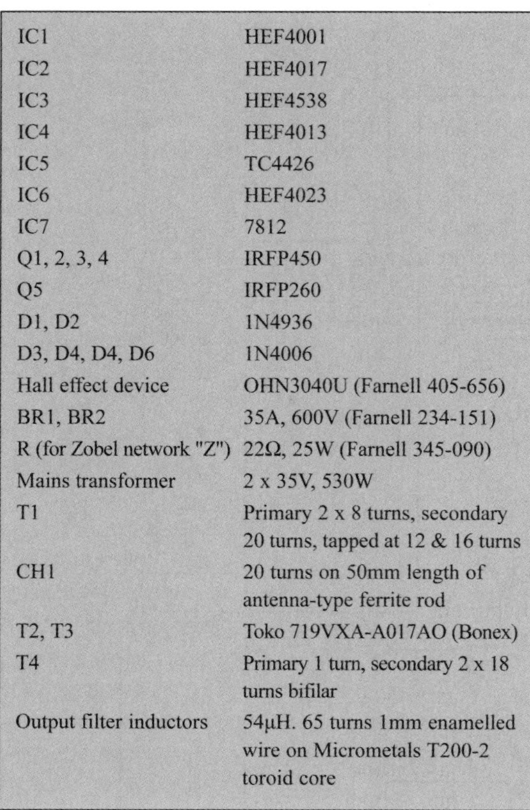

IC1	HEF4001
IC2	HEF4017
IC3	HEF4538
IC4	HEF4013
IC5	TC4426
IC6	HEF4023
IC7	7812
Q1, 2, 3, 4	IRFP450
Q5	IRFP260
D1, D2	1N4936
D3, D4, D4, D6	1N4006
Hall effect device	OHN3040U (Farnell 405-656)
BR1, BR2	35A, 600V (Farnell 234-151)
R (for Zobel network "Z")	22Ω, 25W (Farnell 345-090)
Mains transformer	2 x 35V, 530W
T1	Primary 2 x 8 turns, secondary 20 turns, tapped at 12 & 16 turns
CH1	20 turns on 50mm length of antenna-type ferrite rod
T2, T3	Toko 719VXA-A017AO (Bonex)
T4	Primary 1 turn, secondary 2 x 18 turns bifilar
Output filter inductors	54µH. 65 turns 1mm enamelled wire on Micrometals T200-2 toroid core

Table 6.1: Component details for the G3YXM 1kW transmitter

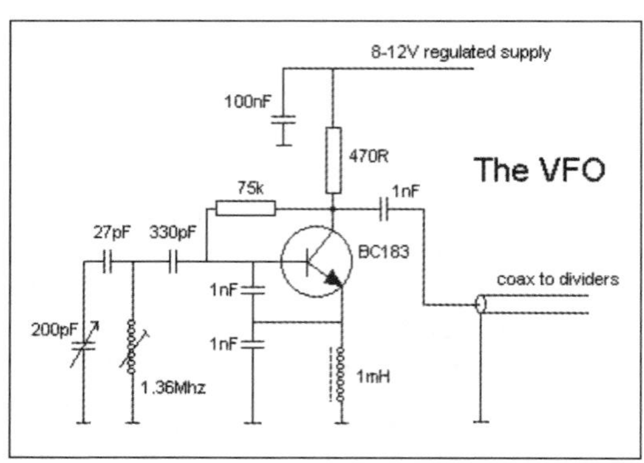

Fig 6.10: 1.36MHz VFO for the G3YXM 136kHz transmitter

square wave, driving the output mosfets via gate driver IC6. Each mosfet shown is actually two devices in parallel. The output transformer ratio is set by switch S2. Higher output is obtained with more turns selected. Across the primary of the transformer the Zobel network marked 'Z' (22Ω and 4n7 in series) reduces ringing. The output is fed to the antenna via a low-pass filter. The cut-off frequency is quite high at about 220kHz as virtually no second harmonic is produced.

The SWR bridge consists of T4 and associated components. It is a bifilar winding of 2x18 turns which forms the centre-tapped secondary and the coax inner passing through the toroid core forms the single-turn primary. The protection circuit which cuts the drive for about a second is triggered by high SWR via IC1B, or over-current signal from the Hall-effect device, which is triggered by the magnetic field of CH1, which is made from a 50mm piece of ferrite antenna rod wound with 20 turns of 1.5mm enameled copper wire. The Hall-effect detector is placed near one end of CH1 and the spacing adjusted to trip at about 20A. The receive pre-amp uses coupled tuned circuits giving a band-pass response over the 135 to 138kHz range A single JFET (Q7) makes up for the filter loss.

No guarantees of performance are implied and no responsibility for loss or damage can be accepted. This project requires a high level of constructional experience.

The mains transformer used in the power supply has two series 35V windings. The DC voltage is either 50V from the centre tap or 100V from both windings. An auxiliary 12V winding was added by winding 30 turns of 16SWG wire through the toroid. At full output the HT will drop to about 80V. The keying circuit uses a series mosfet with shaping of rise and fall times to prevent key-clicks. To turn this mosfet fully on, its gate must be at least 5V positive of its source which is close to the main supply voltage. Diodes D5 and 6 are supplied via a high voltage capacitor from the 12V winding to produce an extra 20V bias for this purpose.

The low-level circuitry was built on strip-board, taking care to keep the tracks short and earth unused inputs. The TC4426 chip IC5 is capable of driving 1.5A into the gate capacitances of the mosfets and the decoupling capacitors must be fitted close to the chip with short leads. The 6R8 series resistors are mounted on the gate pins of the mosfets, the resistor leads forming the connections to the strip board. It is probably best to use one resistor for each gate. The strip board should be grounded to the earth plane as near as possible to the mosfets, which should have the source leads soldered to the ground plane. The two 4n7 capacitors should be connected directly across the mosfets.

Output transformer T1 is constructed from two-core 'figure of eight' speaker cable wound eight times through the ferrite toroid, connected as a centre-tapped primary by connecting one end of one winding to the opposite end of the other. The secondary is wound over it with 20 turns of thin wire tapped at 12 and 16 turns. The Zobel network should be wired from drain to drain with short wires.

Get the PSU, VFO and CMOS stages working first. Check with a scope that you have complementary 12V square waves on the gates, the waveform will be slightly rounded off due to the gate capacitance. Connect the transmitter to a 50Ω load and, having selected the first tap on SW2, apply 50V (SW4 in low position) with a resistor in place of the fuse to limit the current. The mosfets should draw no current without drive. Press the key and the output stage should draw a few amps and produce a few watts into the dummy load. If the shut-down LED comes on, either the load is mis-matched, the SWR bridge is connected backwards or the 60pF capacitor needs adjustment. If all seems well, remove the current limiting resistor and increase the power by selecting taps, key the rig in short bursts and check for overheating of mosfets and cores. When you are happy that the transmitter is working OK, load it up to 15A PA current and slowly move the Hall device nearer to the end of the ferrite rod (CH1) until the protection circuit trips. Move it just a tiny bit further away and fix in position with silicone rubber. The receive preamplifier filter inductors can be aligned using a signal near 137kHz; the tuning is very sharp.

G0MRF 300W Class-D 136kHz Transmitter

The following article by David Bowman, G0MRF is abridged from RadCom, January/February 2003

With no commercial equipment available from the established 'big four' manufacturers, LF designs have relied on individuals bringing a variety of ingenious

Front panel of the G0MRF transmitter [Photograph Maurice de Silva, G0WMD]

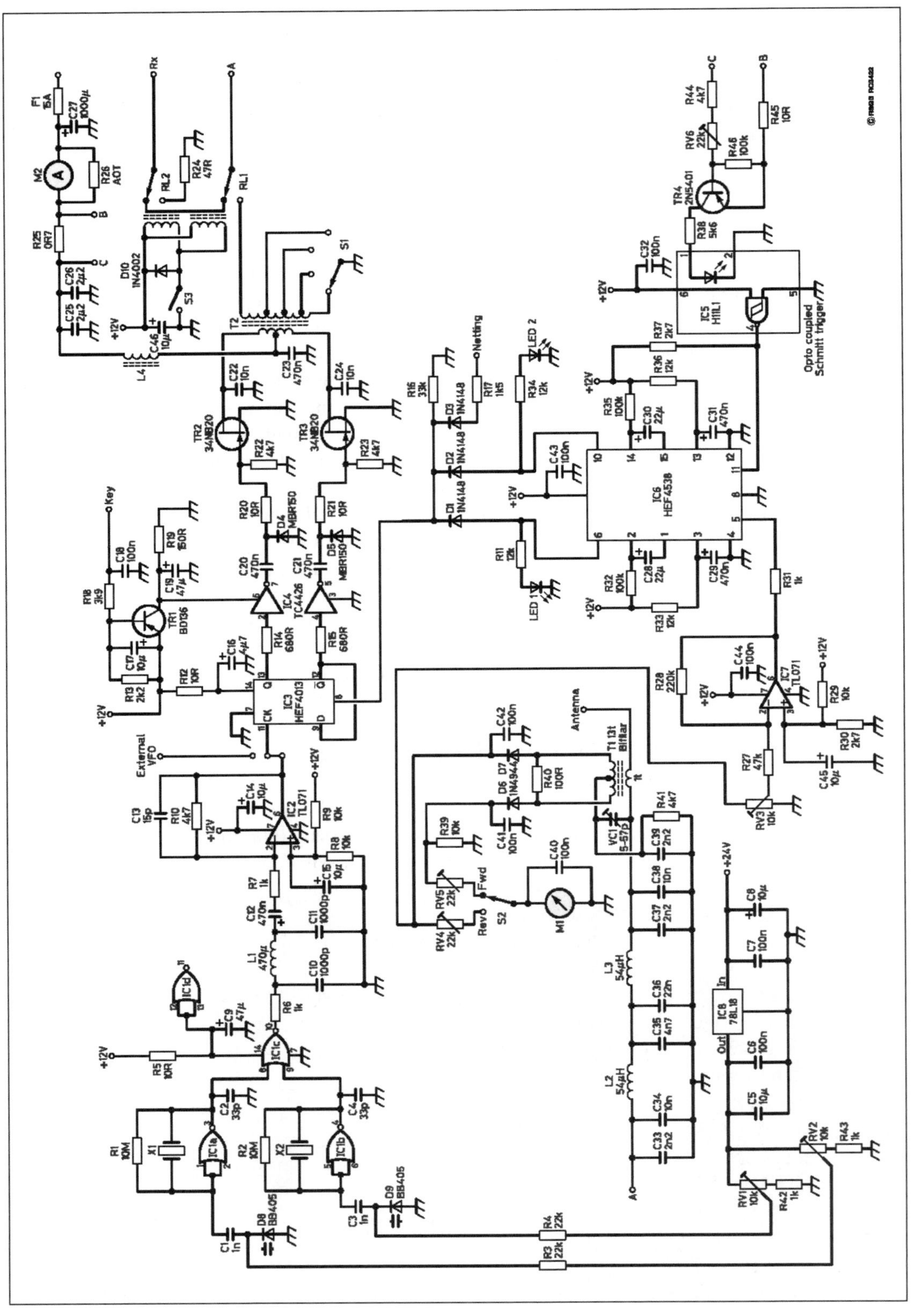

ideas to the band. This transmitter combines a number of proven techniques and, with over 300W output, allows you to get on to this exciting amateur allocation with a good signal. It is based around an amplifier using two low-cost power FETs in a high-efficiency class-D configuration. The transmitter is protected against over-current and high-VSWR conditions. The single PCB also includes forward- and reflected-power metering, output filtering and transmit /receive switching.

Fig 6.11 (opposite): Complete circuit diagram of the G0MRF 300 watt transmitter

Circuit description

The transmit drive is generated by a pair of crystals operating as variable crystal oscillators. Crystal X1 is 8000kHz while Crystal X2 is 8274kHz (**Fig 6.11**). Each crystal is connected across a CMOS NAND gate, which functions as an oscillator. Varicap diodes are used for differential-tuning of the crystals.

The two outputs are applied to a third NAND gate which, because logic gates are non-linear, functions as a mixer. The output of IC1(c) contains several products including the difference frequency at 274kHz. A low pass filter, comprising L1, C10 and C11, removes the high-order products, leaving a sine-wave at twice the required output frequency. The filter is terminated by R7, which is part of the inverting amplifier IC2. C13 in the feedback loop adds some additional low-pass filtering before the signal is applied to the clock input of a 4013 D-type flip-flop. A small PCB jumper provides the option of driving the transmitter from an external source [11].

IC3 has two functions. Firstly, it divides the input frequency by two, producing 136kHz at the (Q) and (not Q) outputs. The second function of IC3 is to act as a switch in the event of a fault condition. In normal operation the Set Direct input, pin 8, is held at 0V by R16. The circuit uses D1 - D3 as a simple discrete OR gate to provide control and protection functions. Diodes D1 and D2 feed in signals from the reflected power and over-current protection circuits, while D3 is used to provide a netting facility on receive.

If D1 or D2 or D3 conduct, the Set Direct input will go to 12V, causing IC3 to shut down, removing the drive from the power amplifier. **Fig 6.12** shows how these functions can be controlled with a double-pole centre-off switch. One pole is used to drive the transmit / receive relays, while the other switches on a cooling fan during transmit periods.

Netting is carried out with the switch in its centre-off position. This puts the relays in the receive position, but keeps the 4013 divider active.

IC4 is a dual-inverting FET driver. It amplifies the CMOS-level signal from IC3 and is capable of driving up to 1.5A into the gates of the power FETs. A fast charge / discharge time is essential for highly efficient, and disaster-free operation of a class-D amplifier. C20 and C21 AC-couple the drive to the FETs. Schottky diodes, D4 and D5, restore the correct DC level at the gates while R20 - R23 ensure stability.

The Class-D push-pull output stage comprises FETs TR2 and TR3 and output-matching transformer,

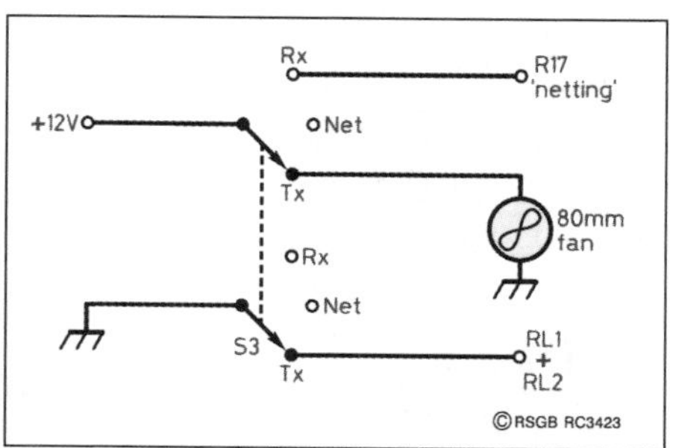

Fig 6.12: Transmit-receive switching using a DPDT centre-off switch

Warning

If you apply hundreds of watts at 136kHz to a high Q aerial system, the antenna voltage will very high - in excess of 20kV is not uncommon. Most insulated wire will break down and arc across to anything nearby. Keep all aerial wires well clear of everything and use good insulators. Many aerials have fallen down the moment the key was pressed, including mine. Remember that RF burns hurt and those voltages could be very dangerous!

T2. Initially, I selected a large E-core transformer for T2. This ETD44 core worked well and was used in the prototype. Unfortunately, it proved both expensive and difficult to reproduce. Finally, it was replaced by a toroidal design, which was easier to construct. The drain-to-drain impedance of the FETs is matched to 50 ohms by the turns ratio of T2. A series of taps on the secondary allows the turns ratio of T2 to be changed, allowing the power delivered to the antenna to be selected via a front panel ceramic switch. The highest number of secondary turns provides the highest output power.

The DC supply is passed through an ammeter and current-sense resistor and is decoupled by C26 and C27. DC is applied to the centre tap on the primary of T2. L4 and C23 provide additional filtering.

The RF output passes from the secondary of T2 through transmit / receive relay, RL1. A second relay, RL2, has been included to terminate the receiver input when in transmit mode. These relays are rated at 12A, and have been tested at 136kHz with power levels of 1000W. Diode D10 is included to protect any semiconductors included in the external switching arrangements.

From the relays, the RF passes through a multi-element low-pass filter to the output. The LPF is essential for removing the high levels of harmonics which are present in the square-wave output from the amplifier. The T157 core used for L3 is rated to about 400W, while the polypropylene capacitors are all specified at 1kV and are capable of handling much higher power levels. The cut-off frequency of the filter is 200kHz, ensuring a very low insertion loss at 136kHz.

Reflected power protection

Forward and reflected power are detected by directional coupler, T1. A single wire passing through the centre of the toroid acts as a single-turn primary, while

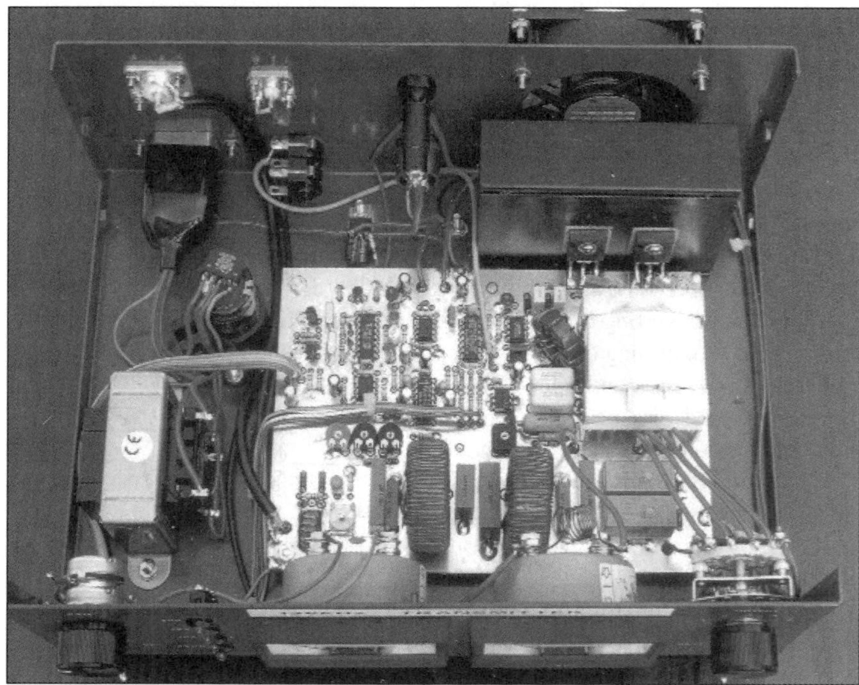

Inside the G0MRF transmitter [Photograph Maurice de Silva, G0WMD]

Rear panel showing the fan and connectors [Photograph Maurice de Silva, G0WMD]

the secondary is a bifilar winding of 13 turns. The secondary produces outputs proportional to forward and reflected power. These AC signals are rectified by diodes D6 and D7. Preset potentiometers, RV4 and RV5, set the sensitivity. Switch S2 selects whether forward or reflected power is displayed on the meter. Resistors R29 and R30 define the reference voltage at the non-inverting input of IC7 and hence set the trip point of the protection circuit. Under normal operation, pin 6 of IC7 is at 12V. When the voltage at the wiper of RV3 exceeds the voltage at pin 3, the output at pin 6 rapidly falls from 12V to zero. This circuit was adapted from a Motorola application note [12] and is very fast-acting. It is claimed to be capable of switching off the drive in about 10 microseconds. The op-amp output is connected to the input of IC6, a 4538 dual-monostable. Once triggered, the output of the monostable changes from 0 to 12V. This voltage forward-biases D1, which causes the Set Direct function of the 4013 to shut down the device. The output of the 4538 also illuminates a front panel LED giving a visual indication of the cause of the shutdown. Having cut off the drive, the monostable maintains this condition for a period determined by R32 and C28, about 2.2s. The circuit resets automatically.

Over-current protection

Over-current protection has been implemented by utilising current-sense resistor, R25, with TR4 and opto-coupler IC5. When the current flowing through R25 causes a potential difference of 0.7V to be developed across it, the PNP transistor, TR4, will switch on. Current then flows through R38 and the diode contained within the opto-coupler.

When the LED forward current reaches 600μA, an internal Schmitt trigger causes the output voltage to fall rapidly from 12V to zero. This triggers the other half of the dual-monostable, IC6. To preserve the speed of the overcurrent trip, there are no decoupling capacitors around TR4 or IC5. Once again, the response time of this circuit is very fast and it can reduce the output to zero in about 10-20μs. The exact value of the trip point can be adjusted over a small range by RV6.

Construction

The PCB should be assembled and tested before being fitted into an enclosure. Start by constructing the VXO and logic circuits, leaving the low-pass filter coils, transformer T2, and directional coupler T1, until last. The power FETs can be temporarily fitted for testing and then mounted permanently after testing is complete. The coils L2 and L3 in the low-pass filter are quite large and can be held in place using a little epoxy glue for extra support. When fitting inductors, ensure that the enamelled wire does not come into direct contact with the earth plane.

Components for the G3MRF 300W Class-D Transmitter

Resistors

R1, R2	10M
R3, R4	22k
R5, R12, R20, R21, R45	10R
R6, R7, R31, R42, R43	1k
R8, R9, R29, R39	10k
R10, R41, R44	4k7
R11, R33, R34, R36	12k
R13	2k2
R14, R15	680R
R16	33k
R17	1k5
R18	3k9
R19	150R
R22	4k7 mounted off board
R23	4k7 mounted off board
R24	47R
R25	R07, 6W, RS Comp'nts.
R26	Shunt for 15A FSD
R27	47k
R28	220k
R30, R37	2k7
R32, R35, R46	100k
R38	5k6
R40	100R
RV1, RV2	10k dual-gang pot
RV3	10k preset
RV4, RV5, RV6	22k preset

Capacitors

C1, C3	1n
C2, C4	33p
C5, C8, C14, C15	10µ
C17, C45, C46	10µ
C6, C7	100n
C9, C19	47µ
C10, C11	1n
C12, C29, C31	470n electrolytic
C13	15p
C16	4µ7 tantalum
C18, C32, C41, C42	100n ceramic 50V
C20, C21	470n polyester 63V
C22, C24	10n 50V pulse capacitors (polypropylene)
C23	470n 250V polyester
C25, C26	2µ2 100V polyester
C27	1000µ 63V - not on PCB
C28, C30	22µ tantalum 16V
C33, C38	2n2 1kV polypropylene
C34, C37	10n 1kV polypropylene
C35	4n7 1kV polypropylene
C36	22n 1kV polypropylene
C39	2n2 polystyrene 160V
C40, C43, C44	100n ceramic 50V

Semiconductors

IC1	HEF4011B
IC2	TL071CN
IC3	HEF4013B
IC4	TC4426CPA
IC5	H11L1 Opto-isolator
IC6	HEF4538B
IC7	TL071CN
IC8	78L18AZ
D1, D2, D3	1N4148
D4, D5	MBR150
D6, D7	1N4944
D8, D9	BB405 varicaps
D10	1N4002
TR1	BD136
TR2, TR3	STW34NB20 MOSFET
TR4	2N5401
LED 1, LED 2, LED 3, LED 4	Two green for power: 12V & 40V Two red ultrabright: VSWR and current trip.

Inductors

L1	470µH 7BA Toko
L2	54µH T157-2 powdered iron toroid 59 turns of 0.8mm wire
L3	54µH T157-2 powdered iron toroid 59 turns of 0.8mm wire
L4	11t 1.5mm on powdered iron toroid T94-2
T1	Pri: 13 t 0.4mm bifilar. Sec: 1t (RG58 inner) on 15mm 3C85 ferrite
T2	42mm 3C90 ferrite toroid. Pri: 10 turns 1.5mm CT. Sec: 21 turns 1mm with taps at 6, 10, 15, 18 turns.

Miscellaneous

X1	8.000 MHz crystal
X2	8.275 MHz crystal, QuartSlab. Fundamental mode, 20pF parallel load
RL1, RL2	12A relay. Single-pole change-over
VC1	5-57pF 809 series PTFE 300V trimmer, Farnell.
M1, M2	1mA FSD meter
S1	Rotary ceramic switch, single-pole 5-way, break-before-make.
S2	Forward / Reverse switch, single-pole 2-way switch.
S3	2-pole, centre-off toggle
Heat sink.	Single-sided 1.2°/W
Isolating washers	TO247
PCB	
Fan	80mm 12V, Farnell / Rapid / RS Components / Maplin, CPC, etc

A kit of parts for this project, or a PCB, is available from the author [12].

This avoids high voltages arcing through the thin insulation and other damage due to abrasion. The primary of T1 is a single wire passing through the centre of the toroid. I used a small length of the inner conductor from RG58 coaxial cable.

The powder-coated ready-punched enclosure used in the prototype is available from H J Morgan Smith [14].

Testing

Testing should follow a logical procedure. Apply DC to the 12V and tuning voltage inputs. Check that the two crystals in the VXO are oscillating by looking for the 8MHz signals at pin 8 and 9 of IC1. With the oscillators running and tuning correctly, you should be able to see 274kHz at pin 6 of IC2 and 136kHz at the (Q) and (not Q) outputs of the 4013.

The range of the VXO at 136kHz will be typically 1.5kHz. While this is not sufficient to cover the entire 2.1kHz allocation, it is possible to adjust the values of C2 and C4 and select which portion of the band you wish to cover. On my prototype, I decided to cover the slow CW (QRSS) portion at the top of the band, down through the CW section to 136.3kHz.

Start by setting all the presets to mid position and VC1 to 80% mesh. Connect the output to a 50-ohm dummy load. At LF, almost any load will suffice, even wirewound resistors are a good match at 136kHz! Fit a 5A fuse temporarily to the main FET supply and switch on. Select the lowest power tap at six turns. Ground the transmit / receive pin and key the transmitter. If luck is on your side you should see between 50 and 100W output. Don't be tempted to switch to high power at this point. Instead, spend some time checking the other functions at this power level. Measure the efficiency of the amplifier and you should see a value above 70%. Values up to 86% are not uncommon. The power meter should read correctly, but if it reads backwards this can be corrected by reversing the connections on the directional coupler. With a 50Ω load, the trimmer, VC1, can be adjusted to show zero reflected power. When you are satisfied that the transmitter is operating correctly, replace the fuse with a 15A component, and test at the higher power levels. The total number of turns on the secondary of T2 has been specified as 21. In practice, you may only need to use this number of turns if you are using a supply of around 36V. If you have a higher voltage (around 45V), you will be able to achieve maximum power output using the 18-turn tap.

The final part of the setting-up procedure is to adjust the reflected power and over-current trip points. I suggest that you turn up RV3 to maximum sensitivity and see how it responds. The current trip should be set for 10-11A with a supply of 36V, but if you're using a higher voltage supply, then the trip should be arranged to cut in at 400W DC input. At 45V supply, this equals 8.9A. Preset RV6 provides a fine adjustment of the over-current trip point. Coarse adjustments can be can be made by adding 1Ω, 0.5W, resistors in parallel with R25.

Alternative circuit

Following the publication of the above article in *RadCom*, Jim Moritz, M0BMU, suggested the alternative output circuit shown in **Fig 6.13**. He says:

"My unit gives 400W out with a 37V supply - for 300W out with a 48V supply, I reckon the primary windings of the output transformer should be changed from 4 to 6 turns. The value of the choke in the DC supply is not critical - the

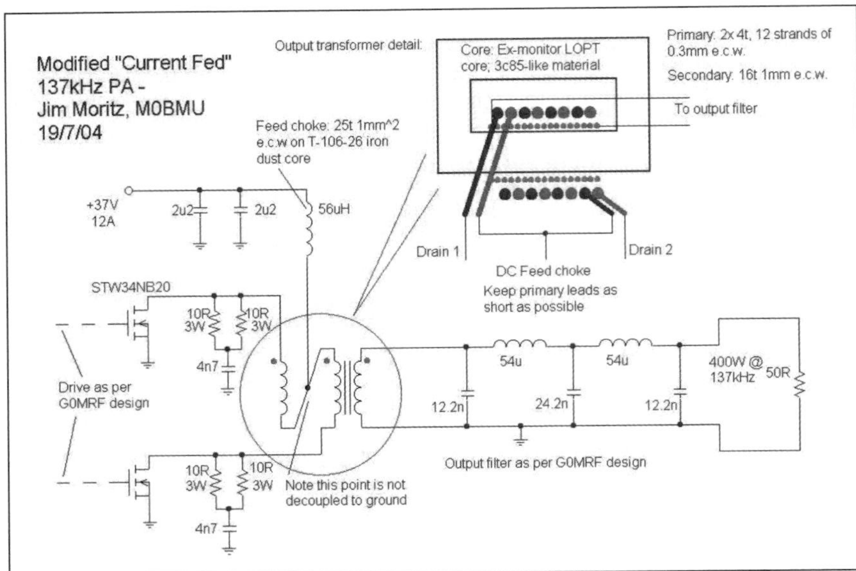

Fig 6.13: M0BMU's alternative to the G0MRF PA circuit

iron dust cores can often be found in old PC SMPSUs. The most significant change to the original circuit was to remove the decoupling capacitor from the centre tap of the transformer primary and increase the inductance of the choke, converting the circuit into a 'current feed' class D configuration. This means the DC supply has a high impedance at 137kHz, which prevents high transient currents into the low pass filter capacitors when the mosfets switch. The ideal drain voltage waveform would be a half sine wave, although in practice there is still considerable ringing at the switching transitions, allthough much reduced. The value of the damping resistors and capacitors is a compromise; reducing R and increasing C reduces the amount of HF ringing, but increases dissipation in the resistors."

Transmitters for 500kHz

At the time of writing, power requirements for 500kHz transmitters are relatively modest, due to the greater antenna efficiency achieved at the higher frequency, and the lower radiated power permitted by the terms of the 500kHz Notice of Variation. Achieving the current limit of 0.1W ERP with typical amateur antennas requires power levels of a few watts for larger antennas, and perhaps a few tens of watts for smaller, less efficient antennas. 500kHz transmitters currently used can be scaled-down 136kHz designs, or borrow from HF QRP transmitter practice. As with 136kHz, low-cost switching MOSFETs are effective as output devices, as well as devices specified as RF power amplifiers. A number of amateurs have successfully used simple valve transmitters on 500kHz.

G3XAQ ECL82 500kHz CW Transmitter

This transmitter (**Fig 6.14**) was designed and built by Alan Ibbetson, G3XAQ. It uses a single ECL82 valve, is crystal controlled, and produces just under 7W output with well suppressed harmonics and a clean keying waveform.

The triode section of the ECL82 is used as a Pierce oscillator. The tuned anode circuit uses the primary of an IF transformer from an old valve broadcast radio.

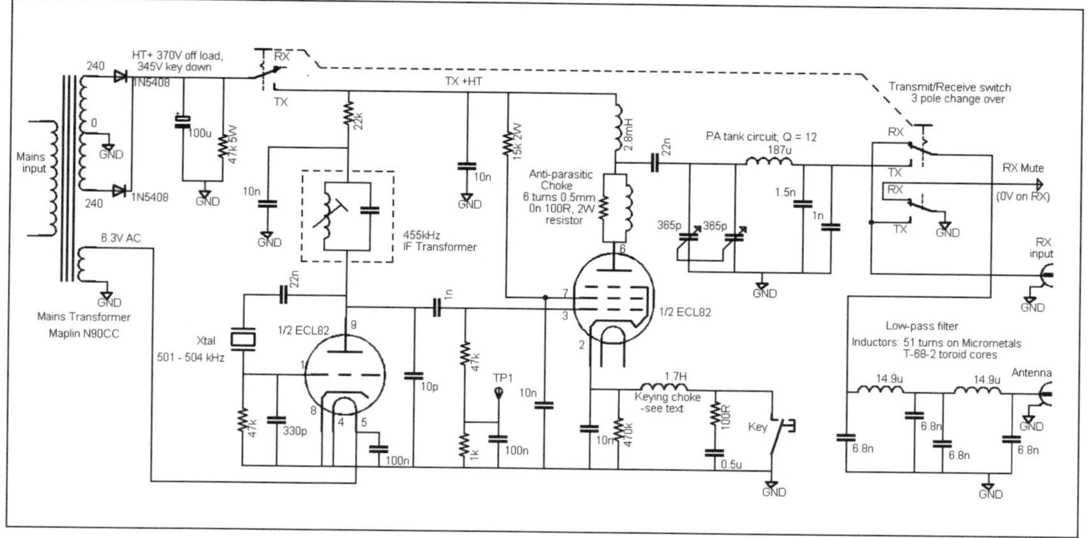

Fig 6.14: G3XAQ ECL82 500kHz transmitter

Feedback is determined by the ratio of the 330pF and 10pF capacitors. The values required depend on the activity of the crystal. Adjust the 330pF if necessary for reliable oscillator starting and freedom from chirp when the PA is keyed. The 22k anode feed resistor is selected to give 0.5-1mA PA grid current (1V DC at TP1); for very active crystals a value as high as 100k might be needed.

The crystal was originally a 500kHz frequency standard. The quartz plate was removed from the holder and ground up to 502kHz with grade P600 emery paper laid on a flat smooth surface, such as a glass mirror. Note that isopropyl alcohol or acetone is useful for washing away traces of grease, which can reduce crystal Q to the point where oscillation ceases.

The pentode section forms a cathode keyed class C PA. The pi tank is designed for a loaded Q of 12. Fixed loading capacitance is used to save chassis space. The two 115v primaries of a miniature 6VA mains transformer are used in parallel as a keying choke. The measured inductance is 1.7H with a DC resistance of 230W. This resistance contributes 11.5v of PA bias, which offers some protection to the valve should the drive fail. The choke and capacitor values are chosen to give a rise and fall time on the keyed envelope of 3ms. The cathode bias together with the limited perveance of the valve results in a modest 6.5W RF output at 50mA cathode current. The 15k screen resistor sets the screen voltage to 175v, but values up to 100k can be used to reduce the output power to less than 2W. Simple cathode keying does not quite cut off the PA. This, and the lack of neutralisation, results in a backwave of only -40dBc. However, tests with stations 20 miles away show this not to be detectable in practice.

Transmitter harmonics fall within the Medium Wave broadcast band, so an additional ‘half wave’ low pass filter is added after the PA pi tank to avoid EMC issues. With the addition of this low pass filter the measured level of the second harmonic is -60dBc and the third harmonic is -63dBc.

Change over between the transmitter and a separate receiver is performed with three poles of a miniature four-pole changeover toggle switch. This arrangement gives 58dB of receiver isolation when transmitting, which may mean that the muting circuit is not needed if the receiver possesses effective AGC.

The power supply is built onto the same 8x6 inch chassis as the rest of the transmitter. A full wave rectifier and capacitor filter provides 345v HT at 60mA, and 6.3v AC at 0.8A for the ECL82 heater.

The chassis and the mains transformer were supplied by Maplin. Other parts were from the junk box.

Note: John Fielding, ZS5JF, suggests the following circuit improvements: “Fig 6.14 shows the filament of the ECL82 being grounded at pin 4. The two filaments are internally connected in the ECL82. When the key is up the cathode of the pentode section will rise towards the anode voltage. The limiting value of cathode to filament voltage is approx 100V. It would be a better idea to lift the filament pin 4 and the heater transformer winding and float the 6.3V AC supply above ground to prevent possible damage to the valve. As an added safety device a zener diode of 30V/1W can be wired between the cathode of the pentode and ground. This will ensure the valve is cut-off when the key is up. There should also be a safety RF choke across the pi tank output to ground in case the 22n anode DC blocking capacitor fails short circuit.”

M0BMU 500kHz Class D MOSFET Transmitter

This transmitter (**Fig 6.15**) has a class D voltage-switching output stage with approximately 11W CW output and mismatch protection. It operates from a 13.8V DC supply. A VFO using a ceramic resonator is used to cover the whole 500kHz band.

The VFO Q1 uses a Murata CSB 4MHz ceramic resonator with a series tuning capacitor. The 4MHz output is shaped by amplifier Q2 and divided by eight by the 74HC4020 counter IC to obtain 500kHz. The frequency tolerance of ceramic resonators is relatively loose; several resonators were tried, and all were able to cover the whole amateur band, however the value of C3 had to be selected for each resonator.

The power output stage uses complementary N-channel and P-channel switching MOSFETs in a half-bridge push-pull configuration. The symmetrical waveform produced helps to minimise the unwanted second harmonic output at around 1MHz. The logic level VFO signal is converted to 12V level by the TC4427 gate driver IC. The resistor/capacitor/diode gate circuit ensures the cor-

Q4, 5 are mounted on 20°C/W heatsinks
Q7 is mounted on 4°C/W heatsink
L1 is a 4u7 choke, rated at least 1.2A DC
L2, L4 are 53 turns of 0.4mm wire on a Micrometals T-68-2 toroid core
L3 is 70 turns of 0.25mm wire on Micrometals T-68-2 toroid core
D1 - D5 are 1N5819 30V 1A Schottky rectifier diodes
RL1 is a changeover relay with 12V coil, contacts rated 2A.
T1, the PA output transformer is wound on a Fair-Rite 5943007061 toroid (22mm dia, #43 material). The Primary is 3 turns of 0.8mm wire; the Secondary is 15 turns of 0.6mm wire, tapped at 10 turns (5W out), 13 turns (8W), 15 turns (11W)
C3, 4, 5 are stable polystyrene, silver-mica, CG0 ceramic etc.
C14, 15, 17, 18, 19, 20, 21, 22 are low-loss types, eg polystyrene, silver-mica, polypropylene, etc.
All resistors are 0.25W, except R20, R21 - 1.0 , 0.5W

Table 6.2: Notes on the components for the 500kHz Class D MOSFET transmitter

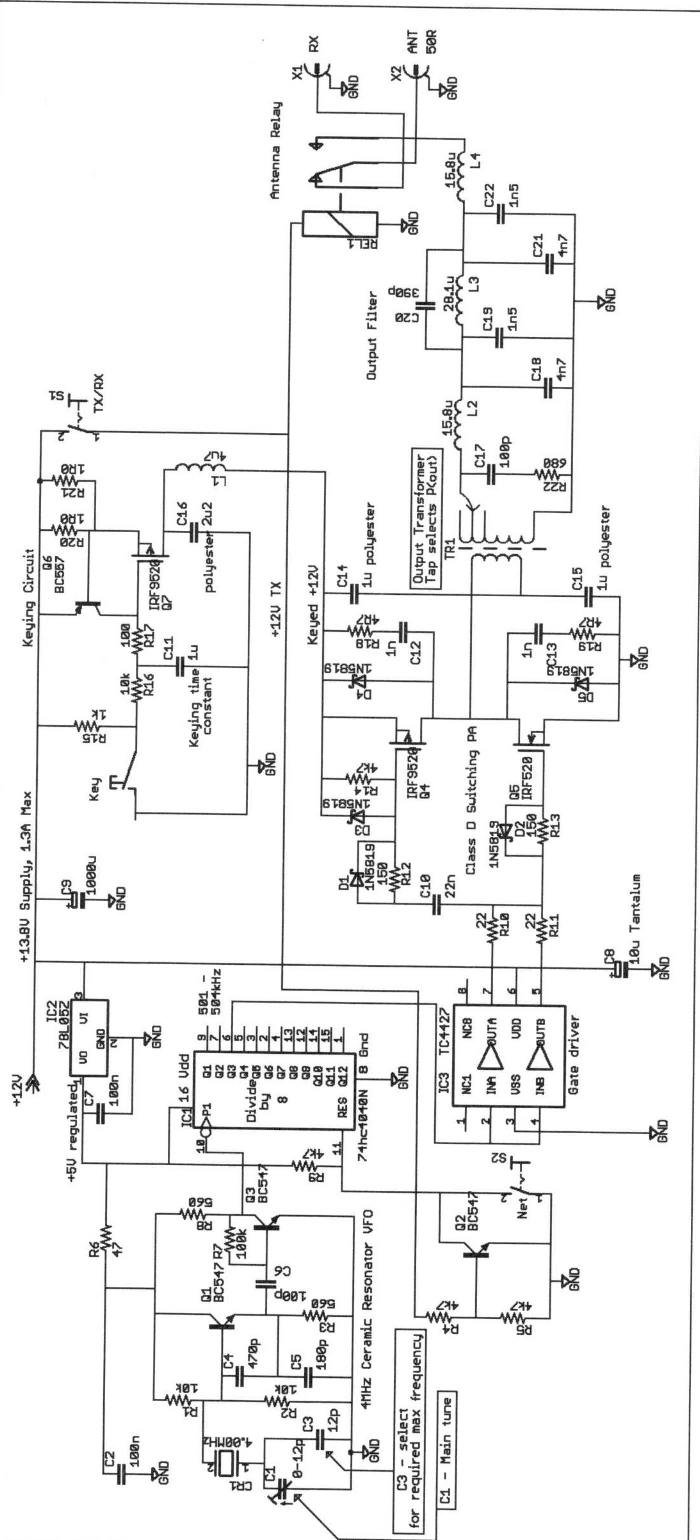

Fig 6.15: 500kHz Class D MOSFET Transmitter. Component values are as shown and additional notes are in Table 10.3

rect DC levels at the MOSFET gates, and also provides slow turn-on and fast turn-off of the MOSFETs, ensuring both MOSFETs are never 'on' simultaneously.

The MOSFET drains connect to the output via a tapped transformer TR1. The tapping point on the secondary sets the output power level. A smaller number of turns reduces the output; the output can probably be 'stretched' to 20W by increasing the number of turns. The tank circuit / output filter is a modified choke-input half wave circuit; C20 is added to produce a rejection notch at around 1.5MHz to enhance filtering of third harmonic output. C12/R18, C13/R19 and C17/R22 damp unwanted 'ringing' at high frequencies during switching transients, and reduce levels of high-order harmonics at the output.

The DC supply to the output stage is keyed via MOSFET Q7; DC current in Q7 is limited by Q8 to about 1.3A, which protects the switching MOSFETs in the event of a short circuit at the antenna output.

The antenna is switched between transmitter output and receiver by a changeover relay. Also, when on receive, the 500kHz VFO output is disabled by setting the reset input of the divide-by-eight counter. The VFO output can be enabled for netting on the receive frequency by the 'net' switch.

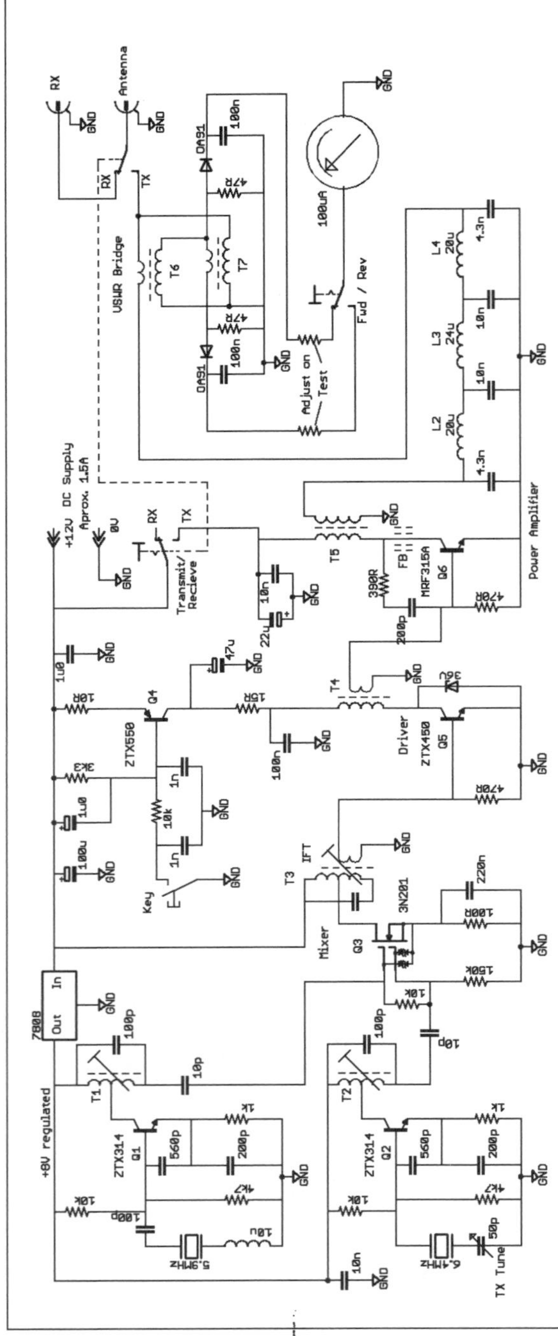

Fig 6.16: G3YMC's 500kHz transmitter. Inductor details are shown in Table 6.3

T1, T2	30 turns wound on quarter-inch slug-tuned formers, tapped 10 turns from the 'earthy' end
T3	470kHz IF transformer
T4	14 turns primary, 8 turns secondary, on a T-50-61 toroid core
T5	2 turns primary, 8 turns secondary on a 26mm diameter 3C85 ferrite toroid core
T6, T7	1 turn primary, 70 turn secondary, wound on a T-50-61 toroid core
L2, L4	64 turns on a Micrometals T-50-2 toroid core
L3	70 turns on Micrometals T-50-2 toroid core

Table 6.3: Inductor details for G3YMC 500kHz transmitter

To monitor output power and antenna matching, a tuning meter system was incorporated into the transmitter circuit. This is described separately in the Measurement and Calculation chapter.

G3YMC VXO-Controlled 500kHz Transmitter

The transmitter in **Fig 6.16**, was designed and built by Dave Sergeant, G3YMC. The output frequency is derived from a HF VXO and can be tuned over the whole band. CW output power is about 6W from a 12V, 1A DC supply.

The 500kHz signal is obtained by mixing the output of a VXO operating at around 6.4MHz (Q2) with the output of a fixed-frequency crystal oscillator at 5.9MHz (Q1) using dual gate MOSFET Q3. Output is taken from T3, a salvaged 470kHz IF transformer re-tuned to the 500kHz difference frequency. With the values shown, the prototype covered the full 501 - 504kHz allocation with a little overlap. The oscillators are supplied with regulated 8V via a three-terminal regulator IC. Power is supplied to these stages on both transmit and receive.

Driver transistor Q5 increases the VXO output to provide sufficient drive for the PA. The driver is keyed by switch Q4. The RC components around the base of Q4 are chosen to give rise and fall times of around 4ms to minimise key clicks. The keying and driver stages are also powered during receive; operating the key on receive produces a low-level signal for netting to the receive frequency.

The PA stage is based on a surplus MRF315A VHF transistor in a turnstile package, operating in class C. To maintain stability, a ferrite bead threaded onto the collector connection is required. The output low-pass filter was designed by G0MRF with values to give good suppression of the second harmonic near 1MHz. One pole of the transmit/receive switch connects the 12V supply to the PA on transmit. The second pole is used to switch the antenna between the transmitter output and the receiver.

An SWR bridge is connected at the transmitter output and is useful as an antenna tuning aid and to indicate output power. Low forward voltage diodes such as the OA91 germanium type shown are required. The value of the 'adjust on test' resistors will depend on the sensitivity of the meter movement available; the prototype used values of 680 ohms to achieve full-scale deflection in the forward direction with a 100 microamp meter.

A longer article describing this transmitter is available on G3YMC's web pages [15]

Low pass filter for 500kHz

The 500kHz allocation has its second harmonic in the Medium Wave AM broadcast band, so a filter with a sharp cut-off at 600kHz is desirable. The filter in **Fig 6.17**, designed by G0MRF, can also be used on receive to reduce blocking from strong AM broadcasters. The result of measurements on the prototype are shown in **Fig 6.18**.

Component values are: C1 and C4, 4400pF made from two 2200pF in parallel; C2 and C3, 10nF; L1 and L3, 20.6uH, 49 turns of 0.56mm dia on T-94-2; L2, 24.3uH, 54 turns 0.56mm on T-94-2. The capacitors are polypropylene from RS Components [8]. The maximum power level is limited by the core and wire size to about 100 watts. More information can be found on G0MRF's web site [13].

Power supplies

Most amateur radio shacks have a high current 12 volt stabilised supply, so it may seem obvious to use that for a low frequency transmitter. Indeed some of the 500kHz transmitters shown above are designed for that voltage.

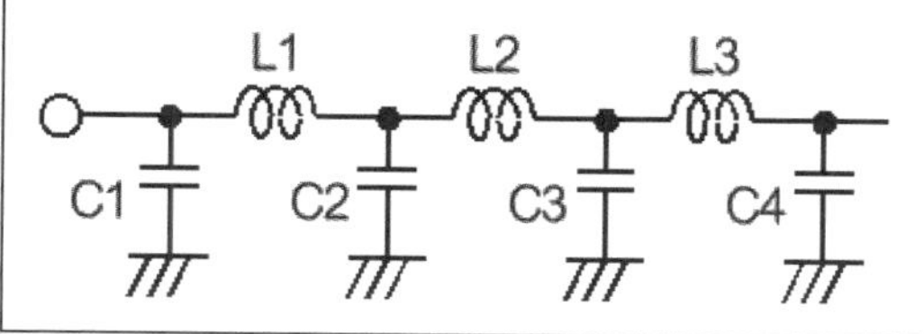

Fig 6.17: Low pass filter for 500kHz

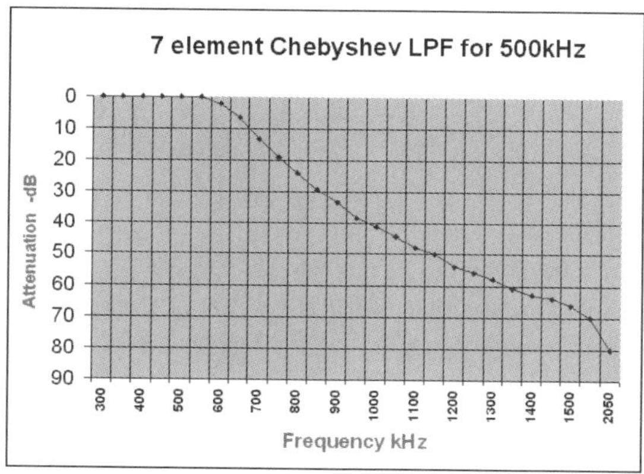

Fig 6.18: Measured performance of G0MRF low pass filter

Higher voltages are often used, however, with power FETs because it keeps the current down, and hence the need for very thick wiring and very short leads.

A simple 100V supply is shown as part of the kilowatt transmitter (Fig 6.9), together with a low-current stabilised 12V supply for the VFO. The high voltage line is unstabilised as the PA is not required to be linear - it is either on or off. Any stabilisation would in any case be complex and would generate a great deal of heat.

It is possible to find surplus high voltage, high current, stabilised supplies, for instance those formerly used in telephone exchanges, at rallies. Chargers for computer back up supplies can also be useful.

Take great care when using high voltages and/or high currents. Avoid working on equipment when it is powered up. If you must do so, remove metal objects such as rings or watches, and keep one hand in your pocket to avoid an electric shock across your heart. Make sure someone knows where you are, and how to turn off any power.

References

[1] The Decca system. *http://www.radarpages.co.uk/mob/navaids/decca/decca1.htm*

[2] BK Electronics, Units 1, 3 and 5 Comet Way, Southend-On-Sea Essex SS2 6TR. Tel: 01702-527572. *http://www.bkelec.com/*

[3] Linear amp: *http://www.hafler.com/techsupport/pdf/P3000_datasheet.pdf*

[4] Linear amp in use: *http://www.w1tag.com/XESTX.htm*

[5] GW4ALG's valve power amplifier. *http://www.alg.demon.co.uk/radio/136/400w_pa.htm*

[6] LF combiner: *http://www3.telus.net/sthed/lf/tx/*

[7] G4JNT's 600W PA: *http://www.wireless.org.uk/jnt.htm*

[8] RS Components web pages and on-line catalogue: *http://rswww.com*

[9] Farnell web pages & on-line catalogue: *http://www.farnell.com*

[10] Transmitters for 136kHz: *http://www.wireless.org.uk/136rig.htm*

[11] PIC- or PC-controlled 0-6 MHz DDS VFO (AD9832). Johan Bodin, SM6LKM. *http://home4.swipnet.se/~w-41522/minidds/minidds.html*

[12] 'AR510: .VSWR Protection of Solid State RF Power Amplifiers.', by H O Granberg, *RF Design*, Feb 1991.

[13] David Bowman, G0MRF. E-mail: *g0mrf@aol.com*. Web: *http://www.g0mrf.freeserve.co.uk/*. Tel: 020 8572 8615.

[14] H J Morgan Smith, sheet metal engineers. Tel: 01293 452 421.

[15] G3YMC: *http://www.btinternet.com/~dsergeant/136.htm*

7

Measurement and calculation

In this chapter:

- Test gear for setting up the station
- Dummy loads
- Measuring a working station
- Calculating ERP
- Field strength measurement
- Scopematch tuning aid
- 500kHz antenna tuning meter

TO GET THE BEST OUT OF your LF station, it will be necessary to use a combination of readily available and home constructed test gear. The basic requirements are to be able to measure the transmitted frequency and the radiated power.

In order to obtain a 500kHz Special Research Permit, you must describe to Ofcom how you will ensure your station complies with the 0.1W ERP (effective radiated power) limit for this allocation. Compliance with the licence conditions for the 136kHz band also requires you to stay within the 1W ERP limit for this band. ERP can be determined either from measurements of the antenna current and dimensions, or, more directly, by measuring the field strength produced by the station. Both these approaches are described in this chapter.

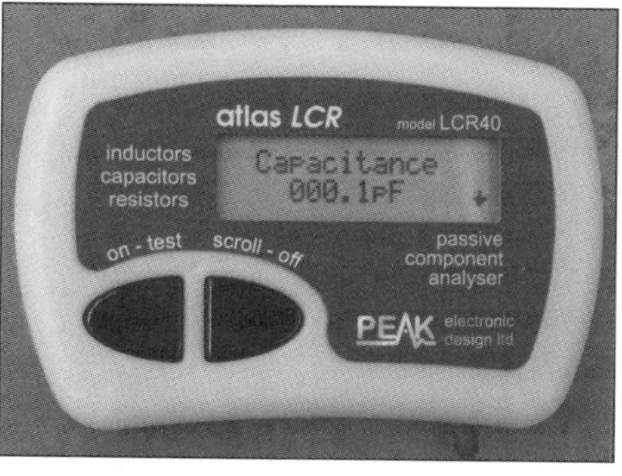

This small box measures resistance, capacitance and inductance over a wide range of values

Additionally, it is useful to have a convenient means of being able to check that the antenna system has been tuned to resonance. For anyone building their own transmitter, it may be necessary to obtain, or borrow, a good range of test gear, including an oscilloscope.

Maths have been largely avoided in the previous sections of this book, In this chapter you will find the calculations necessary to design, test and ultimately improve your low frequency station.

Test gear for setting up the station

The most obvious piece of test gear for the constructor is a multimeter. Preferably you should have both a digital meter for accuracy and an analogue meter for reading the changing results when making adjustments.

An oscilloscope is a boon for development or testing of a homebrew transmitter, since examining the waveforms and measuring signal levels at various

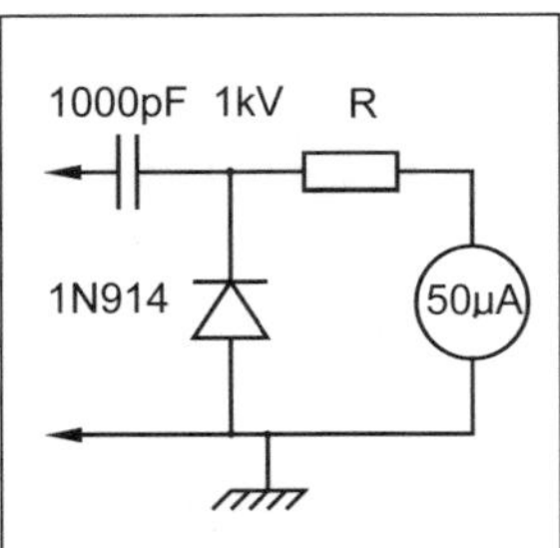

Fig 7.1: A simple RF probe is a useful tool for constructors

points in the circuit allows correct circuit operation to be verified.

For experimenting with the construction of large loading coils, an inductance meter is useful. These are available for a few tens of pounds and cover from one or two millihenries to several henries. Check that the range is suitable for the coils you want to build.

The simplest item to build is an RF probe (**Fig 7.1**) which has many uses for anyone building a transmitter or even an oscillator.

A frequency counter can be helpful to check that the transmitter's stages are working at the correct frequency. A great deal can be done simply by using the station receiver to check on frequencies, harmonics, sub-harmonics and distortion.

Some LF operators have managed to buy a second hand Selective Level Meter (SLM) originally used in analogue telecommunications systems. As well as being useful as receivers, SLMs provide accurate signal level measurements over a wide dynamic range. This makes them useful for measurement of spurious and harmonic output levels of transmitters and numerous other types of measurement, especially field strength measurements when used in conjunction with a calibrated antenna..

For setting up the resonating and matching of low frequency antennas, G3LDO recommends using the Array Solutions AIM4170 Antenna Analyser.

Dummy loads

Conventional dummy loads intended for the HF and higher bands will of course work perfectly well at LF and MF. However, higher powers are often required for 136kHz. Fortunately, many types of relatively cheap, high power resistors will give good results at low frequencies.

Wirewound resistors with values from a few tens to a few hundred ohms usually have manageable inductance at LF. For example, a 50 ohm load made up of two 100Ω, 150W (Arcol HS150 metal clad wirewound) resistors in parallel was found to have an impedance of (50.5 + j6.2 ohms) at 137kHz. This amounts to an SWR of 1.13:1, which would be adequate for many applications. Connecting two 1.5nF, 1kV polypropylene capacitors in parallel with the resistors to 'tune out' the inductive component of the impedance resulted in SWR of 1.02:1.

More recently, 'power metal film' resistors have become available at reasonable cost in ratings of tens to hundreds of watts (eg Vishay RCH50 series rated at 50W, available from RS components [1]). These have very low inductance and give good performance as dummy loads into the HF range and above. Like

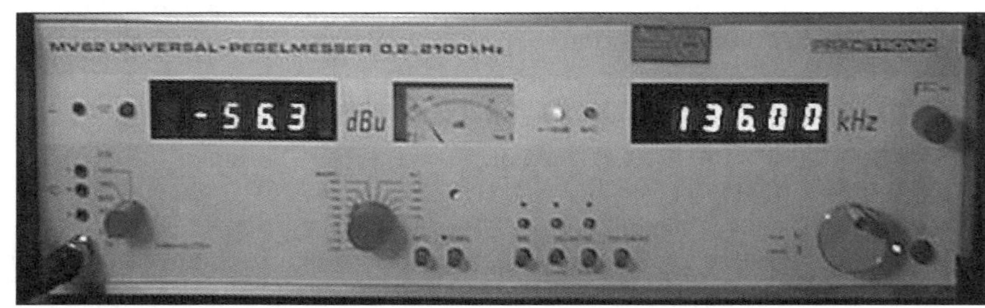

A selective level meter is designed for accurate measurement of LF signals on a telecom network

the metal-clad wirewound resistors, these are designed to be bolted to a heatsink, and suitable series-parallel combinations can be used to build a high power dummy load.

Several amateurs have pressed various types of heating element into service as high power 136kHz loads, including such things as toasters and electric fan heaters. These often have resistance in the vicinity of 50 ohms, with elements of wire or strip in a zig-zag shape that has a reasonably low inductance. It is advisable to run such a load at considerably less than its mains rated power, since the resistance rises considerably when at its normal operating temperature.

Most secondhand thermocouple RF meters are stand-alone, but this Russian one is in a bakelite case

Measuring a working station

RF current

The most important piece of test equipment when transmitting at low frequencies is an antenna current meter - actually this should be called 'antenna system' meter as it is often convenient to measure the current in the earth wire, not the antenna. The two most common ways of measuring current are a thermocouple meter and a transformer-coupled meter. Do not try to use the current range of an ordinary multi-meter to measure RF. The range required depends on your output power and the type and size of your antenna. A Marconi antenna is likely to be fed with 0.5 to 3A on 136kHz, and rather less than this at 500kHz; a loop antenna may be tens of amps. It is useful to have a really low current meter as well for low power experiments or for tuning your antenna.

RF ammeters using the heating of metals to produce a voltage - thermocouples - are available from time to time on the surplus market. Although they are convenient, they have square-law scales which can be difficult to read at the low end and can easily burn out (permanently) if overloaded. If you can get hold of one, use it to check your transformer-type meter and then put it away safely.

Fig 7.2 shows a much more useful RF meter that can be easily constructed and can be switched to cover several current ranges. Although the description that follows is for a current meter with an FSD of 1A the information given will enable you to construct a meter with any current range.

A small ferrite-cored transformer can be used to precisely sample the current flowing in a conductor. The sampled current flowing from the secondary winding of the transformer is equal to the primary current multiplied by the transformer turns ratio (primary turns)/(secondary turns). Rectifying the sample and applying the output to a moving coil meter provides a predictable and reliable method of current indication which will tolerate large overloads, is linear scaled and will respond quickly.

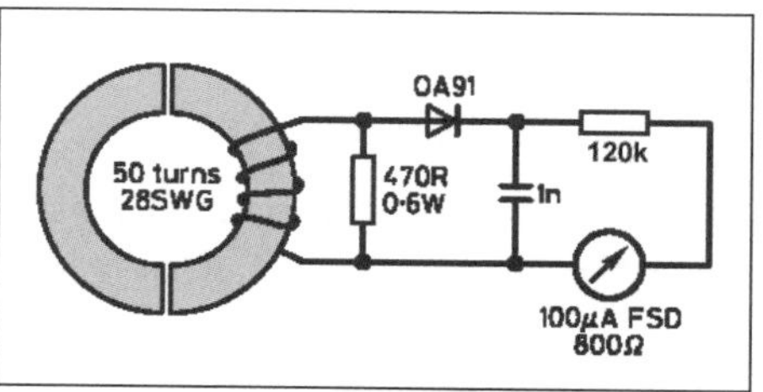

Fig 7.2: This RF current meter is linear and versatile. The ferrite ring can be split as illustrated to enable it to be clamped onto a wire without disconnecting it

With a single turn on the primary side and 50 turns on the secondary we can expect precisely 20mA to circulate in the secondary for each amp of primary current (1A / (50) = 0.02.

In dealing with toroid ring cores a 'turn' simply means a pass through the central hole - it does not need to be complete.

The secondary load resistance must be small compared to the secondary winding impedance in order to get an accurate current ratio. With typical high-permeability ferrite toroids, a 50 turn winding will have an impedance of the order of kilohms. A load of 470 ohms is suitable. Due to the 50:1 transformer ratio, the transformed load in the primary will be (470 /502), or 0.18 ohms , which is low enough to have minimal insertion loss in a typical vertical antenna system. A larger turns ratio will be required for loop antenna current measurements.

With 20mA passing through 470 ohms we will have 9.4 volts RMS available for rectification, corresponding to 13.2 volts peak. We can expect to lose approximately 0.5 volts at the detector diode leaving a DC voltage of 12.7 to drive the moving coil meter. To obtain full scale deflection of 100µA with 12.7 volts requires a total resistance of 127 kilohms. The meter itself will contribute about 800 ohms so a practical 120k resistor will fit the bill with negligible error. Finally. the effective resistance of the detector circuit will be much greater than the 470 ohms, so there will be negligible error due to loading here.

A useful variant is to use a split toroid so that the meter can be clamped onto an existing wire, such as an earthing cable, rather than having the wire passed through it. There's more on current meters, including calibration and making a clip-on meter at G3SEK's web site [2].

SWR

SWR bridges, as widely used at HF or VHF, can also be used at LF. The SWR bridge indicates the degree of mismatch between the impedance at the antenna feeder and the design impedance level of the SWR meter (normally 50 ohms), and so is useful for adjusting and monitoring the antenna tuning. Commercial SWR meters intended for the HF bands may be usable, but usually have reduced sensitivity at lower frequencies. Check for correct operation with a dummy load before using with a real antenna. Examples of SWR bridges designed specifically for 136kHz and 500kHz use are included in some of the designs in the Transmitters chapter. Some SWR bridges provide a power measurement facility but, at 136kHz and 500kHz, antenna current measurement is much more useful for power determination, as will be discussed in the next section.

Calculating ERP

Licensed amateurs will be familiar with calculating the DC input power to a transmitter, which is the DC voltage applied to the PA, multiplied by the DC current drawn by the PA:

$$P_{DC} = V_{DC} \text{ x } I_{DC}$$

Also familiar is calculation of RF output power into a load resistance R if the RMS RF voltage or current in the load is known:

$$P_{RF} = I^2R, \quad \text{or} \quad P_{RF} = V^2/R,$$

Which allows calculation of transmitter power delivered to a resistive load, eg a dummy load, or an antenna tuned to resonance.

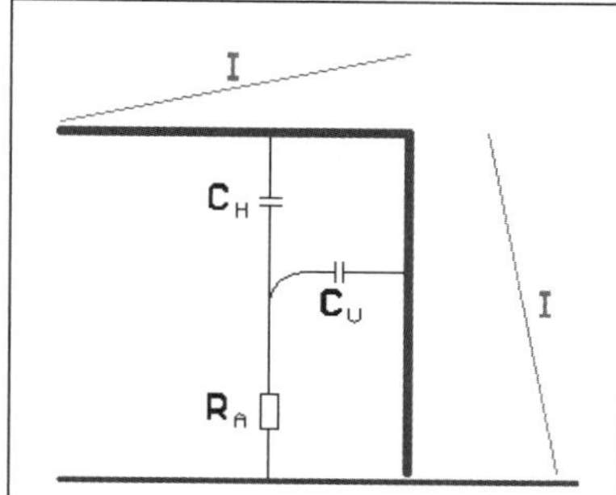

Fig 7.3: Capacitance to earth from the vertical and horizontal sections of an inverted-L Marconi

However, the licence conditions for the 136kHz and 500kHz allocations specify a power limit in terms of effective radiated power (ERP). To calculate ERP, we need to know how much power is actually radiated by the antenna, and what directivity (ie directional gain) the antenna has. At HF and above, we are used to the idea that the radiated power will be close to the transmitter output, because antennas in this frequency range have quite high efficiency. However, the efficiency of amateur antennas in the LF/MF range varies greatly, and is extremely small - a fraction of one per cent - so the radiated power will be much less than the amount of RF power fed into the antenna. So we must take into account the efficiency of the antenna to calculate radiated power. For 'electrically small' Marconi (vertical) or loop antennas, (ie antennas whose dimensions are a small fraction of a wavelength) the directivity can be assumed to be 1.8 (2.62dB) compared to a reference dipole. It sounds paradoxical that a small, inefficient antenna can have 'gain' over a dipole, but directivity is only a way of including the difference in directional patterns of the antennas in the calculation, and so takes no account of efficiency.

The efficiency of an antenna as a percentage is:

$$100\% \times R_{rad}/(R_{rad}+R_L),$$

Where R_{rad} is the radiation resistance, and R_L is the loss resistance of the antenna.

The radiation resistance represents the proportion of the power fed into the antenna that is converted into a radiated signal. R_{rad} can be calculated for a Marconi (vertical) antenna from the effective height H_{eff}, and the wavelength λ, using the well-known formula:

$$R_{rad} = 160\pi^2 H_{eff}^2 / 2$$

The wavelength $\lambda = (3 \times 10^8)/f$, where λ is in metres and f hertz.

Effective height was described in the chapter on transmitting antennas, and it can be calculated from the antenna dimensions. For simple antenna shapes, such as the L and T configurations, the following formula can be used:

$$H_{eff} = H_{actual} \times (2C_h+C_v)/2(C_h+C_v)$$

Where H_{actual} is the actual height of the top loading wires above ground, C_h is the capacitance to ground of the top loading wires, and C_v is the capacitance to ground of the vertical downlead (see **Fig 7.3**). A reasonably accurate estimate of C_h is 5pF per metre of wire, and C_v 6pF/m. See Chapter 3 for a discussion of the effect of multiple wires.

Example:

A Marconi vertical antenna has a top loading wire 40m long at an actual height above ground of 13m. C_h = 40 x 5pF = 200pF, C_v = 13 x 6pF = 78pF, H_{eff} = 11.2m. At 137kHz, λ = 2190m, R_{rad} = 0.041 ohms.

H_{eff} will be between 50% and 100% of the actual height of the antenna, depending on the length of the top loading wires. When the top loading wires are sloping, for example in the umbrella configuration, the above formula can be used by making H_{actual} the average height of the sloping wires.

For a loop antenna, the radiation resistance depends on the enclosed area A of the loop and the wavelength:

$$R_{rad} = 2 \times 320\pi^4 A^2/\lambda^4$$

(The factor of 2 in the formula is due to the presence of the ground plane under the antenna, which increases R_{rad}.) The shape of the loop does not affect Rrad.

Example:

G3YMC's loop in Chapter 3 has enclosed area of 100m^2. At 137kHz, λ = 2190m, R_{rad} = 27$\mu\Omega$ (micro-ohms).

The loss resistance R_L represents the proportion of the power fed to the antenna that is lost, being dissipated as heat in the antenna wire, tuner, ground, and lossy objects near the antenna. In amateur antennas, R_L is invariably much larger than R_{rad}. The loss resistance can be found by measuring the RF resistance at the antenna feed point when the antenna is tuned to resonance (strictly, this will be R_{rad}+R_L, but in practice R_L is so much larger than R_{rad} that the antenna resistance can be taken as equal to R_L). R_L could also be found by measuring the transmitter power output and the antenna current I:

$$R_L = P_{RF} / I^2$$

Once R_{rad} is calculated, and R_{loss} determined, the efficiency can be calculated, and the radiated power is then:

(Tx power x Efficiency/100%).

An easier and more accurate approach to finding the radiated power, which avoids the need for RF impedance and transmitter power measurements, is to measure the antenna current. Radiated power P_{rad} is then just:

$$P_{rad} = I^2 R_{rad}$$

To get ERP, we multiply the radiated power by the antenna directivity:

$$P_{ERP} = P_{rad} \times 1.8 = 1.8 \times I^2 \times R_{rad}$$

These formulas can be combined to give ERP directly.

For a Marconi (vertical) antenna:
PERP = 1.8 x 160 π^2 I^2 H_{eff}^2 / 2

At 137kHz, this becomes P_{ERP} = I^2 H_{eff}^2 /1687
At 503kHz, P_{ERP} = I^2 H_{eff}^2 / 125.1

Example:
A 500W transmitter produces 2.4A antenna current in the Marconi antenna with H_{eff} of 11.2m in the previous example.
P_{ERP} = 2.4^2 x 11.2^2 / 1687 = 0.43W.
We can also calculate R_L and the antenna efficiency:
R_L = P_{RF} / I^2 = 500 / 5.76 = 87 ohms,
Efficiency = 100% x R_{rad}/(R_{rad} + R_L) = 100% x 0.041Ω/(87 + 0.041) = 0.047%

For a loop antenna:

P_{ERP} = 1.8 x 2 x 320 π^4 I^2 A^2 / λ^4

At 137kHz, this becomes P_{ERP} = I^2 A^2 / (205 x 10^6)
At 503kHz, P_{ERP} = I^2 A^2 / (1.13 x 10^6)

Example:
The G3YMC loop in Chapter 3 has an antenna current of 8A at 137kHz and area of 100m^2.
Therefore P_{ERP} = 8^2 x 100^2 / (205 x 10^6) = 3.1mW.
The loss resistance of the loop is 0.65Ω, and the radiation resistance 27μΩ.
Therefore efficiency = 100% x 27μΩ / (27μΩ + 0.65Ω) = 0.0041%.

The formulas for radiation resistance and ERP show that the power radiated for a given amount of antenna current is much greater at 500kHz than 136kHz. Therefore antenna efficiencies tend to be much higher on 500kHz.

Field strength measurement

A more direct way of determining your ERP is by measuring the field strength. As pointed out in the section on antennas, the definitive way of determining the effective radiated power of a station is to measure the field strength at a known distance from the antenna. The relation between field strength E (volts/metre) at a distance d metres, and ERP is given by the formula:

$$P_{ERP} = \frac{E^2 d^2}{49}$$

For this relationship to be valid, the distance d must be in the far field region of the antenna, where the field strength falls away in inverse proportion to the distance from the antenna. The near field region is closer to the antenna, where the field strength decreases more rapidly with distance, and the formula above does not apply. For small antennas at 136kHz and 500kHz, a safe minimum distance is about 1km. At distances much greater than a few tens of kilometres, the

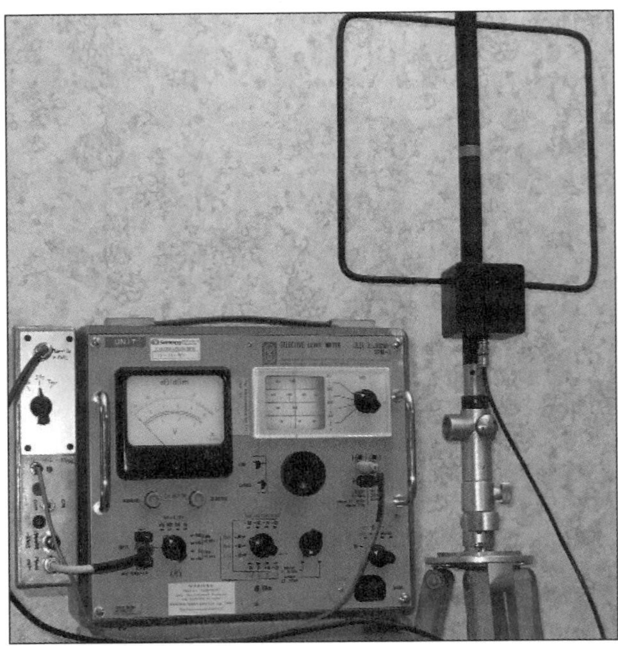

Fig 7.4: Field strength measuring system at M0BMU

formula also becomes invalid, due to the effects of ground loss on the propagating wave close to the ground, and ionospheric reflections. For amateur stations, the signal is also likely to be too weak to accurately measure at larger distances

Two pieces of equipment are required to measure field strength, a calibrated receiver and a calibrated 'measuring' antenna (**Fig 7.4**). The calibrated receiver must be capable of accurately measuring signal levels down to a few microvolts, and have sufficient selectivity to reject unwanted adjacent signals; the ideal amateur equipment for this purpose is the selective level meter (see section on receivers).

Calibrated antennas have a specified antenna factor (AF), which is the number of decibels which must be added to the signal voltage measured at their terminals to obtain the field strength. Quite good accuracy in the LF and MF ranges can be obtained using a simple single turn loop antenna. Such loops have a low feed point impedance, so the received signal level is little affected by the load impedance. The output voltage of an N-turn loop with area A square metres at a frequency f hertz is given by:

$$V = 2.1\times10^{-8}\times fNAE$$

From this, the antenna factor of a single turn loop at 137kHz is:

$$AF(dB) = 20Log_{10}\left(\frac{1}{2.1\times10^{-8}\times137\times10^{3}\times A}\right) = 20Log_{10}\left(\frac{350}{A}\right)$$

At 503kHz, AF = $20Log_{10}(94.7/A)$. A square or circular loop made of tubing is usually used, with an area between $0.5m^2$ and $1m^2$. As an example, suppose a signal level of 7.5dBμV (ie 7.5 decibels above 1 V, or 2.4 V; selective level meters usually give a decibel-scaled reading) is measured at a distance of 5km from the transmitting antenna, using a $1m^2$ loop at 137kHz. From the formula above, AF is 51dB, so the field strength is 58.5dBuV/m, or 840uV/m. Using the ERP formula gives P_{ERP} = 350mW.

A more compact alternative to the loop is a tuned ferrite rod antenna, however this requires calibration with a known field strength to determine the antenna factor. A field strength measuring system, including ferrite rod antenna, measuring receiver, and calibration set-up has been described by Dick Rollema, PA0SE [3].

Field strength measurements are prone to errors caused by environmental factors. The measured field strength is particularly affected by conducting objects giving rise to parasitic antenna effects. Such parasitic antennas can be large steel-framed structures such as buildings and road bridges, overhead power and telephone wires, even such things as fence wires and shallow buried cables. Such factors are difficult to entirely avoid, so several field strength measurements should be made at different locations over as wide an area as possible. Locations giving widely different values of ERP can then be rejected; it will be found that a few decibels of variation still exists between different measurement sites, so the ERP should be taken as an average of several measuring sites [4].

The Scopematch tuning aid

This device developed by Jim Moritz, M0MBU, is used to simplify matching an LF antenna to 50-ohms. It is basically an SWR bridge without the detectors and meter. With this device the current and voltage amplitude and phase relationships can be monitored on a dual trace oscilloscope to establish a matched condition.

Construction

The circuit and construction is shown in **Fig 7.5**. Any high permeability 18mm diameter ferrite toroid ferrite core can be used for the transformers although a 3C85 core is ideal. The one in the prototype came from an old SMPS common mode choke. Do not use iron dust cores.

T1 secondary comprises 50 turns of enamelled wire. The primary is a single wire passing through the middle of the toroid, as used in an SWR bridge. Power handling is not really an issue.

T2 uses the same the same construction, but in this case the 50 turns are on the primary, with a single loop of wire to the output connection. Note that the 50-turn winding has the full transmitter output voltage across it, so the winding has to be well insulated from the core to withstand a few hundred volts of RF. The small core worked fine at the 400W level, but saturated with 600W. If high power is contemplated it would be advisable to use a larger core for T2, and to increase the primary and secondary turns from 1:50 to 2:100.

Operation

T1 is a 1:50 current transformer, which samples the current at the transmitter output and together with the 50 ohm resistor the scale factor is 1V = 1A. T2 is a 50:1 voltage transformer which samples the output voltage, 1V out = 50V at Tx output.

The oscilloscope is set for the same volts per division on both channels. The scale factors are chosen so that when the antenna system is resonant at 50 ohms (or a 50 dummy load is used), both voltage and current traces are identical (see **Fig 7.6**). If the load is inductive, the current waveform will lag the voltage; if capacitive it is the other way round. Getting the antenna resonant is just a matter of adjusting the loading coil until the two waveforms are in phase. Once the antenna is resonant, if the current waveform is bigger than the voltage waveform, the

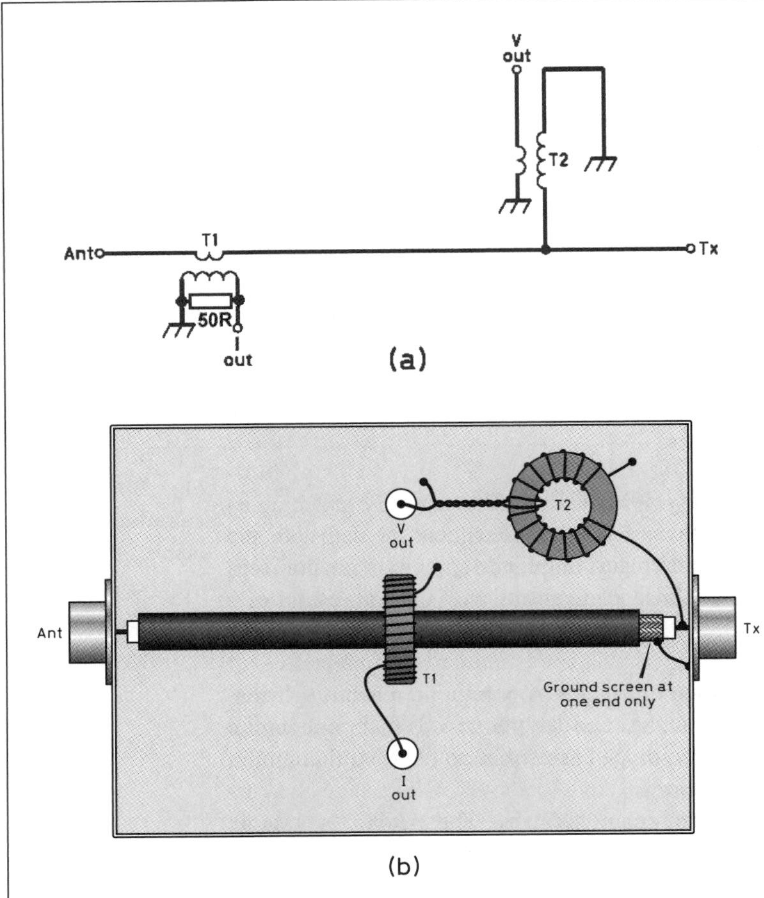

Fig 7.5: The construction and circuit of the ScopeMatch. Note that the coaxial cable screen within the box is grounded on one side only

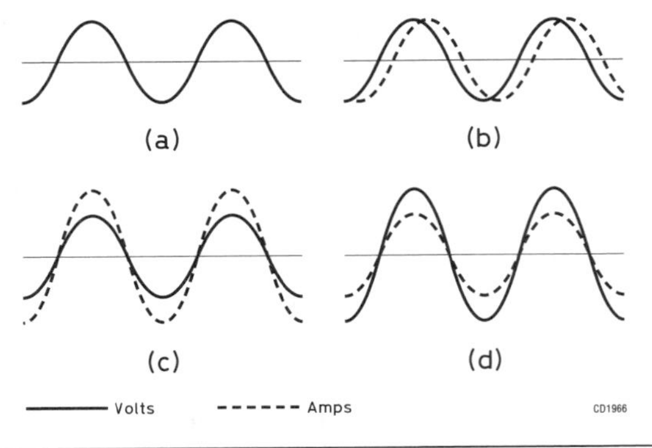

Fig 7.6: (a) Perfect match. Current and voltage waveforms have the same phase and amplitude and only one trace discernible. (b) Antenna off tune and inductively reactive (voltage leads current). (c) Antenna resonant but resistive component of impedance low (voltage 25V, current 1amp, 25ohms) (d) Antenna resonant but resistive component of impedance high (voltage 50V, current 0.5A, 100 ohms)

load is less than 50 ohms, and if smaller the load is greater than 50 ohms. You can calculate the actual R by measuring V and I off the screen and using Ohm's law.

This gadget has proved very useful both for setting up an antenna and while operating it takes out most of the guesswork that occurs when using SWR bridge circuits. You can also tune up on low power.

T2 can be replaced with a capacitive divider. This comprises a 100p capacitor connected to the inner of the coaxial cable at the 'Transmitter' socket in series with a 5000p capacitor connected to ground. The centre of the capacitive divider is connected to the voltage-sampling socket. The 100p capacitor must be rated to take the transmitter output voltage.

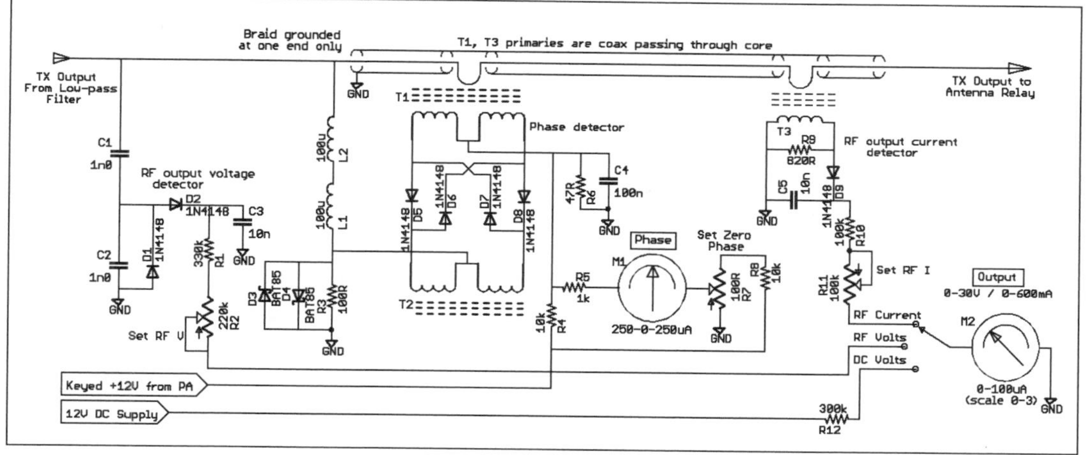

Fig 7.7: 500kHz antenna tuning meter

500kHz antenna tuning meter

The tuning meter system shown in **Fig 7.7** was designed for use with the 500kHz Class D MOSFET transmitter described in a previous chapter, but would also be useful with other 500kHz transmitters with output powers of a few watts and above. When tuning up a transmitting antenna at LF or MF, the operator wants to know if the antenna impedance is inductive or capacitive, or tuned to resonance and, once resonance is achieved, whether the resulting resistive load matches the transmitter output. The usual type of VSWR bridge circuit only indicates the degree of mismatch, so is of limited help. This circuit includes a phase detector to indicate resistive or reactive loads, and RF voltage and current measurement which allows the output resistance and power level to be checked. The operator first resonates the antenna by adjusting the loading coil inductance for zero phase, then checks the voltage and current levels to find the load resistance, and adjusts the matching circuit accordingly.

The phase detector circuit senses the RF output current via transformer T1, and the RF output voltage via inductors L1, L2 and applies both signals to the diode ring D5 - D8. D3, D4 act as a clipper to keep the signal level fairly constant with changing transmitter power. When the load is resistive, the output current and voltage are in phase. The signals applied to the detector are approximately in quadrature due to the inductive voltage divider. This results in a DC output from the phase detector close to zero. A reactive load results in the RF voltage and current no longer being in phase, and a positive or negative deflection of the centre zero phase meter depending on whether the impedance is inductive or capacitive. Due to phase offsets and diode mismatches within the circuit,

C1, C2 are 1nF polystyrene, polypropylene or silver-mica.
L1, L2 are Axial chokes, 100uH.
T1: secondary is 2 x 20 turns bifilar 0.25mm wire on 14mm 3C85 ferrite toroid, and the primary is RG58 coax passing through the core.
T2 is 2 x 20 turns bifilar 0.25mm wire on 14mm 3C85 ferrite toroid.
T3 secondary is 50 turns 0.25mm wire on 14mm 3C85 ferrite toroid, and the primary is RG58 coax passing through the core.

Table 7.1: Tuning meter component notes

the phase detector output is not quite zero with a resistive load; R4, R7 and R8 provide an adjustable DC bias to allow the meter deflection to be set to zero with a dummy load attached to the transmitter output.

The RF voltage is sensed via a capacitive divider C1, C2. The reactance of C1, C2 cancel the reactance of L1, L2, minimising the loading effect of the meter on the transmitter. A diode voltmeter produces a DC voltage to drive the meter. The RF current is sensed via current transformer T3, and applied to a second diode voltmeter circuit. The scale-setting resistors are chosen so that the voltage scale is 50 times the current scale; thus, when the load is 50 ohms, the meter deflection is the same on both voltage and current ranges, and the operator can see at a glance the load is matched, greater than, or less than 50 ohms. A third meter range is provided to measure the DC input voltage, for use with a battery supply.

The scale-setting resistors are chosen to suit the available meter movements and scales. R5 sets the phase meter sensitivity to provide near full-scale deflection with the maximum power level, but an accurate calibration is not required since the phase meter only has to indicate zero, positive and negative. Operation of the phase meter can be checked by connecting a capacitor of 5 - 10nF across the dummy load, which should produce near full-scale deflection. R1, R2 set the voltmeter scale, R10, R11 set the RF ammeter scale. The meter can be calibrated using an oscilloscope or known RF voltmeter or ammeter with a dummy load. Accuracy is not critical; the main thing is that the meter registers equal deflection on voltage and current ranges with a 50 ohm load.

A version of this circuit designed for higher power levels at 136kHz is described in [5].

References

[1] RS Components web pages and on-line catalogue: *http://rswww.com*

[2] *http://www.ifwtech.co.uk/g3sek/clip-on/clip-on.htm* (note that this web site is aimed at VHF operators and a suitable core must be used for LF)

[3] *http://www.wireless.org.uk/pa0se.htm*

[4] 'Experimental investigation of very small low frequency transmitting antennas', J.R. Moritz, IEE 9th International Conference on HF Radio Systems and Techniques, June 2003, *IEE Conference Publication n. 493* pp 51 - 56.

[5] *http://www.picks.plus.com/software/LFtunemeter.pdf*

8

Low frequency propagation

In this chapter:

- □ Ground waves
- □ Skywaves
- □ The effect of the Sun
- □ Can we predict good conditions?
- □ 500kHz

IT IS GENERALLY BELIEVED that propagation in the LF bands is stable, almost boring. This is only loosely the case. Historically the LF bands have been used where a wide service area is required which is relatively immune from interference and ionospheric effects such as fading. Prime commercial uses have been radio navigation systems, wide area military communications, and to a lesser extent, mainly in Europe, broadcasting. A lot of the research that has been carried out has had as its objective a determination of the severity of interference from signals beyond normal service range. In the years after WWII this was more to determine the reliable range of long distance navigation systems such as Decca Navigator, Loran-C and Omega. The critical factor being the reliability with which the phase or timing of the signal could be determined.

By contrast, the radio amateur, often working at the threshold of possibility, is willing to wait for and use whatever short-term effects are available to achieve his ambition of long distance communication.

The signal from a transmitter may reach a receiving site in two ways. Firstly by way of waves which follow the curvature of the Earth to some extent, known as ground waves. Secondly by the return of skyward travelling waves by the ionosphere, referred to colloquially as skywaves, or more correctly ionospheric waves.

Ground waves

The so-called ground waves follow the curvature of the Earth because the speed of the wave is slowed slightly by the dielectric constant of the ground (**Fig 8.1**). This has the effect of tilting the wavefront downwards, and allows the signals to be detected far beyond the normal visible

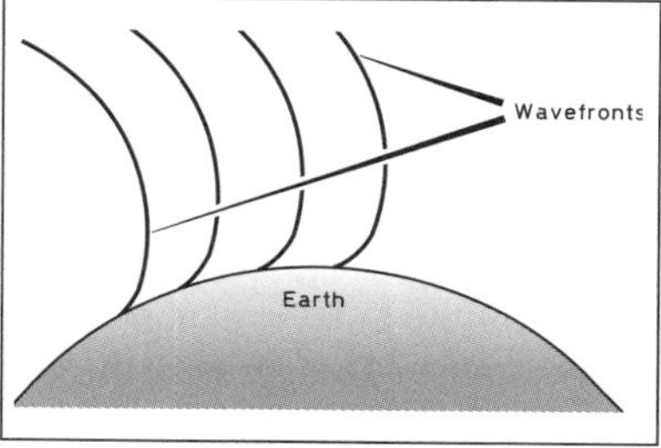

Fig 8.1: Ground wave signals are tilted downwards, allowing them to 'hug' the earth and propagate far beyond the visible horizon

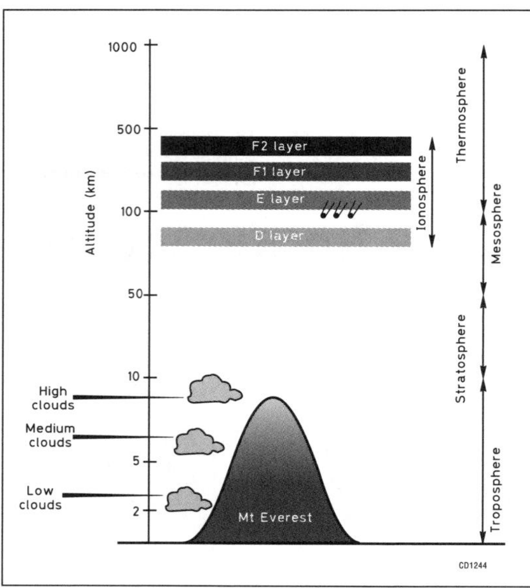

Fig 8.2: The ionospheric layers. Note that their height will vary with the time of day. LF signals are propagated by the lowest part, the D layer

horizon. Unlike higher frequencies the strength of the ground wave signal is not reduced significantly by absorption. As a result there is no 'dead zone' on low frequencies and ground wave signals can be detected at over 2000km from the transmitter.

Skywaves

Because most amateur sized aerials are small compared to the wavelength, a considerable amount of the radiated power is launched at higher angles and rapidly leaves any influence of the ground. These waves travel upwards until they reach the ionosphere at around 50 to 100km altitude (**Fig 8.2**). Vertical incidence signals will penetrate deeply into the ionised regions but will suffer a great deal of attenuation. At lower angles the waves will be gently 'bent' (refracted is a more accurate term) back towards the ground. Skywave returns have been detected at as little as 300km from the transmitting station and result is a slow shallow fading in the strength of the signal.

The change in strength is due to the change in the distance the skywave travels as the altitude of the 'bending' region alters. The skywave arrives at the receiver with a different phase to that of the ground wave and the two waves may either add, to reinforce the signal, or cancel to reduce it. Complete cancellation only occurs if the ground and skywave are the same strength as well as 180 degrees out of phase. Most of the published data suggests that the skywaves become approximately equal in strength to the groundwaves at around 700km from the transmitter. Beyond this distance the skywave is stronger.

A case of 'dead zone' can appear when very low power signals are transmitted. In this situation the ground wave is weakened, by the nature of its outwards spread, to levels below the detection level of the receiver before the angle of the skywave becomes low enough to cause them to return. This is often experienced by US FCC Part 15 stations (operating between 160 and 190 kHz), who are limited to one watt RF input power and a maximum antenna length of 50ft.

A simple geometric construction (**Fig 8.3**) allows us to calculate the distance covered by a single ionospheric 'bounce' provided we know the height at which the signal is bent back towards Earth. For simplicity we can consider a mirror like reflection from an altitude we will call the 'apparent reflection height' and we will assume that the signal leaves the transmitting site tangentially to the ground. Experience suggests that the daytime 'reflection level' is around the bottom of the D-layer at about 50 km altitude whilst at night the reflection level is in the upper D-layer near the bottom of the E-layer at around 100km altitude.

Our calculations then show that in daytime a single hop will be of around

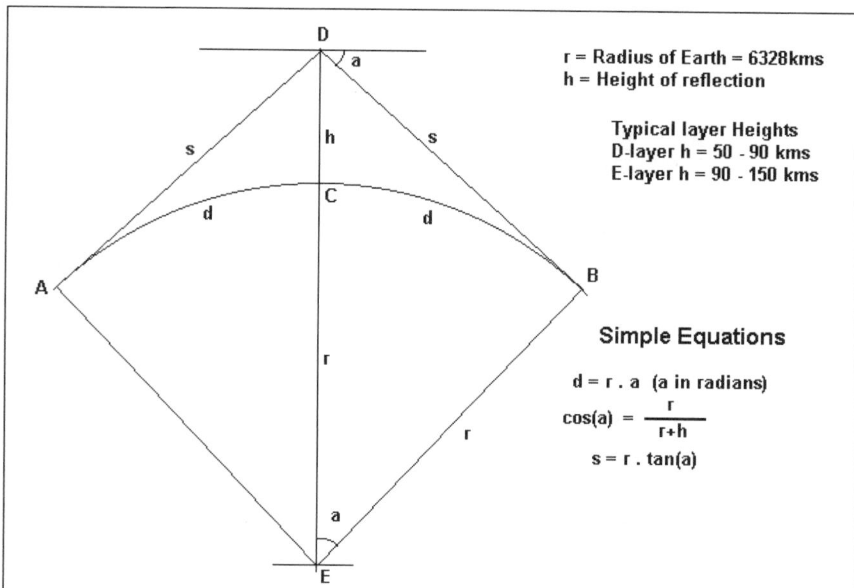

Fig 8.3: Simple geometry of ionospheric reflection

1000km, whilst at night-time a single hop will be around 2000km. It is important to realise that the returning skywave approaches the ground at grazing incidence or tangentially, it does not bounce at high angles like a tennis ball as shown on many sketches. Thus the wave does not need to be 'reflected' from the ground to go upwards for a second hop, it merely slides past barely touching the ground.

Low frequency radio paths can comprise several such 'hops'. The regular signal heard from VO1NA during 2003 and 2004 at 3600km was probably a two hop path, whilst the record contact between Quartz Hill in New Zealand and Vladivostok in Asiatic Russia at over 10,000km was probably around five hops. One-way signals from Quartz Hill were detected and identified in western Russia at 16,000km. These exceptional distances were achieved at night with the path in full darkness. The daytime path lengths are usually restricted to around 2000km, due mainly to the higher signal absorption (attenuation) levels in daytime and the loss at each 'hop'. Nevertheless, under exceptional circumstances VO1NA has been copied in the UK at 1200z, but this is a rare event. Even the powerful (20kW ERP) naval station CFH at Halifax, Nova Scotia, is not often heard in Europe during the day-time.

In practice the situation is a little more complicated. The 'reflection' of the waves is not without loss. At lower altitudes the daytime ionisation of the D-layer produces a belt of ionisation below the 'reflection height' that absorbs power from the radio waves. At the lower HF frequencies (160m, 80m and 40m) this shows up as the severe restriction in day-time range, because the skywaves are completely absorbed by the D-layer. After sunset this ionisation in the D-layer decays and the lower HF waves can pass through to be reflected from the F layer and so called 'skip' signals appear. In the LF frequency range the daytime absorption is not so complete and it is possible to receive daytime skywave signals at distances of about 2000km, which probably requires two hops. For a given path these signals are never as strong as those received after dark.

The effect of the Sun

Propagation conditions are further affected by solar disturbances. At the height of the sun spot cycle, the Sun emits bursts of intense x-rays and ultra-violet light called solar flares. Because the output of a solar flare is an electromagnetic emission (like a radio wave), it is almost instant and will only affect the side of the Earth that is currently illuminated. Intense flares cause radio blackouts at HF frequencies, because they produce extra ionisation in the D-layer which strongly absorbs most HF radio frequencies (**Fig 8.4**). Surprisingly at LF the effect is usually the exact opposite. The intense radiation converts the normally absorbing level ionisation to a state where it easily 'reflects' LF waves. The result is that LF signals show a strong peak in strength which is a similar shape in time to that of the X-ray flux (as can be seen on the NOAA web site [1]).

This flare enhancement can cause an increase of up to 10dB in the strength of a signal being received in daytime. This can be useful, but the enhancement is much less than is normally achieved on night-time paths.

The solar magnetic disturbances that produce flares also throw off huge clouds of ionised gas or plasma.. The plasma travels much more slowly and takes between 36 and 56 hours to reach the vicinity of Earth, a journey of 96 million miles.

When these clouds reach the earth they buffet the atmosphere. Because they are composed of fast moving charged particles, the cloud caries with it a magnetic field, and its interaction is with the Earth's magnetic field. The magnetosphere is a distorted doughnut shaped 'cage' formed by the lines of magnetic force generated in the Earth's core. The magnetosphere protects us from most of what the Sun can throw at us. Without it, the majority of Life on Earth could not exist.

If the magnetic field of the plasma is in one direction the cloud bounces off fairly harmlessly, like similar poles of small bar magnets. In the opposite field direction the field lines of the plasma are said to 'connect' with the geomagnetic field, like the bar magnet opposite poles. This situation opens up 'cracks' in the Earths 'defences' and charged particles flood into the atmosphere. The most notable visible effects of this phenomena are the aurora seen mainly in high latitudes after a magnetic storm.

The event also causes the Earth's field to vary wildly for a short period, an event which can be observed on magnetometers, and hence the term 'Geomagnetic Storm'. This was though to be the main source of injected particles, but since then the use of satellites and the discovery of the Van Allen radiation belts has refined ideas of the process. It has been realised recently that the majority of the particles are swept

Fig 8.4: Effects of solar disturbances on the ionosphere

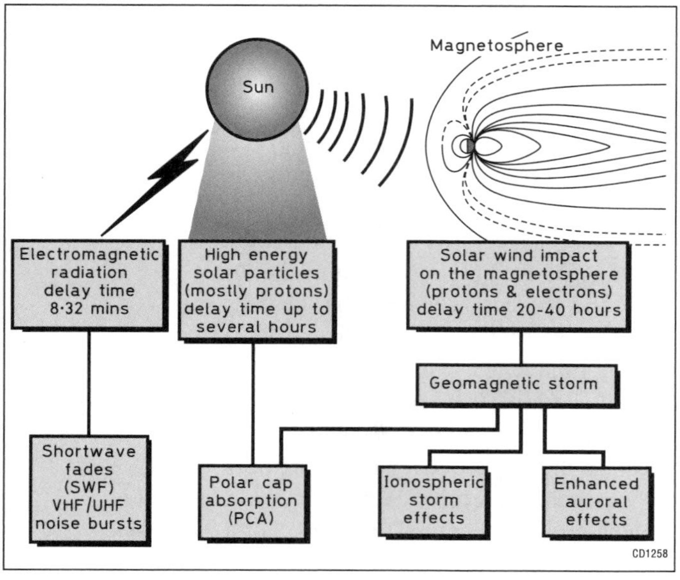

past Earth and are sucked into the long tail of the magnetosphere on the side of Earth opposite to the Sun. The Geomagnetic field then draws them back into the Van Allen belts, forming a series of circulating rings. Electrons travel one way and ions, because of their opposite charge, the other. More than this, the electrons being much lighter follow paths that spiral round the Earths magnetic lines of force from one hemisphere to the other. They are 'turned round' by the 'cramping' of the lines of force near the poles. Together these rings of circulating charges, which are known as the Equatorial Ring Current, generate a magnetic field of their own, which can be detected and measured by magnetometers at the Equator. The Rings exchange charged particles, mainly electrons, with the ionosphere

It had been noted by many researchers prior to the advent of satellite measurement, that the injection of electrons (called electron precipitation) into the ionosphere, after a geomagnetic storm, lead to severe reductions in distant radio-signal strengths. The effect did not build up until a day or so after the storm and could often persist for up to 28 days. It is not physically possible for electrons, even very energetic ones, to exist in the relatively high atmospheric pressure at the D-layer for very long. So that the signal attenuation should decay with the passing of the storm. It has recently become clear that the Ring Current acts as a reservoir of electrons which are bled into the ionosphere at the daylight edge, where the magnetosphere is distorted by the pressure of the Solar wind. Thus the after-effects of a Geomagnetic storm on LF radio transmissions will be felt until the Ring Current is depleted of its trapped electrons.

Fortunately the Ring Current can be measured by the field it generates. It is not an easy task because the field due to the Ring Current is about one thousandth of the Earth's field. (50 to 400nT against 50,000nT)

Daily estimates of an index,which effectively measures the Ring Current, are published by several institutes. Most useful for LF radio propagation prediction are the (hourly) real-time estimates from Colorado University and Kyoto University, which are both available on the Internet [2, 3]. The Index is referred to as 'Disturbance Storm Time' and carries the mnemonic Dst.

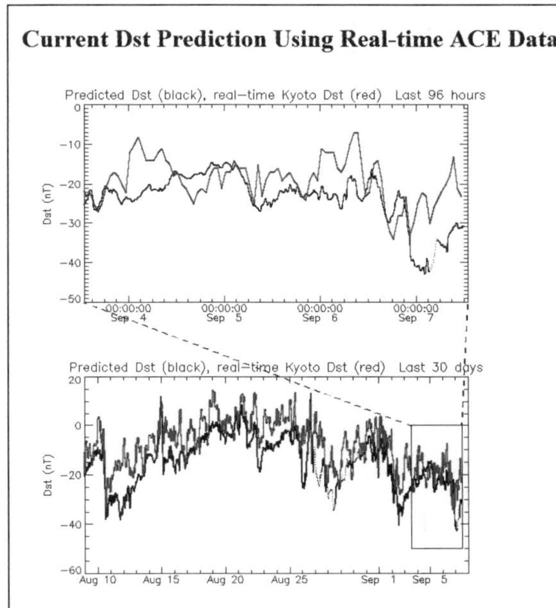

A very useful indication of ionospheric propagation at LF can be derived from the data provided by Colorado University [2]

Plasma clouds (referred to on solar web sites as coronal mass ejections or CMEs) can also be produced by disturbances in the solar atmosphere known as coronal holes. Whilst flare-associated events are more prevalant in years of high sunspot activity, coronal hole events occur throughout the Solar cycle including periods when the visible face of the Sun is totally devoid of spots.

The most familiar effect of these disturbances is intense aurora. A rarer, but more serious problem, is that these events can induce massive currents in long northern power distribution systems. Canada suffered a power black-out for several hours some years ago due to one such event . Submarine cables and satellite communications systems can also be disabled. The arrival of a CME can herald the onset of a period of poor HF communications. Absorption, due to the enhanced ionisation of the D-layer by the trapped electrons, causes all the bands to go 'flat'. Again the effect at LF is different. The daytime signals up to about 2000km can be significantly enhanced by up to 10 or 12 dB above normal levels. The effect on night-time paths is more dramatic with absorption at LF increasing significantly above normal and signal levels on long paths dropping as much as 20dB below normal levels.

Can we predict good conditions?

It might seem that with the knowledge built up it should be possible to predict good LF conditions. This can be done to some extent, but it is much easier to predict bad conditions particularly for night-time paths. Flares cannot easily be predicted and the best that NOAA will say is that there is a likelihood of a flare of particular strength in the next three days. However, by carefully watching the background levels via the NOAA SEC internet site [1], it is possible to see the Solar X-ray flux, measured by the GEOS satellites, increasing. This gives a good indication that a predicted flare is imminent. Flares are more likely around the sunspot maximum and their likelihood is directly related to the sunspot number, which is a measure of solar activity.

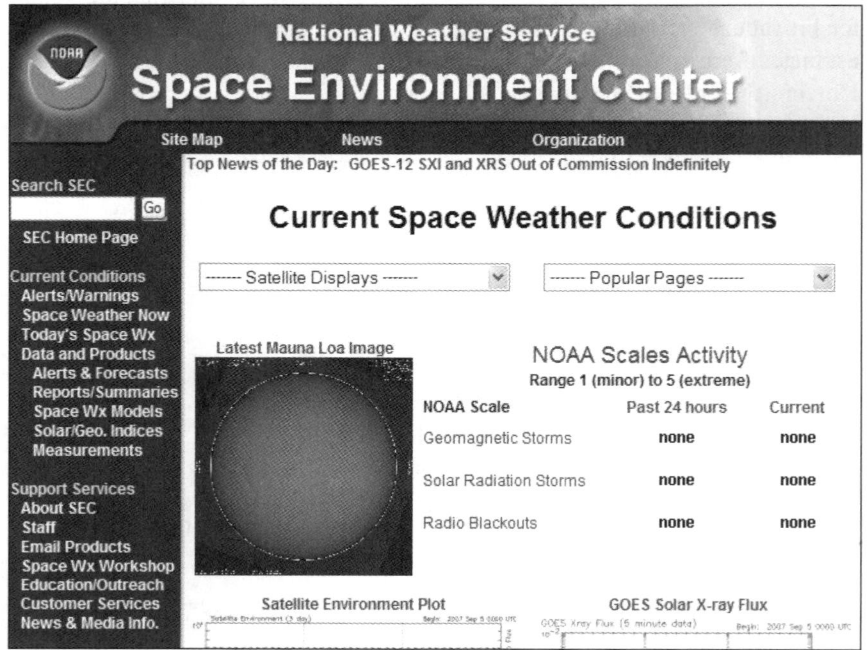

Check the NOAA SEC web site [1] for solar flare information

Coronal mass ejections are detected as they form and their impact on Earth can be predicted about two days ahead of their arrival, which is denoted by a large increase in the geomagnetic index Kp, known as a geomagnetic 'storm'. One problem is that a CME will sweep past Earth, the Kp will indicate the storm and return to the 'quiet' state in a matter of hours. The effect of the storm is not felt in radio terms for about two days at mid latitudes, despite aurora occurring on the night of the impact. This may be due to the time taken for electrons trapped in the ionosphere to diffuse down and spread out at lower latitudes. It may also be due to the fact that the charged particles are collected in the magnetosphere 'tail' as the plasma cloud sweeps past the Earth, and these must travel back, under the influence of the magnetic field, into the Ring Current. Then 'precipitation' from the Ring Current takes place mainly at the 'dawn edge'.

An intense storm will produce a depression in night-time signal levels that can last for 21 to 28 days and the Kp index is no indicator of the return of good conditions but a study of Dst during this period is more rewarding.

A correlation between this index and signal levels of well known commercial stations suggests that the Dst index mirrors the return of good radio propagation. The Dst index has a range from small positive values (0 to +40) for quiet conditions to -100 to -400 for intense storm conditions. The units are nanotesla (nT) because this is a magnetic field. Unlike the Kp index it will show the effect of small events following a major storm which tend to extend the recovery time to good radio conditions, because of the "reservoir" being topped up.

Radio amateurs have had access to LF for almost a whole solar cycle now, and we can say what the effect of the 11 year solar cycle on LF conditions might be. The cycle is usually defined in terms of sunspot numbers and solar flares will be directly related to the sunspot number. Geomagnetic events seem to peak a year or two past the sunspot maximum. Geomagnetic storms still occur during the quiet years but the period between them becomes longer allowing more time for propagation conditions to recover. Perversely it would seem that the very best results are not achieved in dead quiet solar conditions and a small amount of geomagnetic activity can be an advantage.

We can now see that the higher level of daylight solar flux during the years around the maximum produce stronger daylight skywave signals. On average the daylight path of in excess of 1000km, can be 10dB lower at the Solar minimum. There is a further effect which cannot yet be quantified which shows that night-time signals seem to decline below expectation levels in a long geomag-

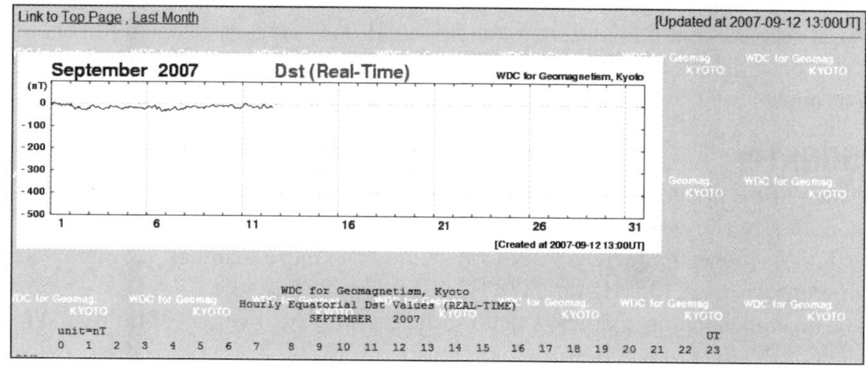

Dst readings are available on the web site at Kyoto [3]

netically quiet period in the Solar minimum. This may be due to the lack of a sufficient radiation to to retain the necessary level of ionisation in the lower E layer. In effect the E-layer may be becoming slightly transparent to 136kHz signals, and some is 'leaking away'. It is noticeable that there can be a dramatic recovery to good levels following immediately after a small geomagnetic disturbance which only measures at a Kp of 4. During a long quiet spell in January 2003 a minor geomagnetic storm raising Kp to only 4, produced record levels on transatlantic paths.

There is a mythology that LF propagation only exists in the winter months, between the autumn and spring equinoxes. This is not true, daytime levels are better in summer because the sun is stronger at mid-day and the ionisation for daytime skywave is higher. The darkness period is shorter and some paths may not have a period of total darkness for a month around the summer solstice. What normally limits operation in summer is the level of static, interference from lightning crashes. This makes listening very uncomfortable and tiring, but some data modes and QRSS can be operated successfully through this period on nights when the interference is not continuous.

The best information about the state of propagation is derived from listening to reliable commercial stations and logging their strength. Propagation is very frequency dependent and it is only really useful to listen to stations in the same frequency area. The frequency band from 75 to 200kHz is totally different to the bands above and below, so suitable indicators for 136kHz conditions should be chosen from that range. This runs from the Frequency Standard transmission HBG on 75 kHz in Switzerland, to BBC Radio 4 on 198kHz. Choose a station that is at least 1500km away so that you are receiving only skywave at night. BBC Radio 4 and the German utility station DCF39 on 138.83kHz are too close to the UK to be useful as propagation indicators in this country.

The Canadian naval station CFH at Halifax Nova Scotia on 137.00kHz is ideal at a distance of about 4500km from the UK, but it does have long periods of inactivity. The Greek naval station SXV located near Athens on 135.75 is one choice at a path length of 2200km from the UK, but it is difficult to understand the strength variations. This may be due to the long reach up the Adriatic followed by a passage over the Alps, but it is also suspected that the power is reduced at times. Under generally good conditions the received level from SXV can swing violently up and down, probably due to multi-hop fading. Because fading is a function of the path distance, it can be very dependent upon the location of the receiving station. Two stations just 50 miles apart may experience what seems like totally different conditions, if one is ideally situated to benefit from constructive (additive) interference between paths with numbers of different hops.

500kHz

Much of the above information is also applicable to the experimental allocation at 500kHz. The major differences are of course a function of the reduced wavelength or higher frequency. Radio Amateurs have more than half a Solar cycle of experience on 136kHz but 500kHz effects are new to us.

The higher frequency means that the absorption (attenuation) of the signal in daytime by the D-layer is much higher than at 136kHz. The result is that the first

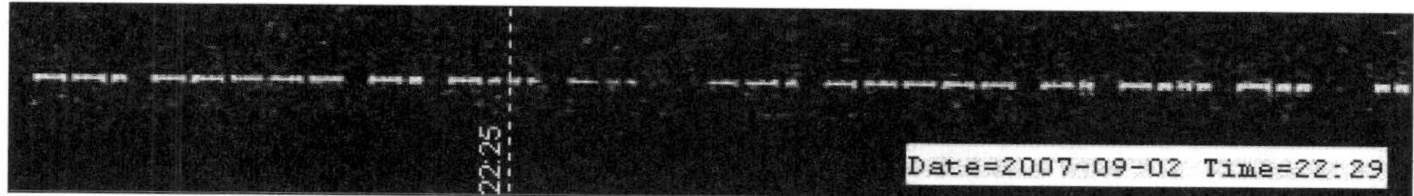

Fading on 500kHz is illustrated by this ten minute section of G0NBD's QRSS3 transmission received over a path of a few hundred kilometres by Hartmut Wolff in Germany

contacts on this band in daytime have only been possible at short ranges. However it must be remembered that this occurred during the bottom of the Solar Minimum when daytime signals levels on 136kHz were much lower as well. We must wait to see if daytime ionospheric signals are possible when the solar flux increases as we progress towards the next Solar Maximum.

The relative abundance of stations with 500kHz permits in the south of England has also meant that a lot of the night-time contacts have also been at relatively short range,although longer than that achievable in daytime. The most noticeable characteristic on these signals has been fading which is deep and has quite a short period. The relatively short range (100 to 300km) means that the signal is entering the ionosphere at a relatively high angle, and the fading suggests that there are 'returns' from two distinct altitudes.

It might be though that the fading would be between the ground wave and the one-hop skywave, but the lack of a daytime path shows that these ranges are beyond the ground-wave reach at the powers currently allowed. It was initially though that this rapid fading would rule out the use of very narrow band techniques like QRSS, because the fading would destroy large chunks of the information. It turns out after some careful study of longer paths where QRSS becomes necessary for communication, that the fading is much shallower at ranges over 700km. It may be that when the 500kHz signal strikes the ionosphere at an angle nearer to grazing incidence, much more is returned, and less leaks through to be returned from a higher 'reflection level'. Certainly QRSS signals have been copied at ranges of over 1000km without identification problems. There is fading but it does not seem to be as catastrophic as was feared.

Longer ranges are undoubtedly possible, but a higher power allowance than the current 100mW ERP would be needed to take advantage of that. Some amateur stations in the USA with a 'commercial' FCC Part 5 permit sponsored by the ARRL, have been copied on QRSS in Europe.

What can we expect as we approach the next Solar Maximum? This is purely surmise but we can probably expect better daytime ranges as daytime skywave increases, but this may be accompanied by deep fading that we do not currently see at the Solar Minimum. Night-time conditions may not improve materially because increases in geomagnetic activity will lead to increased night-time signal absorption in the D-region after magnetic storms. Solar flares may produce both enhanced signals and also degraded signals depending upon the strength of the flares.

Continuous propagation monitoring is more difficult around 500kHz as surprisingly there are few usable or suitable propagation beacons, close to the allocation.

. . . and finally . . .

G3NYK's weekly forecast of LF propagation - part science, part experience, part rabbit's foot - can be found at [4].

References

[1] National Oceanic and Atmospheric Administration (NOAA). *http://sec.noaa.gov/*

[2] Colorado University Dst data: *http://lasp.colorado.edu/space_weather/dsttemerin/dsttemerin.html*

[3] Kyoto University Dst index page. *http://swdcwww.kugi.kyoto-u.ac.jp/dst_realtime/presentmonth/index.html*

[3] G3NYK's propagation forecast. *http://www.alan.melia.btinternet.co.uk/latest.htm*

9

Operating practice

In this chapter:

- □ Operating on 136kHz
- □ Operating on 500kHz
- □ Must I use Morse?
- □ QRSS and other special modes
- □ QRM and QRN
- □ Awards and activity

THE MAIN THING that differentiates the low frequency bands from most other amateur allocations is their tiny size. The 136kHz band is just 2.1kHz wide and the experimental slot just above 500kHz is almost as narrow at 3kHz. Although various modes are permitted in the UK, it is obvious that anyone using conventional SSB would be very unpopular.

The key to success is to listen first. Listening will give you an idea of what stations are available and when, what frequencies and modes are common and what conditions are like from day to day. Many operators appreciate reception reports, particularly from those new to low frequencies, so there is no need to

G3LDO's 136kHz station. The large box on the right is an ex-Decca system 1kW transmitter, with DDS driver, centre. Far right is the primary tuning and matching coil and variometer; the main loading coil is located outside the shack because of the high voltages involved. The transmitter is remotely controlled from a shack in the house where the main receiver (TS-850) is located

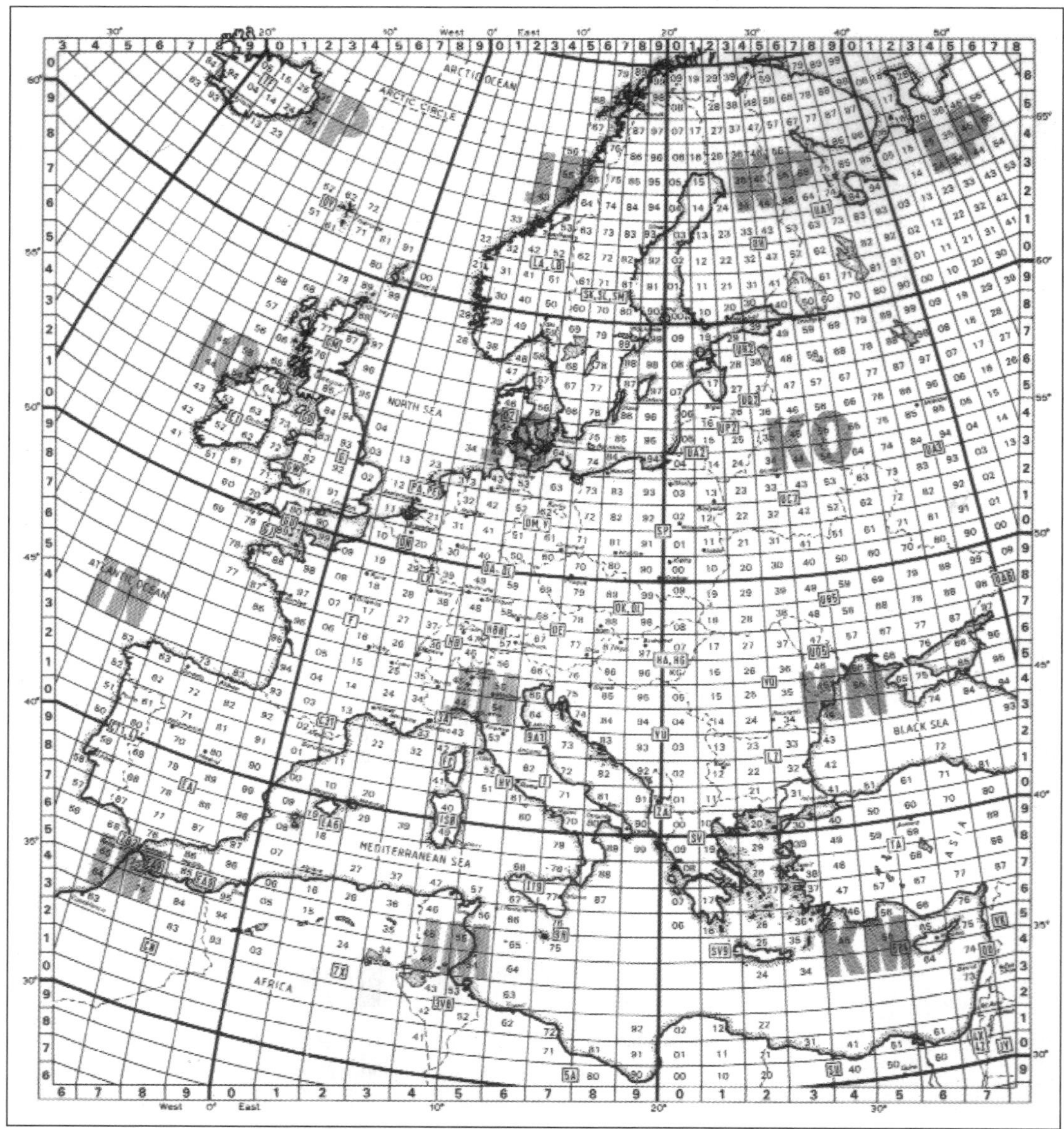

Fig 9.1: The IARU Locator system, known as 'loc' provides a useful way to abbreviate a town name as well as calculate distance

be in too much of a hurry to get transmitting. If you have access to e-mail, you can join the rsgb_lf_group and become part of the experimental community; see Appendix 1 for how to do this.

Because the experimental nature of the low frequency allocations, activity levels are lower than on HF. However, there is activity most evenings and every weekend. If no signals are heard, do not assume that there is no-one on the band. Often there are people monitoring for activity who will respond to a CQ call, even during the working day. Most operating is co-channel, that is both stations are on the same frequency. However, occasionally split frequency operation is used. It may be because one or both stations are crystal controlled, or to avoid reception of a DX station being swamped by locals. If you don't get a co-channel reply to a CQ call, it is normal to tune the band for any other callers; and on these narrow bands this doesn't take long! Cross-mode skeds, for example between CW and QRSS, should be set up with each station in the appropriate part of the band.

A CW contact exchange is very much the same as on the HF bands. This ranges from the 'rubber stamp' contact - often when signals are weak or between stations who do not share a common language - to the 'ragchew' which is just a normal conversation between two friends.

An exchange of information differs from that given at HF in the addition of a 'locator'. Like the bands above 30MHz, distance is important on low frequencies, so the IARU Locator (usually called 'Loc' or QRA) is often sent during the first contact between stations or in beacon transmissions. If you are unfamiliar with this grid system, shown in **Fig 9.1**, or need to work out your own locator, full details can be found in the RSGB Yearbook [1]. Alternatively, a web site containing a calculator that will convert latitude and longitude into a locator and even calculate the distance between you and the station you worked, is at [2].

Operating on 136kHz

Narrowband modes, such as CW, are popular on the 136kHz band, as are machine-read transmissions such as QRSS, PSK31 and data modes especially developed for LF work.

Almost all European countries (including all of Russia) now have an allocation at 136kHz, most with a 1W ERP power limit, and several UK operators have had two-way contacts with over 20 countries. Some special experimental licences have also been issued in Canada, the USA and New Zealand. Amateur LF transmissions have been received by enthusiasts in many parts of the world.

Random QSO activity is mainly at weekends and evenings. Listen around 136.65kHz for CW or watch for QRSS3 around 137.7kHz. As with the other amateur bands, 136kHz has a voluntary bandplan that separates incompatible modes and gives an idea of where to look for contacts on each mode. **Table 9.1**

Table 9.1: Bandplan for the 136kHz band

No rigid bandplan is proposed for the 136kHz band, but amateurs are asked to work within the following conventions, giving long distance communications and experimentation priority.

135.7 - 136.0	**Station tests and transatlantic reception window.** {135.900 - 135.980kHz preferred transatlantic window for Europe to North America transmissions of very slow telegraphy (QRSS) - *but see note below*}
136.0 - 137.4	**Telegraphy (CW)** {135.980 - 136.050 preferred transatlantic window for Europe/North America contacts.}. *NOTE: Due to local interference, at the time of writing the Europe to North America QRSS window is around 136.3kHz*
137.4 - 137.6	**Non-Telegraphy** digital modes.
137.6 - 137.8	**Very slow telegraphy (QRSS) centered on 137.7kHz.** {137.700–137.800 preferred transatlantic window for North America to Europe transmissions.}

shows how the band is divided into modes as well as certain specialist activities. Adhering to the bandplan gives the best likelihood of successful contacts and minimises the risk of causing interference to other stations. Having said that, interference from strong utility stations inside or close to the band may cause centres of activity - particularly for DX working - to be moved (see, for instance, the Note in Table 9.1). It can be seen that normal CW is in the centre of the band, data and experimental modes towards the top and very slow CW (QRSS) right at the top. The bottom extremity is used for testing. DX working is often split-frequency to enable intercontinental contacts where local transmissions would cause undue interference to the extremely weak DX signals. Formal beacons are frowned upon as the band is really too narrow, but from time to time individuals make beacon transmissions for specific purposes, such as intercontinental tests or demonstrating experimental modes.

Operating on 500kHz

At the time of writing, NoVs permitting 500kHz operation have been issued by Ofcom to about 30 - 40 amateurs around the UK, with a power limit of 0.1W ERP. The UK 501 - 504kHz allocation is currently unique in allowing two-way contacts between amateur stations, although several experimental permits have been issued to European amateurs to transmit beacon-type signals, mostly in the range 505 - 506 kHz. In the USA, several 'Part 5' experimental licenses have been issued for operation in the vicinity of 500kHz [3].

With the currently existing low power limit on 500kHz, inter-UK contacts up to about 1000km have been achieved using conventional CW techniques under good propagation conditions. During daylight, propagation mainly via ground wave results in reliable signal levels at distances up to a few hundred kilometres over land, beyond which signal levels rapidly decrease. Therefore, daytime operating tends to be 'ragchewing' contacts with fairly local stations, although when the signal path is mostly over the sea, ranges of 600 - 700 km have regularly been achieved in full daylight. At night, sky-wave propagation greatly improves signal levels over longer paths, enabling DX operation. This is accompanied by deep fading that often results in strong signals fading into the noise every few minutes, returning a few minutes later. Under these conditions, CW contacts to any part of the UK are achievable with a well set-up station and a little patience.

Activity levels for random two-way contacts tend to peak at the weekends, or when some special event occurs, such as an expedition station operating from a

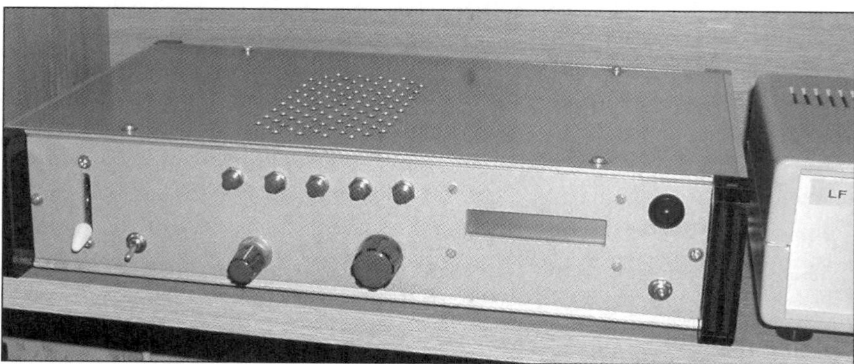

The synthesiser and driver for the OK0EMW beacon on 505.06kHz

Finbar O'Connor, EI0CF/GI4DPE, has given many people their first Irish contact

portable location. Often, stations will announce when they intend to be active on the RSGB LF reflector (see Appendix 1) which is the best source of such information.

No licences for permanent beacon operation at 500kHz have so far been issued in the UK. However, there are often 'personal' beacons in operation. These may be general tests, inviting signal reports from anyone hearing them, or specific experiments may be underway, for example trying to establish communications between two stations, or technical investigations, such as field strength measurements or tests of new communications modes. When they have been previously announced on the LF Reflector, these beacons are useful for newcomers in that a steady signal is provided for a considerable period of time, allowing a receiving set-up to be optimised, different antennas tried, etc. Most beacon transmissions are either in CW mode, or use the QRSS or DFCW narrow-band modes (see elsewhere in this chapter) with CW identifiers periodically inserted.

As well as UK stations, beacon signals are regularly received from Europe; currently there are several beacons frequently operating from Germany (callsigns in the DI2xx series), plus Sweden (SM6BHZ) and Czech Republic (OK0EMW), all within the frequency range 505.0 - 505.2kHz. Activity of these beacons is also often announced on the RSGB LF Reflector. There has also been occasional trans-Atlantic reception of US experimental stations (WD2Xxx series callsigns) in their 505 - 510 kHz allocation.

No formal band plan currently exists for 500kHz, however the informal convention is that two-way contacts take place around a 502kHz 'calling frequency', while beacon and experimental transmissions mainly occur between 503kHz and 504kHz. Obviously one should avoid making long-duration test transmissions around 502kHz, a point that should be considered if a crystal-controlled transmitter is contemplated.

CW is the most widely used mode, being the simplest to implement and adequate for most inter-UK contacts, however a number of stations are experimenting with narrow-band data modes such as PSK31 and narrow-shift RTTY. As on 136kHz, modes requiring a bandwidth greater than about 200Hz are not practical due to the narrow width of the allocation. The extremely narrow-band 'visual' QRSS and DFCW modes are widely used for beacon transmissions due to their weak-signal capability, and the capability to monitor several signals simultaneously using PC 'spectrogram' software (see later). Unlike 136kHz, these modes have not yet been widely used for two-way contacts, most operators preferring CW. However, QRSS and DFCW would be a simple way for operators using very inefficient antennas to enhance the capability of their 500kHz station.

Must I use Morse?

For 'ragchewing' on both bands, and contacts around Europe on 136kHz, the predominant mode is CW, usually at 12WPM or so. Very few operators send fast Morse, even if signals are strong, because there is always a chance that others are listening at a great distance. This makes low frequencies a good place to practise your Morse.

However, there are other modes that do not require proficiency in Morse code and are designed to be machine-read, or at least displayed on a computer screen.

One of these is QRSS which actually uses Morse but at such a very slow speed that any received characters could be looked up in a table by the receiving station. More on this popular DX mode later.

Others include PSK (such as PSK31, or a low bandwidth variant known as PSK08), 'Hell' and modes developed specifically for LF work such as Jason and Wolf. These are dealt with in detail below and in the chapter on Advanced Techniques.

QRSS and other special modes

When UK amateurs first started operating at LF, on the now defunct 73kHz band, it quickly became apparent that there were severe limits on the range of CW, especially for those whose small gardens obliged them to run extremely low radiated power.

Since the signal level could not be improved, noise was seen as the limiting factor. Noise is directly proportional to bandwidth so ways were sought to reduce the bandwidth by a significant amount, well below that required for normal CW, whilst still retaining the ability to transmit information.

In 1997, Peter Martinez, G3PLX, built a system that would display on a computer screen the processed audio output from his 73kHz receiver. The system used a hardware digital signal processing (DSP) unit together with Fast Fourier Transform (FFT) performed in software by his computer.

The screen showed the level of signal plus noise in a bandwidth of just 0.025Hz (yes, 25 millihertz!). When just noise was being received, the screen showed apparently random dots, but whilst a signal was present a line appeared. This enabled the reception of G4JNT's callsign in Morse over the previously unheard of distance of 393km. The transmission power was just one milliwatt ERP and the signal was completely inaudible at the receive end.

So far, so good, but the transmitted bandwidth of a Morse signal is directly proportional to the keying speed. So what speed can be received in a bandwidth of 25mHz? It is just 0.15 words per minute (WPM), requiring dots 80 seconds long and dashes of 240s. In fact, "G3PLX de G4JNT" took all of three hours to

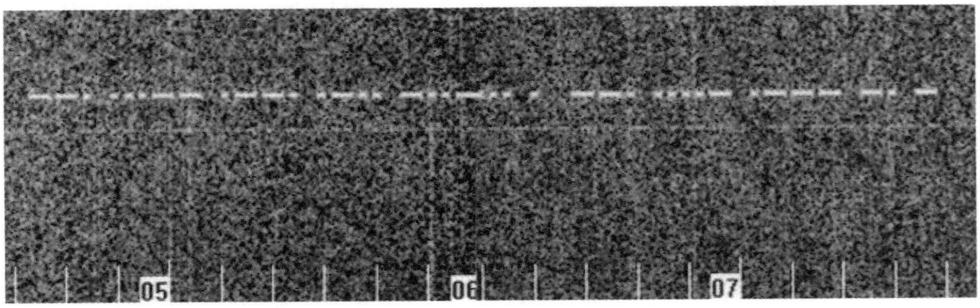

Reception of the first ever extremely slow CW amateur signals by G3PLX. It took nearly three hours to send, but G4JNT's 1mW ERP 73kHz signal travelled 400km to set a new distance record

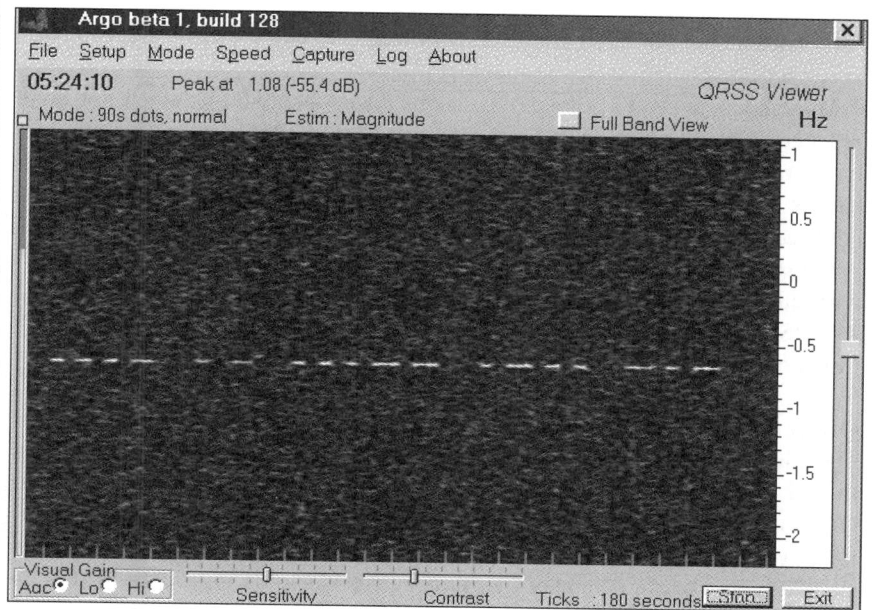

VA3LK received by CT1DRP using the Argo software set to receive a dot period of two minutes. Note that to reduce transmission time, the dashes are just two dot-lengths

send. Plainly, this type of transmission is not for decoding by ear, nor is there much time for ragchewing. **Table 9.2** shows the relationship between speed, bandwidth and signal to noise ratio (SNR).

Some time after this record-breaking test, it was found that freely available software originally written to analyse birdsong could perform a similar function to G3PLX's microprocessor, but using software in association with the computer's soundcard. The program was called Spectrogram and although this method was nowhere near as sophisticated as the PLX original, it was much easier to implement. Spectrogram was used to receive DA0LF's experimental 136kHz transmissions - the first signals heard from outside the UK.

Nowadays, several amateurs have produced soundcard software specifically for LF use, including Argo, EasyGram, Spectran and SpecLab. These are capable of displaying Morse with dot lengths from less than one second to over 100 seconds. Some also provide audio filters and facilities to decode other types of transmission. Further information on this software can be found in Appendix 2.

Table 9.2: Effect of reducing transmission speed

Speed (mode)	Optimum bandwidth (Hz)	SNR vs 12WPM (dB)
12WPM (CW)	10	0
8WPM (CW)	6.67	+1.8
4WPM (CW)	3.33	+4.8
1 sec/dot (QRSS1)	1	+10
3 sec/dot (QRSS3)	0.33	+14.8
10 sec/dot (QRSS10)	0.1	+20
60 sec/dot (QRSS60)	0.0165	+27.8
120 sec/dot (QRSS120)	0.008	+30.8

It is not the aim of this book to go into technical detail on this subject, but a very useful explanation can be found at [4].

Three hours to send a couple of callsigns may not sound like much fun, so in practice a dot length of three seconds is the default QRSS mode. This allows a basic 'rubber-stamp' two-way contact to take place in about half an hour. Slower speeds are used, but usually only for intercontinental DX (see chapter on advanced techniques).

Why "QRSS"? Well, the name came about because "extremely slow CW" was rather cumbersome. QRS is used in amateur radio to mean "slow Morse", so QRSS is "very slow Morse", using the Q-code grammar adopted when QRP (low power) was extended to make QRPP (very low power).

QRSS techniques

The advice to listen first is even more important with QRSS than other modes. In fact, it is look first, as QRSS is a visual mode. The centre of activity for QRSS3 (three second dot length) is 137.700kHz and the screen will display stations within 30-40Hz of this frequency. You may hear local QRSS transmissions, especially on a Sunday morning, recognisable as three-second dots or nine-second dashes. They are even readable by ear if you have a stop-watch, but it's not recommended.

To receive QRSS you will need a PC-type computer with a soundcard. An earlier Pentium PC will work, but the more sophisticated programs may require a more modern, faster machine. Next, download the software. Argo is recommended to the beginner as it is the simplest to use. See Appendix 2 for more details.

Connect the audio output of your LF receiver to the input of the computer's sound card. The receiver output should preferably be at a fixed level; many receivers provide such an output. Failing this, the headphones output will do, but it will be necessary to keep the volume control at a constant setting. The sound card often has two inputs: line and microphone. Choose the one that gives the best result - the microphone input is likely to be the more sensitive.

Run the Argo program and a scrolling display should appear. Signal strength is shown by brightness, and frequency by position on the screen. It is not the intention of this book to provide a detailed instruction manual for the software - they all have Help files - just play with the controls until you have the hang of it. Note that QRSS3 (three-second dots) should be selected for most applica-

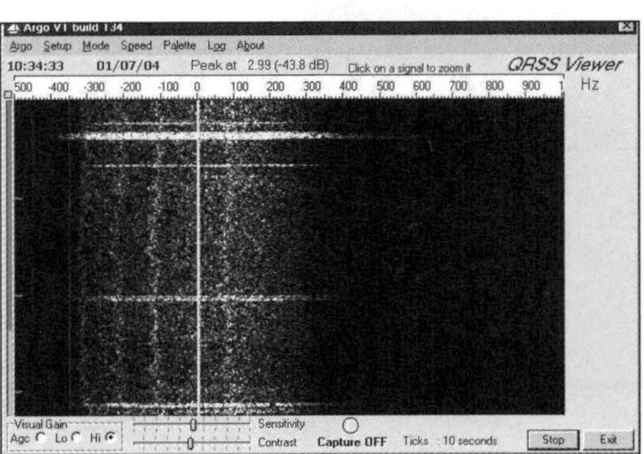

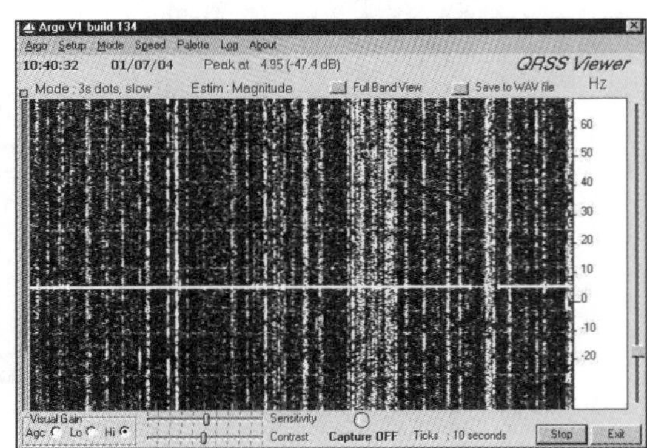

Fig 9.2: Two types of display on Argo: the vertical 'waterfall' (left) and the horizontal QRSS screen. The solid line is a constant carrier and the lines at 90 degrees to it are static crashes.

tions. If nothing is seen on the Argo screen, check the audio connections and if necessary switch the receiver to a strong signal such as the BBC on 198kHz. Note that the correct sound card audio input may first have to be enabled via the Windows "Volume Control" accessory, in order for the receiver output to be displayed. It is also advisable to disable any unused audio inputs. Volume Control can be accessed by right clicking with the mouse on the Windows task bar loudspeaker icon, and selecting "recording devices" or similar.

Once set up, the screen should look like **Fig 9.2**. On the left is a 'waterfall', scrolling vertically. The vertical line is a constant carrier; the horizontal lines are static crashes. The screen is 1.5kHz wide so it can be used to monitor most of the band, though the picture shows the effect of a 500Hz IF filter.

The right hand picture shows the QRSS horizontal display monitoring the same carrier. The static crashes are now vertical and the total height of the screen is about 100Hz. This display is used for decoding the QRSS signals that will appear as dots and dashes horizontally across the screen. The resultant Morse code is deciphered by eye. There is no hurry as even QRSS3 takes about three minutes to display a callsign.

For best reception, the software and audio levels should be set so that noise forms a dim background on the screen. It is likely that Loran-C sidebands (see later) will also be present - they can be seen as the faint horizontal lines in the right hand picture.

QRSS signals at different dot lengths can be received simultaneously but best reception is when the receive software is set to the correct speed. If the receiver is set too fast (wider bandwidth) the signal to noise ratio will be poorer and the Morse will appear 'wide' on the screen. If it is set too slow (narrower bandwidth), the signal will be blurred, often running the dots and dashes together to make it unreadable. It is possible to save to disk an image of the screen, either by clicking on a button or automatically at regular intervals. Distant stations will appreciate being e-mailed a screen shot of their signals.

Having seen and successfully decoded some QRSS signals, it is now time to try transmitting. Because of the long transmissions, it may be necessary to make sure the transmitter cooling is adequate. Also, this is the mode that will really test whether the antenna and tuning components are going to flash over. Be vigilant during your first few QRSS transmissions.

Various methods of slow keying have been used: hand key and stop watch; modified memory keyer; even a rotating disk. The most straightforward, and most popular, is to use software and a small interface (such as the one shown in **Fig 9.3**)

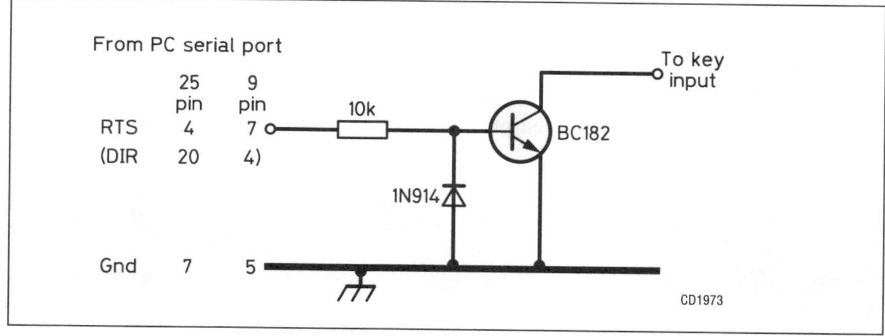

Fig 9.3: ON7YD's suggested simple interface for his *QRS* sending program. A capacitor could be added across the diode to decouple any RF

to connect to the PC's parallel or serial ports. ON7YD's QRS program is designed for all types of QRSS transmission and is freely available. The software is designed to run simultaneously with a spectrogram program on the same PC. More on this in Appendix 2.

Because of the time taken to send QRSS signals, a simplified QSO format has been devised. The 'de' between callsigns is not used and reports are in the form 'O' for perfectly readable, 'M' for readable with difficulty and 'T' for visible but not readable. Callsigns are rarely repeated and are abbreviated after the first full call. However, in common with standard amateur radio practice, a contact is only valid after a successful exchange of callsigns and reports and the final 'rogers'. A typical contact, lasting about 40 minutes in QRSS3, is shown below (the locator is optional and would be omitted if it is already known or in marginal contacts):

CQ ON7YD K
ON7YD G3XDV K
XDV YD O O JO20IX K
YD XDV R M M IO91VT K
YD R TU SK

If someone hears just the end of this contact and wishes to call one of the stations, he may not have seen the full callsign. An abbreviated call may be used provided full calls are sent and received at some time during the contact. For instance:

YD DL3LP K
DL3LP ON7YD O O K
ON7YD LP R O O K
LP YD R TU SK

Because this is still time consuming a mode has been devised to speed up the information transfer whilst still retaining the same bandwidth (and hence signal to noise ratio). DFCW (dual frequency CW) uses two closely spaced frequencies, the higher one for dots, the other for dashes, and can be received using exactly the same software and settings as QRSS. Dot/dash frequency spacing is not critical but is typically 12 divided by the dot length in seconds (eg for QRSS3 it is about 4Hz and for QRSS120, 0.1Hz). The time savings are made by making the dots and dashes the same length, and having only a very short gap between each dot or dash (**Fig 9.4**), resulting in up to 50% time improvement. In all other respects it is used in exactly the same way as QRSS, and cross-mode contacts are common.

If DFCW has these advantages, why is it not used universally? Well, its main disadvantage is the need to switch between two accurate frequencies. It can also be slightly harder to decipher by eye than simple QRSS under noisy conditions. Nevertheless, it has been successfully used for intercontinental transmissions where the reduction in transmission time has a distinct advantage (see the chapter on advanced techniques).

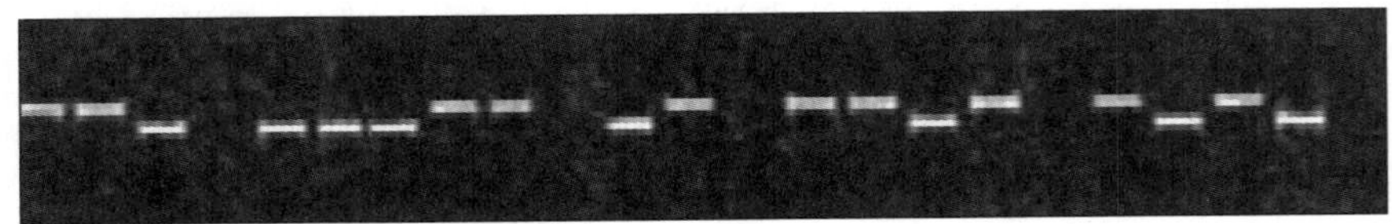

Fig 9.4: Dual-frequency CW (DFCW) uses the same length dots and dashes. Can you read this callsign? Tip: say 'dah' for each white bar on the top line and 'dit' for each on the bottom line

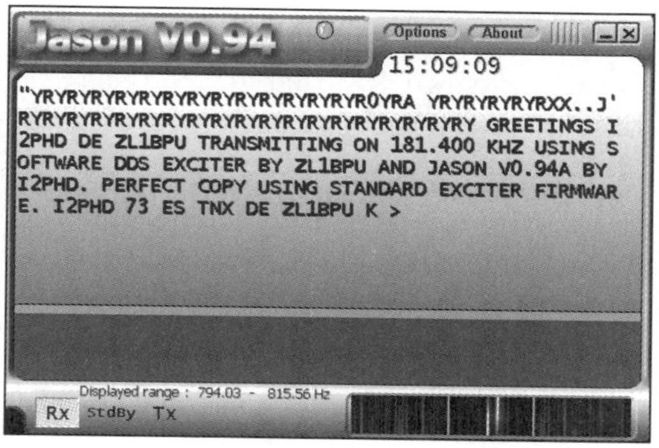

Jason is a slow keyboard to keyboard mode

QRSS vs CW

The sceptical reader may be wondering whether QRSS is worth the bother, or indeed whether it is 'real' amateur radio. These things have been debated for some years by low frequency operators.

The simple answer is that CW is ideal for contacts over a distance of a few hundred kilometres and for having 'conversations'. It is also simple to implement.

QRSS and DFCW give a dramatically increased signal to noise ratio and hence range - perhaps four times the distance with QRSS3 and up to ten times with longer dot lengths. It can be the only way to make regular DX contacts from a modest station. However, a PC is required and the simplest contact takes about half an hour. Little useful information can be exchanged other than: "I am receiving you. Can you receive me?". It can be a useful mode when you are doing other things, eg construction, because the hands-on time is minimal.

And is QRSS really amateur radio? Of course, but it is not everyone's cup of tea. In practice, most operators are capable of running CW and QRSS and use whatever mode is appropriate.

Jason

As an extension of the slow CW technique, the writers of Argo have created a data mode called Jason which uses multiple tones to transmit data at a rate of about 2.5 seconds per character. It is a keyboard to keyboard mode with a bandwidth of about 6Hz. The 'send' output is either tones for input to an SSB transmitter, or serial data for a DDS. Jason is capable of very good performance but can be susceptible to interference from Loran sidebands (see below). Further details can be found at [4 and 5] and the software is at [6]. One advantage of Jason is that it does not need a linear amplifier.

Modes requiring linear transmitters

CW, QRSS and DFCW can all take advantage of the efficient Class D/E power amplifiers such as those shown in a previous chapter. This makes it simpler to build a high power transmitter using these modes, making them popular. However, there are several data modes that have advantages in terms of speed or resistance to interference, but which need a linear transmitter. There is much more about these modes in the Advanced Techniques chapter.

QRM and QRN

After the inefficiency of practical antennas, the next limiting factor to LF success is noise on receive. This can take several forms, but they divide between man-made and natural noises, and again between local and distant. Some noise is unavoidable but others can be eliminated, or at least reduced to a tolerable level.

The 136kHz and 500kHz bands are subject to higher noise levels than amateur allocations at HF and above. Noise in this frequency range has a number of origins:

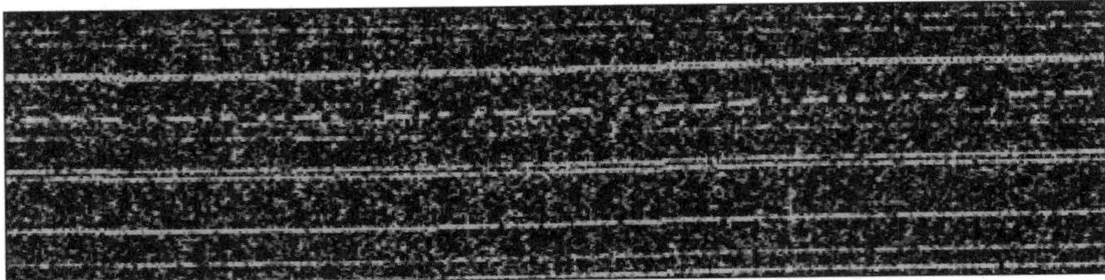

The solid lines are Loran sidebands. In between there is a weak QRSS transmission. Care must be taken to avoid selecting a QRSS transmit frequency that coincides with a Loran line

Natural band noise: Under quiet daytime band conditions, a low level background hiss is present at 136kHz and 500kHz, similar to the band noise in the HF range. But much of the time, the dominant natural noise source is a crackling static (QRN) produced by thunderstorms. In general, thunderstorm QRN levels are higher on 136kHz than 500kHz. QRN on both bands tends to be much stronger at night and during summer, but will also often be present during daytime on 136kHz and, if there is nearby thunderstorm activity, also on 500kHz. Usually it is not very effective to use a directional antenna to reduce QRN, because thunderstorm activity is normally present over wide areas, and the antenna only provides a deep null over a narrow range of angles. Receiver noise blankers have been used to reduce the effects of QRN, with rather mixed results.

Non-amateur signals: The 136kHz band is a secondary allocation, shared with other spectrum users. Sometimes utility signals are present within the band, and the sidebands of powerful utility signals operating near to the band edges are also partially within the band (see Chapter 1). A widespread source of interference in much of the UK, Europe and the northern hemisphere are the sidebands of the Loran C navigation beacon system [7]. Although these pulsed signals are nominally confined to a range of 90 - 110kHz, sufficient leakage occurs outside this range for the rhythmic chattering 'galloping horses' sound to be the dominant band noise at many locations. The radio spectrum around 500kHz has much lower occupancy, so is relatively free from these kinds of interference; however at some locations, significant interference close to 504kHz is caused by harmonics of long wave broadcast stations on 252kHz. These types of unwanted signal can be effectively suppressed using the directional nulls of a loop antenna, provided they are in a different direction to the wanted signal.

Local man-made QRM: In this frequency range, most local sources of QRM are associated with the mains wiring, and electrical or electronic appliances connected to it. Current European EMC regulations do not require testing of mains noise levels below 150kHz, and permit relatively high noise levels in the MF frequency range. It is usually found that appliances generate maximum mains noise levels in the LF/MF range. This sort of noise can propagate considerable distances along the mains wiring, via which it is coupled to the antenna. Other potential sources of local QRM are PCs, monitors and associated digital equipment, TV sets, telecomms equipment and associated cables. Local QRM can sometimes be eliminated by finding and removing the source of interference. If this is not possible, major improvements can often be achieved by using a separate receiving antenna positioned to minimise noise pick-up.

Identifying Local Interference sources

Many LF/MF operators are affected to some extent by local man-made QRM. A good first step in combating such interference is to identify likely sources from the nature of the noise being received. Many noise sources sound very similar when heard through a narrow CW filter, so try listening using SSB bandwidth; setting the receiver to 135.5kHz in USB mode, or 138.5kHz LSB will make the whole amateur band audible while excluding most utility station signals around the 136kHz band. Likewise, most of the 500kHz band can be heard with the receiver set to around 501kHz USB.

A rough 50Hz buzzing noise covering a wide bandwidth typically is due to harmonics of the mains frequency. These may be generated by rectifiers, triac dimmers, motor speed controls and various types of lighting, or by high voltage overhead lines. Almost any mains-powered device containing a rectifier or other electronics can produce this kind of noise.

Drifty carriers with rough 50Hz modulation sidebands, often spreading over several kilohertz, can be caused by switched-mode power supplies. The carriers occur at the switching frequency or harmonics, and the frequency varies with temperature and loading, so often these noise sources drift in and out of the band over time, and are subject to abrupt frequency shifts. Switch-mode power supplies are increasingly used in all sorts of mains-powered appliances, even small plug-in chargers for mobile phones, etc., and are also used in energy-saving compact fluorescent light-bulbs, so are common interference sources.

Noise-like 'hash' sounds, often with a distinctive 'note', can be generated by TV sets and video monitors, and many digital devices such as PCs and their peripherals, computer games and data networking equipment. Occasionally, if the receiver is very close to the noise generating device, noise can be directly induced in the receiver circuits, but connecting cables are more likely to be the source of coupling between noise source and receiver.

If the noise source is within your QTH, it can usually be switched off while operating, or perhaps be replaced by a less noisy substitute. Switching off likely appliances while monitoring the noise level can identify the source. Often, it will be necessary to unplug the appliance to eliminate the noise, since many appliances have a 'standby' mode in which they can generate noise even when not actually operating; it is not unusual for the noise level to be higher in standby than when operating. Switching the mains supply off at the consumer unit is the most certain way of determining if noise sources are inside the QTH; this obviously requires a battery-operated receiver, and be prepared to have to reset videos, alarms etc! If the noise is coming from your neighbour's house, some diplomacy is called for. Advice on tackling this sort of problem can be obtained from the RSGB [8, 9].

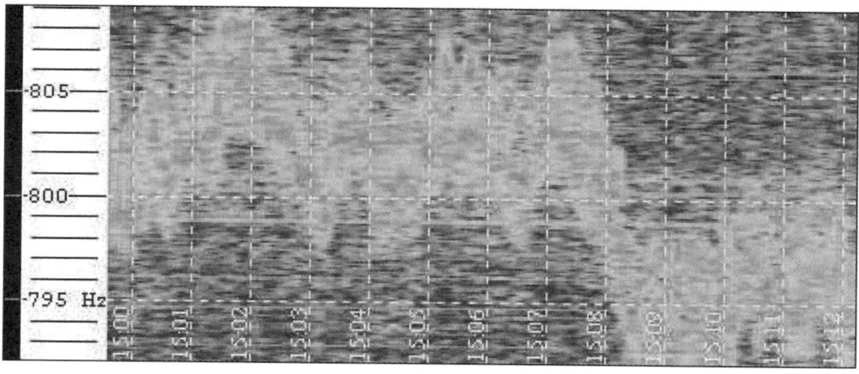

W3EEE's spectrogram of interfering noise - probably from a power supply

RSGB 136kHz Award

The award is available in three categories, with endorsements for additional countries heard/worked.

The basic award is for confirmed two-way QSOs on 136kHz with 5 countries from the ARRL DXCC/WAE country list.

The SWL Award is for confirmation of SWL reports from 5 countries. The SWL award may also be claimed by amateurs working cross band to stations transmitting in the 136kHz band.

The third category is for cross band contacts, where the stations claiming the award has worked 5 countries by transmitting on the 136kHz band and receiving stations on other amateur bands.

Cross mode contacts will be allowed for this award. The categories of this award may not be mixed, but awards from some or all of the categories may be claimed and endorsed concurrently.

Once the basic award has been claimed, it may be endorsed in steps of each additional 5 countries worked or heard.

(Full details are available from the RSGB Spectrum Committee [10])

Awards and activity

There are a few awards available for LF operation. The RSGB's 136kHz award is for two-way contacts with five DXCC entities (countries). The RSGB and AMRAD sponsor an award in connection with transatlantic tests and in memory of LF pioneer Peter Bobek, DJ8WL/DA0LF. Each year, the RSGB awards the LF Experimenters Cup to the person who has contributed most to LF work during the year. In recent years, this cup has been sponsored by Nevada Communications. There are no contests on 136kHz - it is really too small.

A major boost to activity is the presence of an expedition or special event station. From time to time, someone will activate a rare country, erect an LF antenna on a decommissioned commercial (large) mast, or simply take their gear on holiday. These events are usually announced on the LF reflector (see Appendix 1), or on G3YXM's web site [11].

In the absence of a special reason for switching on your LF equipment, try putting out a CQ call regularly each weekend; you'll find that activity breeds activity.

References

[1] *RSGB Yearbook*, published annually by the RSGB.

[2] Calculator for locators. *http://www.qsl.net/dl3bak/qrb/en/frame.htm*

[3] ARRL 600 Meter Experimental Group. *http://www.500kc.com/*

[4] ON7YD on QRSS. *http://www.qsl.net/on7yd/136narro.htm*

[5] G3YXM on Jason. *http://www.wireless.org.uk/jason.htm*

[6] Jason software download. *http://www.qsl.net/padan/jason/*

[7] Loran-C: *http://en.wikipedia.org/wiki/LORAN*

[8] RSGB EMC Committee. Contact the RSGB on 0870 904 7373.

[9] *The RSGB Guide to EMC*. RSGB.

[10] RSGB Spectrum Committee. Contact the RSGB on 0870 904 7373.

[11] G3YXM's LF News pages: *http://www.wireless.org.uk/*

10

Advanced techniques

In this chapter:

- Noise Cancelling
- Remote screen 'grabbers'
- DX working
- Frequency stability and calibration
- Operating away from home
- Modes requiring a linear transmitter

ONE OF THE FUN things about low frequencies is that it is possible to improve your station gradually, gaining a quarter of a decibel here and half a decibel there by making your transmitter, antenna and earth system more efficient. But, having got an efficient station, where can you go from there?

Noise cancelling

There is an old adage: "If you can't hear 'em, you can't work 'em." This is as true at LF as on any other band. The limiting factor is often the background noise level which divides into atmospheric noise and local noise. This is dealt with in some detail in the chapter on operating.

A simple way to reduce the effects of noise is to use a directional receiving antenna, such as a loop, to introduce a 'null' in the direction of the noise. Loops are described in the chapter on receive antennas.

A more subtle way is to combine the signal from your main antenna with that from an antenna orientated to receive maximum noise, in such a way as to cancel out the noise. This is particularly effective in nulling out the effects of a strong local noise source that might otherwise have put you off the air.

This form of noise cancelling depends on being able to provide two receiving antennas, with different relative levels (or different phase relationships) between wanted signals and noise. It can work very well when the noise comes predominantly from a single source, but will usually not be effective when there are multiple noise sources.

G3GRO's noise canceller

The basic 136kHz canceller has only five passive components – see **Fig 10.1**. The signal from the omnidirectional wire antenna feeds an adjustable phase shifter with the output from the phase shifter being simply fed directly in parallel with the input from a loop antenna via an isolating variable resistor RV2.

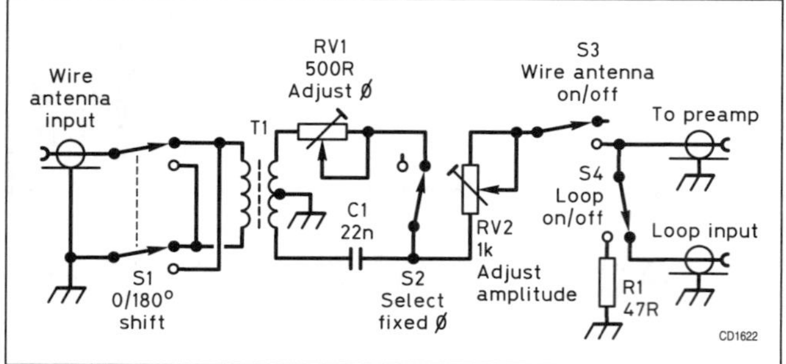

Fig 10.1: Noise canceller. RV1 and RV2 are linear Cermet or carbon. T1 is a trifilar wound toroid three times 18 turns of 28 or 32SWG on a ferrite core (13.25mm diameter Philips C85 material or Fairite FT-50-43, or similar)

This control adjusts the amount of omni-derived signal being combined with that from the loop. A change-over switch S1 at the input allows a 180° phase shift to be added to that of the phase shifter. Capacitor C1 and variable resistor RV1, together with the trifilar-wound transformer, form a variable phase shifter with a range of approximately 180° and reasonably constant amplitude over its control range. The variable phase control RV1 does not quite reach 0° at one end of its travel and so switch S2 is provided which allows a fixed selection of the 0° position.

This simple signal combiner arrangement is based on the premise that the signal from the large omnidirectional antenna will normally be much larger than that from the loop and thus allows the omni signal to be fed simply in parallel with the loop output from the phase shifter via a reasonably high value of resistance in RV2 without adversely affecting the loop signal level. Adjusting RV2 in conjunction with phase control RV1 allows the unwanted signal to be nulled out. It is also useful to be able to switch off the omni or loop inputs individually via S3/S4.

Most general-coverage receivers tend to be somewhat short of gain at LF and although the signal from the main LF antenna is usually adequate, a loop antenna – even a relatively large one – may need some additional gain in order to provide sufficient signal level from the interference source to allow cancellation to be effective. A suitable preamplifier (**Fig 10.2**) has two stages of amplification and is preceded by a band-pass filter. An alternative amplifier can be found in the receivers chapter.

The –3dB bandwidth of the input bandpass filter can be adjusted to approximately 3.5kHz by means of the small top-coupling trimmer capacitor VC1 between coil L1 and L2 to give a flat top response or slightly over-coupled double-hump response, after first peaking the cores of L1/L2 with loose coupling. Diodes D1/D2 at the input protect against unwanted transmitter power.

Switch S5a/S5b is an optional facility that allows this filter to be replaced by a low-pass filter with a 3dB cut-off frequency of around 180kHz so that the preamp can be used from a few kilohertz up to above 200kHz for general LF use.

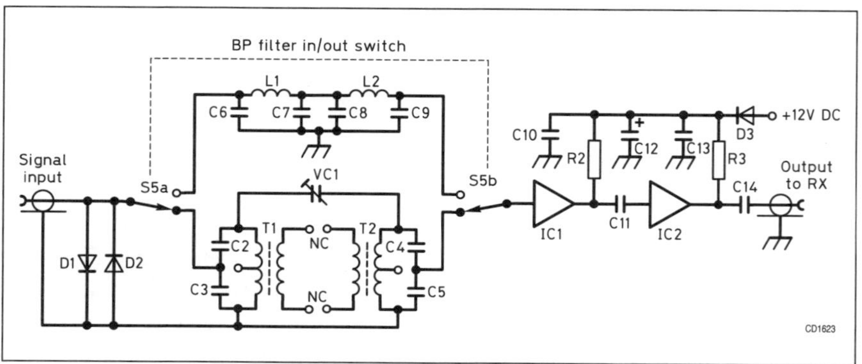

Fig 10.2: Receiver preamplifier. D1, D2, 1N4148; D3, 1N4001; S5, two-pole c/o; T1, T2, Toko 3.5mH CAN 1A350EK (red core); L1, L2, 68µH Toko 283RS-680; C2, C4, 330p; C3, C5, 4n7; C5–C9, 22n; C18, C11, C13, C14, 100n; C12, 47µ electrolytic, R2, R3, 220R; IC1, IC2, MAR3 (see application note for full circuit details)

If the preamp is to be used only for 136kHz then components S5a, S5b, C7, C8, C9, C10 L1 and L2 can be omitted.

Two MAR3 Minicircuits ModAmps are used in series, each having a gain of 12dB and a –1dB saturation point of +10dBm together with a good noise figure. They also have a nominal input impedance of 50 ohms. The choice of two MAR3 gain-blocks, rather than a single MAR6 with a similar total gain, is dictated by the better signal-handling capability of the MAR3.

A strong carrier can be nulled by typically 30dB but the phase and amplitude controls then become quite critical to achieve that depth of null. If the aim is to use the canceller on very strong carriers etc, it may be beneficial to split the amplitude adjustment RV2 into separate coarse and fine controls. Avoid wire-wound potentiometers.

The omnidirectional input to the canceller system is normally the transmitting antenna fed to the canceller system via the transmit-receive switching relay. The loop antenna can be any type, including those in the chapter on receive antenna

Remote screen 'grabbers'

Using 'visual' modes such as QRSS and DFCW, a large number of signals can be monitored simultaneously, provided they fall within the bandwidth of the spectrogram display and the receiver filters. This, combined with continuously-on broadband internet connections has led several LF/MF amateurs to implement 'screen grabbers', where the spectrogram display is periodically uploaded to a web page, typically once every few minutes. Screen grabbers are useful for many purposes - monitoring band activity, finding out how well your own transmitted signal is 'getting out' and monitoring DX propagation are some examples. Since receivers and antennas will be required for other purposes sometimes, most screen grabbers are not permanently operating, but are activated on request, or when there is interesting activity scheduled to occur. The displayed bandwidth, and rate of screen updates, is varied to suit the transmission modes expected. Up-to date information on operational screen grabbers can be obtained via the RSGB LF Group e-mail reflector (see Appendix

G3YXM (*http://www.wireless.org.uk/grab/*): QTH Birmingham, a good indicator of signals detectable in the UK on 136kHz and 500kHz.

W3EEE (*http://www.hifidelity.com/w3eee/dc_graph.html*): Long-term monitoring of received level of DCF39, as a trans-Atlantic propagation indicator.

GM4SLV (*http://www.sighthound.demon.co.uk/pshed/gm4slv_speclab.jpg*): QTH Shetland islands, displaying signals received on 500kHz at the most northerly point of the UK.

KL1X (*http://www.kl1x.com/*): 136kHz and 500kHz band monitoring from locations in the Far East including China and Singapore.

DF6NM (*http://members.aol.com/df6nm/Grabber.htm*): Directional spectrograms, showing strength and direction of signals received in central Europe.

Table 10.1: Selection of screen grabbers on 136kHz and 500kHz

1), or on individual operator's web sites. Some well-known screen grabbers are shown in **Table 10.1**.

DX working

Since there is no international allocation at 500kHz, long distance work has been limited to a maximum of about 1000km within the UK. An exception is US stations receiving AM broadcasters and Europeans receiving US Part 5 stations (see the operating chapter).

On the 136kHz band, day to day contacts at LF are restricted to 1000-1500km, but by using sophisticated techniques and a well-engineered station it is possible to be received at distances of 6000km or even more. The use of the word 'received' was deliberate as there are few transmitting amateurs outside Europe. Nevertheless, there are many in the USA and elsewhere who are equipped to receive on LF and are prepared to monitor for 136kHz transmissions. There have been two-way contacts between western Europe and specially licensed Canadian stations and also with an expedition in Asiatic Russia, as well as transpacific DX, so two-way DX contacts are indeed possible. But until US and Canadian stations have general permission to transmit, most activity concentrates on one-way DX.

Intercontinental contacts are beyond the range of ground-wave so all propagation is via the ionosphere (see propagation chapter). Unfortunately, with the power levels available to amateurs - a maximum of one watt ERP in most cases - the day-to-day sky wave will not support propagation of amateur-level signals beyond 2000km or so. So how is it achieved? Well, as with much amateur radio communication, we wait for enhanced conditions and try to be on the air when they occur.

LF conditions for the necessary multi-hop path vary according to solar activity and darkness levels over the length of the path. Signal levels can vary considerably from day to day and from hour to hour as shown by the graphs on this page from W3EEE [1]. For anyone but the best-equipped stations to stand a

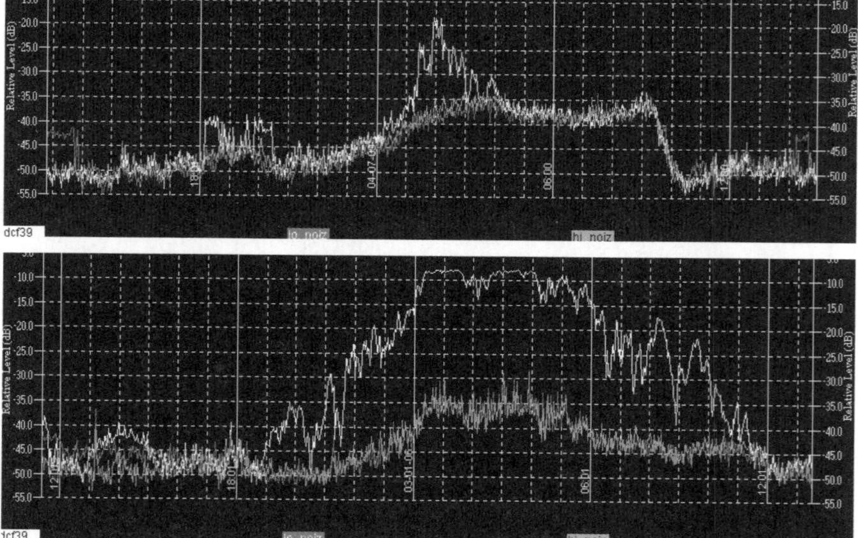

W3EEE's real time plot of the German commercial station DCF39 as received at his Pennsylvania site. The fat line is the background noise level - note that the ionosphere propagates noise, too. The thin line above it is DCF39. The top graph shows a typical day with a short peak between 0130 and 0300UTC. The lower graph shows one of the best ever periods of transatlantic propagation with excellent conditions between 0000 and 0600UTC

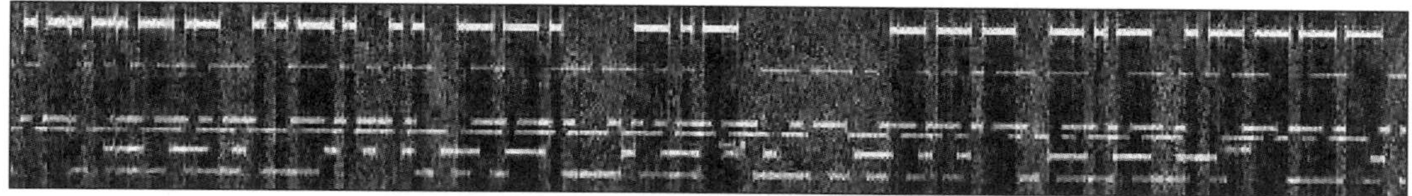

Six European stations attempting to cross the Atlantic using QRSS120. They are all packed into a space only 1Hz wide! The calls are (from the top): OK1FIG, G3XTZ, G3AQC, G3XDV, G3LDO and SM6LKM (pic by Dutch SWL NL9222)

chance of working DX, conditions must be close to the peak of W3EEE's 'best' graph. As can be seen, these last only a couple of hours on a good night and often much less.

So why is this a problem? In the operating chapter, it was established that the signal to noise ratio can be greatly improved by reducing the bandwidth. The downside of a reduced bandwidth is a slower rate of information transfer (Morse speed or data baud rate). In fact, in order to achieve ranges of 3000km or so it is necessary to use dot lengths of 30, 60 or 120 seconds, that is QRSS30, QRSS60 or QRSS120, with the slowest rate having the best chance of being visible. Using QRSS120, a callsign takes about two hours to send and it can be seen that, unless it starts exactly when the conditions start to peak it is unlikely that an entire call will be received. And that's just a single callsign; a two-way contact is much more of a problem - in fact, one of the few successful two-ways was spread over several nights in order to have enough total time to complete the contact.

So the difficulty with DX communication at 136kHz is the time period of the good conditions versus the speed necessary to get an adequate signal to noise ratio. Four strategies have been devised to try to overcome this problem.

Firstly, it is important to be aware of when propagation conditions are likely to be good - or more likely when conditions will be so poor it isn't worth bothering. G3NYK [2] posts propagation forecasts from time to time on the rsgb_lf_group, but it is possible to get an idea of conditions from checking the solar data (see the chapter on propagation).

Next, screen grabbers as described above can be used to check conditions in real-time, either on the 136kHz band or W3EEE's DCF39 monitor.

Listening on 137.000kHz may reveal the Canadian naval station CFH which runs 20kW of teletype. CFH is often off the air so its absence is not a useful guide, but if it is 'S'9 in Europe conditions can be expected to be suitable for amateur DX.

Dual frequency CW (DFCW - see the operating chapter) can be used to reduce the transmission time without reducing the signal to noise ratio. Because DFCW occupies a wider frequency 'slot' than QRSS, more care than usual must be taken to avoid clashing with other operators.

Lastly, a mode such as WOLF (Weak signal Operation on Low Frequency) makes full use of the relatively short periods of very good propagation. WOLF is described elsewhere in this chapter.

Split frequency is almost always used for intercontinental DX working. Europeans use a slot close to 136.32kHz, the actual frequency being agreed in advance depending on noise levels at the receive end. North Americans (at the time of writing Canadian LF amateur licences have been discontinued and US stations are limited to those with 'Part 5' experimental licences with callsigns in the WD2Xxx series) use a slot around 137.770kHz. Although this is close to the frequency used for inter-Europe contacts, these do not take place during the small hours of the morning when the Atlantic path is in darkness, so there is no clash. Because an Argo screen is just 3Hz wide when receiving QRSS60 and half of this for QRSS120, all stations must operate within a 1Hz wide channel (see picture above). Frequency coordination is often carried out on the rsgb_lf_group e-mail reflector to avoid clashes.

Most DX activity is well publicised and most of the two-way contacts have been scheduled, although it is possible to have a random QSO. The exchange of information is kept to the absolute minimum of callsign, report and roger.

Frequency stability and calibration

In order to receive stations using QRSS at the slower speeds, such as QRSS30, QRSS60, QRSS120, it is necessary to have a very stable radio. Fortunately, most modern receivers are good enough. However, a means must be found to ensure that the Argo (or similar) screen is looking at the precise frequency you want. Remember that Argo is monitoring an audio frequency from your radio. Fortunately, there are fairly simple ways of doing this without expensive test gear.

Firstly, current versions of Argo and Spectrum Lab have built-in utilities to facilitate calibration of sound-card frequency errors. The resulting calibration factors are then used to automatically correct the spectrogram frequency scales. This should be done before the steps shown below.

Secondly the LF spectrum is used for some highly accurate transmissions such as the time-standard GBR at Rugby on 60kHz and BBC Radio 2 at Daventry on 198kHz. Other standards are available in the USA and elsewhere.

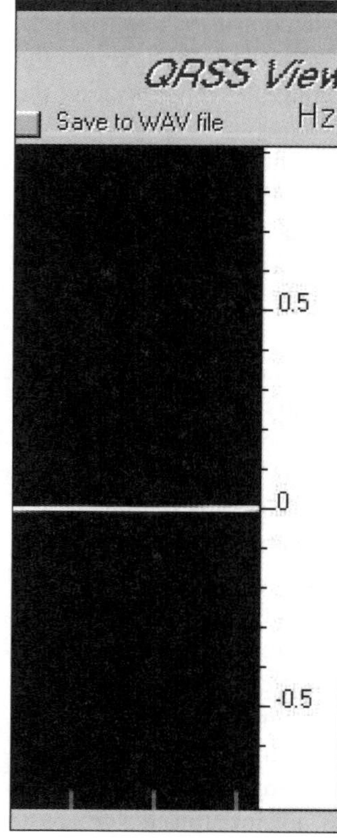

Detail of Argo screen showing the result of calibrating for frequency resolution of better than 0.1Hz

The calibration method is as follows. First tune your LF receiver to one of these stations with the radio's frequency readout displaying the exact frequency, eg 198.000kHz. Set Argo to CW and find the station on the Argo screen - it will appear as a thick horizontal line. Note the audio frequency displayed by Argo. Reduce the receiver's RF gain so that the Argo displays a thin line. Set Argo to QRSS3 and adjust its audio centre frequency to that noted in the previous step. Reduce the receiver gain and alter the Argo frequency until the station displays a thin horizontal line in the centre of the screen. Next, set Argo to QRSS10 and repeat these steps, gradually reducing the Argo speed until you reach the desired dot length. This can take a while as the Argo display slows down considerably at the longer dot lengths. Once the commercial station is drawing a thin line in the centre of the QRSS120 (or whatever) screen, use the calibration facility in Argo (from the set up menu) to set the audio frequency display to zero. Calibration can be fiddly, but is worthwhile. Now you know that the frequency displayed on your receiver equates to the zero on the screen. A signal that appears 0.1Hz above the zero line will be 0.1Hz higher than the displayed frequency; the combination of the receiver and Argo has given you a much more accurate frequency display than the receiver alone. Now set your receiver so that it displays the frequency you want to monitor on the 136kHz band, turn up the gain and you are ready to receive. Note that instead of zero, Argo can display a frequency that ties in with the wanted frequency in the 136kHz band, eg display 989.0 for 136.989kHz. The calibration can be checked at any time by switching your receiver to 198.000kHz and turning the gain down. Note that the above method assumes the receiver is switched to USB.

Note that calibrating the receiver at a frequency that is significantly different from the amateur band frequency of interest may result in a significant error if both the receiver and sound card are subject to relatively large errors. Fortunately, most recent sound cards are reasonably accurate, so large errors using this method are unlikely. Errors of this sort will be minimised by using an off-air calibration signal close to the desired receive frequency, eg the DCF39 "carrier" on 138.830kHz, which has adequate precision to calibrate the receiver to within about 0.1Hz.

Another source of error that cannot readily be eliminated by this calibration method arises due to the use of DDS synthesisers in most modern amateur rigs. The DDS tuning steps do not normally coincide with exact integer numbers of hertz, and the control software in the rig has to calculate the DDS setting that will give the nearest frequency to that set on the display, which in general will not be exactly the same. Fortunately, these "built-in" errors are likely to be only a small fraction of a hertz.

Operating away from home

Many stations have conducted expeditions using LF. Some have shacks set up at alternative locations, others have operated out of doors, whilst a few have had the privilege of a few hours use of a massive commercial mast. In all cases, the effort involved has been worthwhile in terms of the fun of overcoming difficulties and in terms of the activity it has generated from other band users anxious for a contact.

By far the easiest of these is the permanently set up alternative shack, although of course establishing it in the first place entails all of the problems of any LF installation. This includes getting a good earth connection, erecting or locating high antenna supports and tuning the system.

Outdoor LF activity is great fun, although quite difficult. Your transmitter must be capable of running from a car battery (keep the engine running or the battery may flatten rather rapidly), or from a generator. A petrol driven generator providing 240VAC can be hired cheaply, but beware it does not also generate LF noise. The antenna support can be a tree - be careful to use good insulators - a high cliff or a building. Kites or balloons are very convenient as they can be used anywhere, although they can be very dependent on the right weather. It is also very important to master the flying techniques before using one for RF. More information on kites and balloons can be found in the chapter on transmitting antennas. Safety is a vital issue, especially if members of the public are close by. Your activity may attract interested locals, even the police or coast-

This 100m high Decca Navigation mast was available for amateur use for a weekend. The mast was insulated which made the antenna simple. On the right is G3KAU and G3YXM in the equipment hut. Note the antenna feed-through in the window, with the lightning arrester below. More information can be found at [12]

guard, so keep your licence handy and perhaps a leaflet on amateur radio to save endless explanations. Tales of operating from alternative and portable locations can be found at [3].

Several amateurs, usually in groups, have been able to 'borrow' a tall mast - sometimes 100m or more high - from a commercial operator. This is sometimes between the decommissioning of the station and the demolition of the mast. This must never be done without the permission of the mast owner as there are safety (and corresponding financial) issues involved. It may seem that this is an easy way to operate 'portable', as there is often mains power and a building to operate from, as well as the likelihood of the biggest antenna you will ever use. however, if the mast is earthed, it may be difficult to use it as an antenna. You may be lucky and find a mast intended for LF work, or a centre-fed T antenna for MF use. A mast with its own staircase may make it easier to erect a wire, but always get permission to climb and never climb the outside of a lattice tower.

Although impressive signals can be radiated in this way, high received noise levels at the expedition site are a frequent problem; a big antenna often also picks up an impressive level of noise! The result is disappointingly few contacts. If you are planning an expedition, it is a good idea to have available alternative receiving antennas of the types described in Chapter 4, along with some long lengths of coax feeder.

These strong signals may also play havoc with equipment used for tuning up. If at all possible, try receiving at the expedition site before transmission begins, so that noise problems can be investigated and remedied.

Modes requiring a linear transmitter

Although most operation at low frequencies uses modes suitable for high-efficiency class D/E power amplifiers (such as those projects shown in the transmitters chapter), several data modes have been experimented with on 136kHz that need a linear amplifier or advanced techniques (see below) to minimise bandwidth. A commercial linear amplifier for 136kHz, originally intended for audio use, is described in the chapter on transmitters.

Beware that using a non-linear PA will result in a wide transmission that will make you very unpopular with local stations. Operation at low frequencies opens the possibility of advanced transmitter designs which achieve high efficiencies while enabling transmission of 'linear' modes. Such techniques are widely used in modern broadcast transmitters. An example of this has been used at M0BMU to transmit PSK modes at 1.2kW PEP output. A non-linear class-D output stage was used, in conjunction with a high level modulator that supplied a modulated DC supply to the output stage. The amplitude modulation envelope of the PSK signal was extracted and applied to the modulator, while the phase modulation was applied to the carrier input to the class D output stage. This envelope elimination and restoration (EER) technique generates an identical signal to that produced by a linear PA, but achieves an efficiency of 80% or more, while using inexpensive switching MOSFETs as output devices. This transmitter has been used on 136kHz for transmission of PSK31 and 'Wolf' modes (see later), amongst others.

The modes are briefly touched on here, with references to sources of much more information. None of these is widely used but all are suitable for the confines of the 136kHz band.

PSK

The popular HF real-time data mode PSK31 has been used successfully, as has PSK08 which runs at a quarter of the speed with consequent reduction in bandwidth and increased signal/noise. Both can be sent and received using SpecLab (see Appendix 2) and the computer's soundcard. PSK08 contacts have been made between the UK and Germany with copy reported as slightly better than normal speed CW.

Most PSK uses an SSB transmitter in conjuction with a transverter to LF. An alternative PSK modulator, which has been part of the DI2AG 505kHz beacon, uses an old DOS PC without a soundcard and is described at [4].

Hell

This strangely named mode is an electronic version of the mechanical Hellschreiber which was developed by Rudolph Hell in 1927. Hell is closer to fax than a conventional data mode in that each character is sent as an image.

Modern PC sound card based software reproduces the Hellschreiber machine output, for example IZ8BLY's Hellschreiber software [5], along with variants of the mode intended for the HF bands. PA0SE has successfully used an original

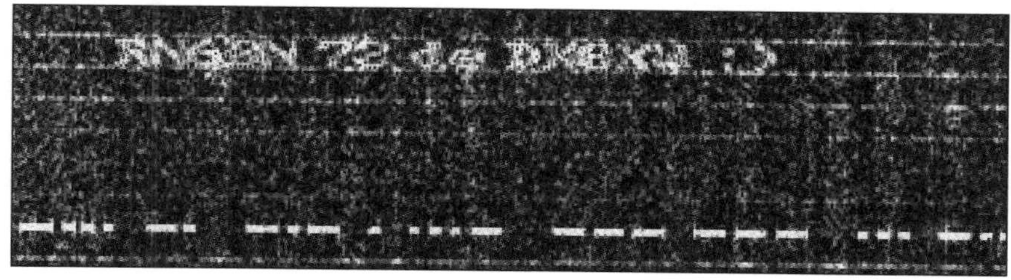

SMT Hell received on a spectrogram program set up to receive QRSS

WWII Hellschreiber machine on 136kHz. More recently, and specific to LF, narrow-band Hell modes, including 'sequential multi-tone Hell' (SMT-Hell) and 'chirped-Hell' have been produced by DF6NM and DL4YHF; the software is available as a component of DL4YHF's Spectrum Lab software [6]. These operate at much lower speed than the original Hellschreiber modes; the speed and bandwidth are compatible with QRSS and DFCW signals, so mixed-mode contacts are commonplace

Wolf

Wolf (Weak signal Operation on Low Frequency)was originally developed by KK7KA from techniques used for communication with deep space probes, and adapted especially for amateur LF operation. Wolf works by encoding a 15 character alphanumeric message as 960 bits using convolutional coding techniques. The resulting massive redundancy in the transmitted signal allows sophisticated error-correcting techniques at the receiving end to reconstruct the original message even if a large proportion of the transmitted bits are corrupted by noise and interference. The signal is transmitted using phase shift keying at 10 bits per second, so the message takes 96 seconds to transmit. Further enhancement of weak signal recovery is achieved by repeatedly transmitting the same message; a further 16 messages can be integrated together at the receiver to improve the signal to noise ratio, at the expense of increasing the time required to transmit and receive a message up to about half an hour (this may seem a long time, but it compares well with the QRSS speeds typically used for intercontinental working). The receiving software attempts to update and decode the signal every 96 seconds, generating the display shown in **Fig. 10.3**.

The original Wolf software [7, 8] utilised 'off-line' processing, where the transmitted signal was first encoded, then played back as an audio recording via the PC sound card. The received signal was recorded, again using the PC, and

```
C:\wolf>wolf -q 10419d.wav -r 8018.527 -f 800.108 -b 5000 -c 7
WOLF version 0.61
t:   24 f: 0.592 a: 0.3 dp:115.6 ci: 9 cj: 85 9O/6R/1R3BK .D0 ?
t:   48 f: 0.247 a:-0.9 dp:113.1 ci:12 cj:215 GGE7MXEPSIHAE28 -
t:   96 f: 0.590 a: 0.5 dp:109.2 ci: 7 cj: 49 7IN937BME53EEAQ ?
t: 192 f:-0.068 pm:  609 jm:602 q:-15.6 -7.6 T7.WE/7LIJWS4/0 ?
t: 288 f: 0.000 pm:  868 jm:796 q:-11.3 -7.6 Q3K*0X0U*FC195Q ?
t: 384 f: 0.000 pm: 1463 jm:796 q: -9.4 -7.8 R6FFJWB27/2FR88 ?
t: 480 f: 0.000 pm: 1739 jm:796 q: -9.5 -7.5 G1XLRUIT5MD26L2 ?
t: 576 f: 0.000 pm: 2228 jm:796 q: -9.3 -8.2  RZMD5AGU4QOXDG ?
t: 672 f: 0.000 pm: 2749 jm:796 q: -7.6 -7.9 QV0SB/5BD.14XJ. ?
t: 768 f: 0.000 pm: 3319 jm:796 q: -6.3 -8.6 88F4*KHBLL2AI83 ?
t: 864 f: 0.000 pm: 3957 jm:796 q: -5.6 -6.6 5A7F7HOBLQ6OTOT ?
t: 960 f: 0.000 pm: 4682 jm:796 q: -4.7 -5.3 M0BMU 10MW ERP  -
t:1056 f: 0.000 pm: 5349 jm:796 q: -3.6 -3.9 M0BMU 10MW ERP  -
t:1152 f: 0.000 pm: 5747 jm:796 q: -3.1 -3.1 M0BMU 10MW ERP  -
t:1248 f: 0.000 pm: 6325 jm:796 q: -2.4 -2.9 M0BMU 10MW ERP  -
t:1344 f: 0.000 pm: 6944 jm:796 q: -1.9 -2.4 M0BMU 10MW ERP  -
t:1440 f: 0.000 pm: 7637 jm:796 q: -1.5 -1.7 M0BMU 10MW ERP  -
t:1536 f: 0.000 pm: 8520 jm:796 q: -1.1 -1.0 M0BMU 10MW ERP  -
t:1632 f: 0.000 pm: 8898 jm:796 q: -0.3 -0.4 M0BMU 10MW ERP  -
```

Fig 10.3: WOLF uses a different approach to low frequency DX working. After several transmissions are processed, the system has accumulated enough information to lock onto the signal and decode the message (bottom right)

the complete recording processed afterwards to extract the signal. Tests using this software achieved the first trans-Atlantic reception of a digital mode on 136kHz. A more recent 'Windows GUI' version of the Wolf software, by DL4YHF and KK7KA [9], greatly simplifies operation by performing all signal generation, reception and processing in real time and using a standard Windows interface on the PC. Successful Wolf operation requires good frequency stability (a small fraction of a hertz) and careful setting up and calibration of frequency errors in the transmitter, receiver and PC sound card using the utilities built into the software.

A Wolf signal requires a bandwidth of nominally 10Hz. Interference from Loran sidebands, which are 8Hz apart, can be a problem in western Europe. The weak-signal capability is comparable with QRSS60, but Wolf has the advantage that speed of transmission is several times greater and is therefore able to take advantage of shorter periods of good propagation conditions.

Better synchronisation

Some of the work of decoding data signals is in gaining and maintaining synchronisation between the transmitting and receiving stations, ie working out when each code element starts and finishes and 'locking' the send and receive frequencies (even phases) together. Work has been done, notably by Peter Martinez, G3PLX, on using cheap Global Positioning System (GPS) modules to derive a 1 pulse per second to calibrate the soundcard, receiver and demodulator to a very accurate degree. One application of this, Clicklock2, can be downloaded from [10].

More modes

As many LF enthusiasts are compulsive experimenters, narrowband modes are constantly being developed. There has even been a two-way 'slow speech' contact using digitally slowed-down audio [11].

References

[1] W3EEE's live chart of DCF39. *http://www.hifidelity.com/w3eee/dc_graph.html*

[2] G3NYK's propagation forecast. *http://www.alan.melia.btinternet.co.uk/latest.htm*

[3] G3YXM's LF expeditions. *http://www.wireless.org.uk/136gm.htm* and *http://www.wireless.org.uk/features.htm*

[4] PSK modulator: *http://members.aol.com/df6nm2/SerPSK.zip*

[5] Hell. *http://xoomer.alice.it/aporcino/Hell/index.htm*

[6] SpecLab *http://freenet-homepage.de/dl4yhf/spectra1.html*

[7] WOLF for beginners. *http://www.mlecmn.net/~lyle/wolf/wolf4beginners.htm*

[8] WOLF software. *http://www.scgroup.com/ham/wolf.html*

[9] WOLF for Windows: *http://www.qsl.net/dl4yhf/wolf/*

[10] Clicklock2: *http://homepages.ihug.co.nz/~coombedn/FILES/Clicklock2.zip*

[11] Slow speech experiment. *http://www.qru.de/slowvoice.htm*

[12] The Puckeridge expedition. *http://lf.apersonalguide.co.uk/decca/index.htm*

Appendix 1

Information sources

In this appendix:

- Web sites
- E-mail group
- Meetings
- Books

EACH OF THE CHAPTERS in this book has a list of references, mostly web sites but also books. In addition, there are many resources available - most of them free - for those seeking more about the fascinating topic of low frequency communication. Those that give the best information at the time of publication are listed below, but new web sites and publications become available all of the time. Of all of these references, the most useful is the rsgb_lf_group e-mail reflector.

Web sites

Operators

The following sites are operated by individuals and organisations with practical experience of LF work. They are all well-established and it is hoped they will be accessible well into the life of this book. As with all information on the world wide web, their content is not edited and cannot be guaranteed to be one hundred per cent accurate. However, the vast majority is well worth a look and will provide the curious experimenter with a host of solutions and many more ideas.

In addition to the topics listed below, most individuals include a description of their station and a log of their best contacts.

CT1DRP: *http://homepage.esoterica.pt/~brian/*
Remote receiver, propagation data.

DF3LP: *http://www.qsl.net/df3lp/*
Antennas, 50W transmitter, magnetic loop, converter, Loran-C, propagation data.

DF6NM: *http://members.aol.com/df6nm*
LF projects including band monitoring using a directional spectrogram, and Loran-C reception experiments.

DK8KW: *http://www.qru.de/*

QRSS intro, 'slow voice' experiments, earth electrode propagation, selective level meters, DDS, 500kHz ship transmitter, DI2BO 505kHz beacon, LF utility stations, dBm to dBμ conversion chart, calibrating receiving equipment.

G3LDO: *http://web.ukonline.co.uk/g3ldo/*

Much technical information, especially about the theory and practice of antennas. Includes errata and addenda for various books and articles on LF and antennas.

G3NYK: *http://www.alan.melia.btinternet.co.uk*

A mine of experimental data and theories on LF propagation, including a forecast of conditions. Also a history of Rugby Radio, and lots on time and frequency.

G3YMC: *http://www.dsergeant.btinternet.co.uk/*

Descriptions of practical experiments on LF loop and Marconi antennas in a very small garden. Experiments on 500kHz. Television receivers as generators of QRM.

G3YXM: *http://www.wireless.org.uk/index.htm*

After the *rsgb_lf_group* (see below), this is the place to go for news of forthcoming LF activity. Also featured are many projects including transmitters and pre-amplifiers, and advice for beginners on both 136 and 500kHz. Articles include expedition reports. The Matrix is a database of who made the first 136kHz between any two countries.

G0MRF: *http://www.g0mrf.freeserve.co.uk/*

Many circuits for 136 and 500kHz. Kits and components at reasonable prices.

I5TGC: *http://fun.supereva.it/dai5tgc.dadacasa/lw_tgc.htm*

How to operate on LF from an apartment block! Antennas for transmit and receive, plus equipment.

IK2PII: *http://www.qsl.net/ik2pii/*

The many 136kHz projects include the design and construction of a 200W transmitter, a direct conversion receiver and a dedicated QRSS receiver.

OK1FIG: *http://ok1fig.nagano.cz/136k.htm*

Pictures of equipment for 136kHz, and expeditions. Recordings of many LF stations in WAV format. Many screen shots of LF stations using QRSS, DFCW and Hell. Transmitter projects and much more.

ON7YD: *http://www.qsl.net/on7yd/136khz.htm*

Lots of information on LF antennas and extremely low bandwidth modes. Many links to articles on LF as well as recommended literature.

RU6LA: *http://136.73.ru/*

Mostly Russian language, but some English including a history of LF radio and list of LF DXpeditions.

SV1XW: *http://www.qsl.net/sv1xv/lw.htm*

An old site, but packed with information. Its title: "The world below 535 kHz" says it all.

VE7SL: *http://www.imagenisp.ca/jsm/136.html*

The Canadian 136kHz scene and advice for beginners.

W3EEE: *http://www.hifidelity.com/w3eee/*
Remote 136kHz receiver for QRSS. Real-time monitor of DCF39. Evaluating receive antennas. Transatlantic LF DX activity from the US end.

W4DEX: *http://www.w4dex.com/*
Details of W4DEX's experimental activities on 136 and 505kHz.

WD2XSH: http://www.500kc.com
The 'official' ARRL Six Hundred Metre Experimental Group site detailing activity in the US 505 - 510 kHz experimental allocation.

Other sites

http://zerobeat.net/G4FGQ/index.html
http://www.radagast.org/~dplatt/hamradio/g4fgq/
Two archive copies of the former web site of the late Reg Edwards, G4FGQ. Computer programs, mostly operating under DOS, including the useful TOROID.EXE.

http://www.amqrp.org/projects/Toroid Design Tool/toroiddesign.htm
Page where you can enter a toroid type and the required inductance and the number of turns will be calculated.

http://home4.swipnet.se/~w-41522/minidds/minidds.html
SM6LKM's direct digital synthesis VFO project.

http://www.dxlc.com/solar/
Solar information, useful for propagation prediction, from the DX Listeners Club.

http://www.hfradio.org/propagation.html
Comprehensive solar and ionospheric data.

http://sec.noaa.gov/
Much propagation data from the National Oceanic and Atmospheric Administration (NOAA)

http://lasp.colorado.edu/space_weather/dsttemerin/dsttemerin.html
Colorado University Dst data:
http://swdcwww.kugi.kyoto-u.ac.jp/dst_realtime/presentmonth/index.html
Kyoto University Dst index page.

http://www.euclid.org/realtime.html
http://www.lightningstorm.com/tux/jsp/gpg/lex1/mapdisplay_free.jsp
http://www.isleofwightweather.co.uk/live_storm_data.htm
Real-time map displays of lightning in Europe and the USA. Useful to check the origin of QRN, or simply abandon that sked!

http://oh2aq.kolumbus.com/dxs/137.html
Real-time reports of activity on 136kHz from all over Europe.

http://www.amrad.org/projects/lf/
The LF pages of AMRAD, a group of keen US experimenters. Includes various low frequency projects and info.

E-mail group

Most amateurs active on the 136kHz band worldwide are 'members' of the RSGB LF Group which is an e-mail forum known as a reflector. After signing up (free), you will receive in your e-mail inbox a copy of every e-mail subsequently sent to the reflector and you will be able to post messages to the group. There is no junk mail, just news and comment, plus technical discussion and advice. This is the place to learn about forthcoming activity and new narrow-band modes, or to ask for skeds. It is also where you can ask questions on LF matters, no matter how simple or complex, with the assumption that you will get replies from experienced, knowledgeable and friendly people.

To join, simply send an e-mail to: *majordomo@blacksheep.org* with no subject and only subscribe rsgb_lf_group in the body of the message. You will receive an automatic welcome message explaining, amongst other things, how to unsubscribe.

Meetings

LF enthusiasts gather every year at the RSGB HF Convention where there are often lectures and a demonstration station. If you bought this book with a view to getting active on 1the low frequencies, but haven't yet taken the plunge, this is the place to learn more and to meet people who have already solved the problems you think you have. There is often the chance to buy specialist items such as coil formers, ferrites, insulators or pre-amplifiers.

Books

Although it was first published in the first half of the last century, *The Handbook of Wireless Telegraphy 1938 Vol II*, is still the place to find useful theoretical and practical information. Published by the Admiralty and reprinted each year for a decade, this tells how LF was used on board ships. Strangely, because of the limited space available on a warship the problems were similar to those facing radio amateurs. Copies are still available from time to time in secondhand shops and on internet auction sites.

Books that are not solely about LF can also contain much useful information. They include the *RSGB Guide to EMC* for information on tracking down noise sources and dealing with your neighbours and *Digital Modes for All Occasions* which includes much simply explained theory and practice for those interested in using some of the modes described in this book. *The Antenna Experimenters Guide* by LF enthusiast Peter Dodd, G3LDO deals with HF antennas but has much to offer anyone keen to understand more about how antennas work. Essential for a general grounding in practical amateur radio, including LF, is the huge *Radio Communication Handbook*. These are all available from the RSGB, Lambda House, Cranborne Road, Potters Bar, Herts EN6 3JE; tel 0870 904 7373; *http://www.rsgb.org/shop/*.

Appendix 2

Components and software

In this appendix:

- Capacitors
- Litz wire - is it useful?
- Ferrite and iron-dust cores
- Component sources
- Software

TRANSMITTERS FOR 136kHz run several hundred watts. The antenna can have very large voltages and/or currents greatly in excess of those found on HF or VHF antennas. These make it important to use high quality, properly rated, components to avoid overheating, or even explosions. At the same time, antenna efficiencies are very low so losses must be minimised by using the correct materials. The low power level currently permitted at 500kHz, together with improved antenna efficiency, makes it less important to use highly rated components, though it is still worth engineering your station properly.

Capacitors

Use capacitors with a high voltage and current rating for most RF power applications. Do not use components straight from the junk box as most types are likely to heat up, especially disk ceramics. For LF/MF, the following types of capacitors are best for high Q:

Ceramic - CG0 or NP0 types, usually restricted to less than 1nF and rated 50V or 100V. Other types of dielectric have high RF losses. Transmitting types are also available with much higher ratings, but are much rarer and expensive.

Mica - Silvered mica up to 10nF or so, rated at 350V or 500V DC are quite widely available and moderately expensive. Occasionally, surplus transmitting mica types are found with much higher ratings; these can deteriorate if very old.

Polystyrene - Up to 10nF or so, usually with voltage ratings of 160V or less are widely available and fairly cheap. Occasionally found with ratings of 1kV or more and values up to 1uF.

Polypropylene, Metallised Polypropylene - widely available in values from a few hundred pF to several uF, rated up to a few kV. Low loss at 136kHz and 500kHz. Best value for money, especially when large capacitance is needed.

Polypropylene types are the best choice in many LF/MF TX applications. If using surplus or second-hand components, be aware that polyester types look just the same, so check the part number on the manufacturer's web site, or test for RF loss, since polyester types have much higher loss. In RF applications, capacitor ratings are usually limited by internal heating due to the RF current, rather than voltage, so generous de-rating is often needed. Polypropylene and polystyrene types in particular should run no more than very slightly warm, because they are limited to quite low maximum operating temperatures.

Litz wire - is it useful?

When a radio frequency signal is passed through a wire, it travels on the outside of the wire. This is known as the skin effect and is the reason that VHF antennas can be made of tubing. It makes the resistance to RF greater than the DC resistance and and causes increased loss in inductors and loop antennas.

The solution is to use Litz wire, which is many *insulated* strands of thin wire bundled together to maximise the surface area. Second-hand Litz wire is sometimes available at rallies or from members of the LF community, although it is prohibitively expensive new.

Using Litz will certainly reduce losses - it can increase Q of an air cored loading coil by a factor of two or three. Although the loss in the coil itself is reduced substantially, the effect on antenna efficiency may well be insignificant due to larger losses in the earth and the environment. However, reducing the loss in the coil also allows higher power operation before the coil overheats. For those who already have a highly efficient antenna system, it may be the next thing to try.

The older type of Litz has dark brown enamel insulation which is extremely hard to remove. Newer types have pink, red or orange 'self fluxing' insulation which can be removed by tinning in a solder pot, or with a hefty soldering iron.

Ferrite and iron-dust cores for LF and MF

Ferrite and iron-dust magnetic cores are familiar components in amateur HF construction projects, in the form of toroids (rings) and tuning slugs. They are also important components in most LF and MF projects. At low frequencies, as well as toroids, other forms of magnetic core are often used, such as transformer 'E' cores and pot cores. The material grades most suited to LF/MF construction are on the whole different to those used at HF. This section offers some general guidance about using ferrite and iron-dust cores at LF/MF; much more detailed information is available in the application notes at [1, 2, 3] and other manufacurers' web sites. Magnetic materials can be classified according to relative permeability (μ). This is basically the factor by which the inductance of a coil wound on a toroid core increases, compared to the same coil wound on a non-magnetic core. Iron dust materials have μ typically 10 - 100, while ferrites have much higher relative permeability, between about 100 and several thousand.

Iron dust cores are used in two general areas by LF/MF amateurs; low loss, high Q inductors for resonant circuits, and RF chokes for feeding DC current to PA stages, supply noise filters, etc. High Q inductors are generally required for transmitter tank circuits and output filters, for which the best material is the Micrometals -2 grade (usually colour-coded red). Toroids in this material are also widely used in the lower HF range, and are available from amateur radio component suppliers. A Q greater than 100 is usually achieved. Large toroid cores are used for LF, for example the T130-2 core is suitable for a 136kHz output filter up to a few hundred watts, and T200-2 up to 1kW or so. Smaller sizes such as the T68-2 are satisfactory for lower power levels at 500kHz.

RF choke applications can use 'power' grades of iron dust core. These cores have higher permeability than the -2 grade, and so achieve higher inductance with fewer turns of wire. RF losses are much higher though, so Q is usually less than 20, but this is usually an advantage for a choke because unwanted resonances are damped. The Micrometals cores of this type usually have a two-colour code, eg -26 grade is yellow/white, -52 grade is green/blue. This type of core can often be salvaged from scrap switch mode power supplies.

The main use for ferrite cores at LF/MF is as transformer cores. Different ferrite grades are best suited to different frequency ranges, with higher permeability materials being best suited to lower frequencies. For use in 136kHz PA output transformers and antenna matching transformers, ferrites with a permeability of around 2000 are best; these are the same grades that are used for switch-mode power supply transformers, and include Ferroxcube/Philips 3C8, 3C85, 3C90, 3C95 etc, Siemens/Epcos N27, N67, N87, Fair-Rite #75 and #77, Neosid F44 and many other similar materials. These are available as toroids, but more widely as transformer assemblies with two 'E' core halves and a plastic bobbin, and also pot cores. The higher numbers tend to be more recent developments with slightly improved characteristics, but differences between grades are not great. For 500kHz, the same cores can be used; the losses in the cores are higher, but since the power levels are normally lower, this is usually acceptable. The Fair-Rite #43 material is very satisfactory for 500kHz with somewhat lower permeability ($\mu = 850$), and lower losses. For small signal transformers, very high permeability cores can be used to achieve wide bandwidth with small windings. Low permeability ferrite cores (eg Ferroxcube/Philips 4C65, Fair-Rite #61) can be used to produce high Q small signal inductors, but these are not suitable for power applications due to non-linearity at high signal levels. Ferrite pot cores, provided with an air gap and a tuning slug for adjustment, are well suited to producing high-Q LF/MF inductors, but are not now widely available.

It is important to be able to either calculate the inductance, or the number of turns required for toroidal or other cored inductors and transformers:

$$L = N^2 A_L, \text{ or } N = \sqrt{(L / A_L)}$$

Where A_L is the 'specific inductance' for the particular core, and N is the number of turns. A_L is usually specified by the manufacturers in nanohenries per turn, so the inductance value will also be in nanohenries. If the A_L of a ferrite core is not known, it can be roughly estimated from:

$$A_L = 4\pi \times 10^2 \times \mu A/l \quad \text{(nH/turn)}$$

Where μ is the permeability (a rough guess will often do for transformer design; most 'switch-mode' materials have μ in the range 2000 - 2500), A is the cross-sectional area of the core (in square metres) and l is the length of the magnetic path through the core in metres (the average of the inner and outer circumference of a toroid). The value of A_L will typically be in the range of thousands of nanohenries per turn for cores likely to be used. Typically, the inductance of a transformer winding is chosen so the reactance will be 5 - 10 times the circuit impedance level at the lowest operating frequency.

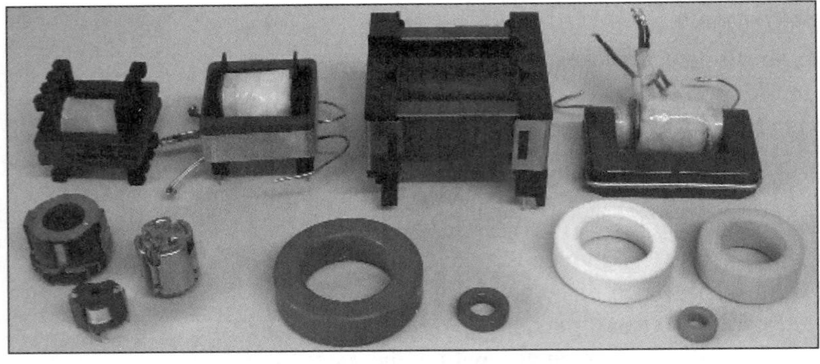

Fig A2.1: Cores for LF/MF. From left to right, back row: EC41, EE42, ETD59 transformer core assemblies; PA output transformer for modified G0MRF 400W TX wound on LOPT core. Front row: Three pot cores, T200-2 and T68-2 iron dust toroids, three assorted 3C85 and 3C90 toroids

For power transformers, it is also important that the magnetic flux density in the core is not too high; a high flux density will lead to high losses, severe heating, and problems with core saturation. Peak flux density (measured in Tesla, T) of about 100mT - 150mT is usually a safe figure for these ferrites. For a sine wave RF voltage applied across a winding, the peak flux density, B_{peak}, can be calculated from:

$$B_{peak} = V_{RMS} / 4.44fNAe$$

Where f is the frequency in Hertz, N is the number of turns on the winding, and Ae is the effective cross-sectional area of the coil (in square metres).

More details on transformer design can be found in the chapter on transmitters, and at ferrite manufacturers' web sites [1].

'Switch-mode' ferrite cores are available from industrial component distributors such as RS components and Farnell (see below), who will also supply private customers. Transformer core and bobbin assemblies are available in several styles (eg EC, EE, ETD) and sizes (for example, an ETD 39 core assembly has overall length of 39mm). Small toroidal ferrite cores are also available from these sources, as well as from amateur radio suppliers; these are sometimes colour coded according to ferrite grade (3C85 toroids are usually a pink colour), but the modern tendency is to have either a plain white coating, or no coating at all. The ferrite core from a line output transformer (LOPT) from a TV set or monitor can also be a useful transformer core (see Chapter 6, Fig. 6.13). They are made from a 'switch mode' ferrite grade. The core can be recovered by carefully sawing away the original transformer windings; take care to remove any plastic spacers or adhesive separating the mating surfaces of the two core halves.

Component sources

Note that this information is believed to be correct at the time of publication. Some suppliers insist on a minimum quantity order so it may be useful to get together with others when ordering.

Abacus Deltron (3C90 toroids)
High Greaves Way, Sawcliffe Industrial Estate
Scunthorpe DN15 8RF. Tel: 01724 281 770. Web: *www.deltron-uk.com/jkcm/*

David Bowman, G0MRF (3C90 toroids, etc)
E-mail: *g0mrf@aol.com*. Web: *http://www.g0mrf.freeserve.co.uk/*.

Farnell Electronic Components Ltd (semiconductors, ferrites, chokes, capacitors)
Canal Road, Leeds, LS12 2TU. Tel: 08701 200 200. Fax: 08701 200 201.
E-mail: *sales@farnell.co.uk*. Web: *http://www.farnell.com/*.

Keytronics (semiconductors, crystals)
88 Hadham Road, Bishops Stortford, Herts, CM23 2QT. Tel: 01279 505543. Fax: 01279 757656. E-mail: *pk@keytronics-uk.co.uk*. Web: *www.keytronics-uk.co.uk*.

Mainline Group (T200-2 toroids)
Mainline Electronics, 192 Little Glen Road, Glen Parva, Leicester, LE2 9TT. Tel: 0116 278 0980. Fax: (+44) 0116 224 8300. Email: anona@mainlinegroup.co.uk. Web: *www.mainlinegroup.co.uk*.

Maplin Electronics Ltd (ferrites, hardware)
National Distribution Centre, Valley Road, Wombwell, Barnsley, South Yorkshire. S73 0BS. Tel: 0870 429 6000. High street presence in many towns countrywide. Web: *www.maplin.co.uk/*.

RS Components: (huge range of semiconductors, ferrites, chokes, capacitors, etc)
UK Orderline: 08457 201201. Web: *http://rswww.com*

Sycom (transistors, RF chokes; capacitors; hardware; good range of iron dust and ferrite toroids)
PO Box 148, Leatherhead, Surrey, KT22 9YW. Tel: 01372 372587. Fax: 01372 361421. E-mail: *robin@sycomcomp.co.uk*. Web: *www.sycomcomp.co.uk*.

TLC Electrical Supplies (screw-ended earthing rods and couplers)
Tel: 01293 565630. E-mail: *sales@tlc-direct.co.uk*. Web: *www.tlc-direct.co.uk*

Software

It is possible to operate on the low frequencies without using a computer and several successful operators have done so. However, to make the fullest use of this part of the spectrum it is very useful to have a computer in the shack. The *rsgb_lf_group* e-mail reflector is the hub of the low frequency amateur radio community worldwide and the shack computer can also be used for making calculations and for working DX using extremely low bandwidth modes (see the operating chapter). Some recommended programs are listed below - all can be downloaded free from the Internet.

Calculators

These two programs are written to run under DOS, but they work fine in a 'DOS' window on a computer running Windows XP. They are a bit fussy to use, but are worth a little trial and error.

TANT136.EXE (G4FGQ). *http://zerobeat.net/G4FGQ/page3.html*
This is designed for those who want to use an 160/80/40m dipole with the feeders strapped to make an LF Marconi, although it can be used for purpose designed inverted-L or Tee antennas. Having input the size of the antenna, the feeder or vertical wire and the dimensions of the chosen coil former, the program calculates the coil winding details, the expected radiation resistance and the output power. TANT136.EXE should only be regarded as a rough guide, but it is a good starting point when building your first LF antenna.

SOLNOID3.EXE (G4FGQ). *http://zerobeat.net/G4FGQ/page3.html*
Good program to use when designing loading coils.

TOROID.EXE (G4FGQ). *http://zerobeat.net/G4FGQ/page3.html*

This one calculates the number of turns required to make a specified inductance on a specified toroid. Very useful.

QRSS programs

With the exception of ON7YD's keying software, all of these display an audio spectrum and use Fast Fourier Transform (FFT) to integrate the received audio. It is essential to have at least one of these if you want to receive QRSS and its variants. All require a sound card to be installed in the computer.

Argo (I2PHD and IK2CZL). *http://digilander.libero.it/i2phd/argo/index.html*

This has presets for most of the commonly used variations of QRSS, and very little is adjustable. This makes Argo the easiest of the FFT programs to use. Time and date can be displayed on screen. It will work with real time audio or a recorded (WAV) file, and will also save audio as a WAV file. Capturing 'snapshots' of screens, for a 'grabber' or simply for later analysis, is easy and may be automated on a timer (great for monitoring DX when you are in bed). Ideal for the beginner.

Spectran (I2PHD and IK2CZL). *http://digilander.libero.it/i2phd/spectran.html*

A version of Argo with fewer pre-sets and many adjustable options. It can be used in through-audio mode which has an anti-hum filter, denoiser, and bandpass and notch filters. USB or LSB are selectable for correct display of frequency.

SpecLab (DL4YHF). *http://www.qsl.net/dl4yhf/spectra1.html*

The big daddy of spectrograms, Spectrum Laboratory is flexible and capable of many things that others cannot do. It is correspondingly complex to use. For QRSS use, the FFT, audio and display settings are fully configurable. There are many data export functions, including the ability to plot the strength of a signal and/or noise band. An audio spectrum analyser is included. For those with two antennas, the unique radio direction finder can be useful. The program will also cope with PSK08 and Hell.

EasyGram (OK1FIG). *http://ok1fig.nagano.cz/EasyGram.htm*

Using the original Spectrogram DLL as its heart, EasyGram has configurable FFT settings. It can automatically save screen shots which can easily be reviewed

QRS (ON7YD). *http://www.qsl.net/on7yd/136narro.htm#QRS*

The most popular way to key a QRSS or DFCW transmission, this program covers a wide range of dot lengths from one second to one hour! From text input it will key the transmitter, and operate the PTT line if required, via the serial or parallel ports. A simple interface must be constructed for each line (see the chapter on operating practice). The QSK function allows you to listen between dots or dashes and an audible alarm sounds when the transmission is about to end.

Other narrowband modes

See the operating chapter for details of where to find the software for Hell, Jason, WOLF etc.

References

[1] Ferroxcube - *http://www.ferroxcube.com.* Fair-Rite Products Corp - *http://www.fair-rite.com.* Micrometals Inc - *http://www.micrometals.com*

Index